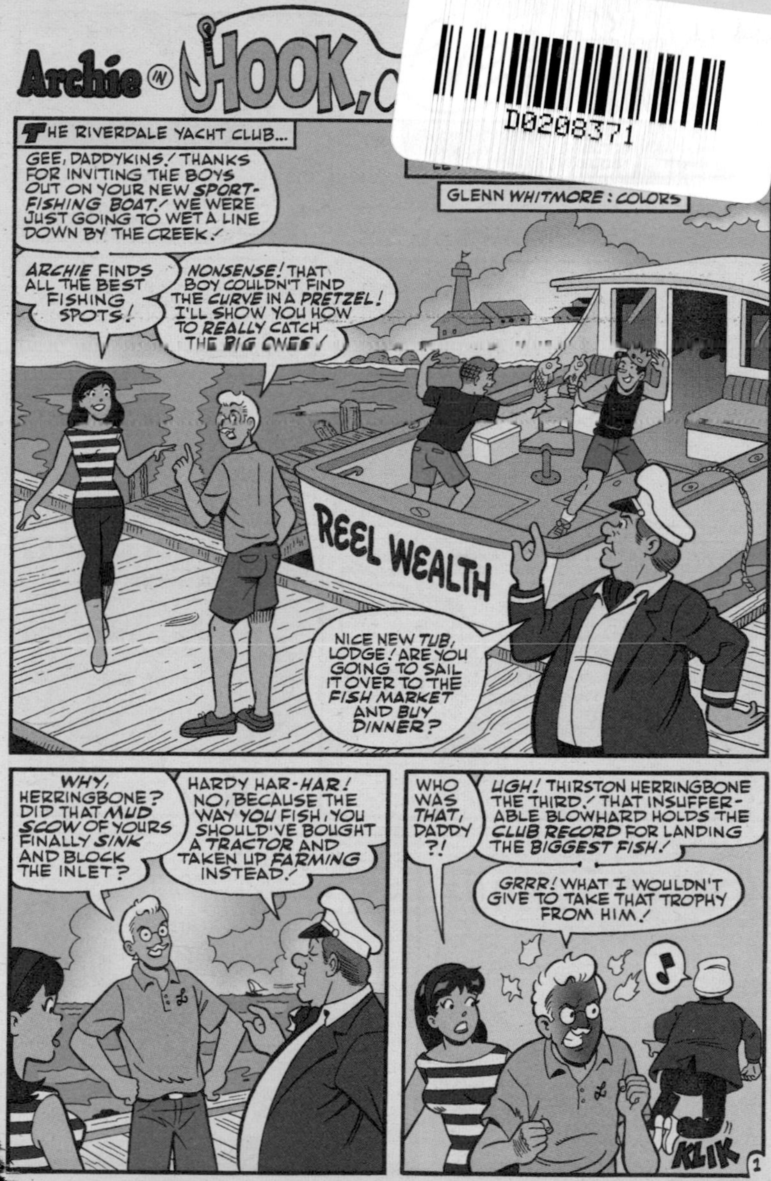

Archie in HOOK, C

THE RIVERDALE YACHT CLUB...

GLENN WHITMORE : COLORS

GEE, DADDYKINS! THANKS FOR INVITING THE BOYS OUT ON YOUR NEW SPORT-FISHING BOAT! WE WERE JUST GOING TO WET A LINE DOWN BY THE CREEK!

ARCHIE FINDS ALL THE BEST FISHING SPOTS!

NONSENSE! THAT BOY COULDN'T FIND THE CURVE IN A PRETZEL! I'LL SHOW YOU HOW TO REALLY CATCH THE BIG ONES!

REEL WEALTH

NICE NEW TUB, LODGE! ARE YOU GOING TO SAIL IT OVER TO THE FISH MARKET AND BUY DINNER?

AND SO...
LOOK, JUGHEAD! THIS BOAT HAS MORE ELECTRONICS THAN THE SPACE SHIP ON "STAR SCHLEP"!
YEAH, ARCH! I ONLY HOPE THE GALLEY IS AS IMPRESSIVE!
I'M STARVED!

WE HAVE EVERY STATE-OF-THE-ART TOOL! DEPTH RECORDERS, GPS, UNDERWATER CAMERAS, MOTION DETECTORS, TEMPERATURE SENSORS...
BEEP BEEP

SEE! THERE'S A SCHOOL OF BAITFISH! THE BIG ONES CAN'T BE FAR BEHIND! HURRY! LET'S GET BACK OUT ON DECK!!
62.9ft.
0.
0.4
7.25
00.2

SOON
OKAY! NOW WE JUST HAVE TO HOPE FOR A STRIKE!
GEE, I NEVER THOUGHT I'D HEAR YOU SAY THAT, DADDY!
CHUM
THE FRIDGE WAS EMPTY...

BUT I FOUND THIS BUCKET LABELED "CHUM". IS THAT A KIND OF CHOWDER?
POP

GAK!
THAT'S HIDEOUS!! TAKE IT AWAY!! AGGH!!

NO, JUGHEAD! CHUM IS GROUND-UP ROTTEN FISH. WE POUR IT IN THE WATER TO ATTRACT LARGE PREDATORS! BUT WE WON'T USE THAT NOW. GET IT OFF THE DECK, ARCHIE!
PLEASE!
CHUM
REEL WEALTH
AYE AYE, SIR!

Oh, DADDY! YOU'VE GOT ONE!!
YOU'RE RIGHT! LOOK AT HIM TAKE OUR LINE!
ZZZZZZ

HE MUST BE ENORMOUS!
GET READY, EVERYONE! HE'S GOING TO LEAP!
ZZZZ

EGAD!
SPLOOSH
HE MAKES HERRINGBONE'S RECORD LOOK LIKE A SARDINE!!

I'LL GET THE NET!
I'LL GET THE TARTAR SAUCE!!

DON'T BE RIDICULOUS! THAT FISH WON'T FIT IN A NET!
BRING THE GAFF HOOK!

Huh?!
YES, SIR!
RIGHT AWAY, SIR!
SHOOF

NO TIME TO WASTE!
HE'S DIVING AGAIN!
HERE I COME!!

?
DOINK

YEEOWTCH!

WATCH THE FISH, YOU RED MENACE! HE'S TAKING ALL THE LINE! BACK DOWN THE BOAT BEFORE WE LOSE HIM!!
ULP! SORRY, SIR!
ZZZZZ

RIGHT! I'M ON IT!
THUNK
ROARR

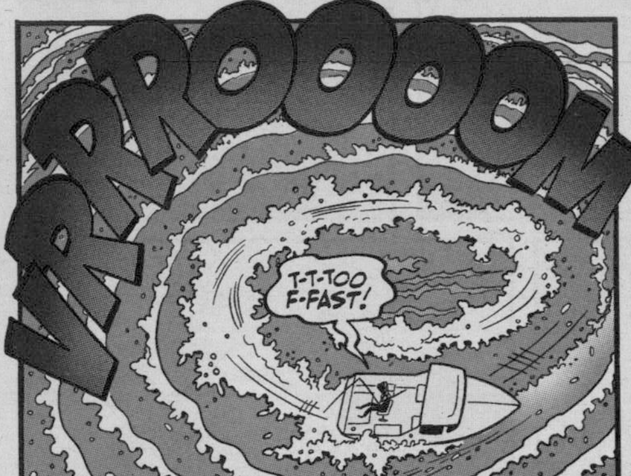
VRROOOOM
T-T-TOO F-FAST!

TH-TH-THE WH-WHEEL! G-GRAB TH-TH-THE WH-WHEEL!!

CHUM

DONK
MM-MNGNFFF!
CHUM
GLOOSH

SNAP
EWW!
CHUM

THE NEXT DAY, AT LODGE MANSION...
BUT DADDYKINS--! IT'S NOT FAIR! ARCHIE TRIED HIS BEST!
LISTEN, VERONICA...

THAT FRECKLED FRANKENSTEIN COST ME THE FISH OF A LIFETIME!!
AND THE CHANCE TO FINALLY STIFLE THAT CROWING HERRING-BONE!!

SO IF YOU WANT TO SEE HIM IN THIS HOUSE, THIS IS HOW IT'S GOING TO BE! MY TERMS ARE NON-NEGOTIABLE!!

OH, REALLY! YOU'RE BEING IMPOSSIBLE, DADDY!!
IT'S OKAY, RONNIE, I UNDERSTAND. BUT I DO HAVE ONE MOUNTING CONCERN...

I CAN'T SEE THE TELEVISION FROM HERE!
THE END

MY INFORMANT PAID OFF, *POWERTEEN!* THE LAVITTO FAMILY'S GOONS HAVE *PUREHEART* IN THAT WAREHOUSE DOWN BELOW!

IAN FLYNN STORY
JEFF SHULTZ PENCILS
BOB SMITH INKS
GLENN WHITMORE COLORS
JACK MORELLI LETTERS

WOW, BLACKJACK! YOU'RE AN ACE OF A DETECTIVE!

BLACKJACK AND POWERTEEN IN PUREHEART RESCUE!

NO ACES HERE, MISS! JUST A JACK OF ALL TRADES!

WHAT I *DON'T* GET IS HOW A BUNCH OF GOONS COULD HOLD A GUY LIKE *PUREHEART*. THE GUY CAN BENCH-PRESS A *FIRE TRUCK!*
YEAH, BUT HE HAS ONE REALLY EXPLOITABLE WEAKNESS...

WASSAMATTER, PUREHEART?
YOU THINK YOU'RE TOO GOOD FOR US?!

WITH YOU BACKING UP THE BOSS, THIS ENTIRE TOWN COULD BE OURS!

NO MORE CURFEWS! GO WHERE YOU WANNA GO; DO WHAT YOU WANNA DO!

C'MON! WORKIN' FOR MR. LAVITTO AIN'T SO BAD! YOU DO WHAT HE SAYS, AND HE REWARDS YOU WELL! THINK OF ALL THE GOOD YOU COULD DO WITH ALL THAT CASH!

AND WITH THAT KIND OF MONEY AND POWER, YOU COULD HAVE ANY GIRL YOU WANT! WHATTAYA SAY, BIG HERO? WANNA GO ON A DATE?

NO WAY! I'M PUREHEART! I'M A HERO, AND I DON'T WORK WITH CRIMINALS LIKE YOU!!
HA!
KEEP TELLING YOURSELF THAT!
BUT YOUR POWERS DRY UP WHEN YOU HAVE IMPURE THOUGHTS!
AND SINCE YOU HAVEN'T BUSTED OUT OF THEM ROPES YET...
THAT MEANS YOU'RE AT LEAST TEMPTED!
KRASH
THEN IT'S UP TO US TO LEAD HIM FROM TEMPTATION!
3

KA-POW

WHOOSH
CARE TO JOIN ME, BOYS?
ZOOM

AND WHERE DO YOU THINK YOU'RE GOING, LADY?!

FLING
YI!

LOOKS LIKE YOUR THREE-OF-A-KIND BEATS MY ONE JOKER!
YEP! WE SURE DEALT WITH THEM!

YOU'RE FREE, PUREHEART!

BUT WHY DIDN'T YOU JOIN IN THE FUN WHILE YOUR CAPTORS WERE DISTRACTED?

YOU WERE AMAZING! I'M CALLED "PUREHEART"!
WHAT'S--

WHAM
OOF!

Ah.
I SEE.

Y'KNOW, I CAME AS "POWERTEEN" AND NOT "MISS VANITY" FOR EXACTLY THIS REASON.
SIGH HE'S HOPE-LESS!
END

Archie in "Beach Nut!"

HI, BETTY! HI, RONNIE!

ARCHIE!?

Script, Art & Letters: Bob White

I'LL BE WITH YOU AS SOON AS I SET THINGS UP WITH SUGAR HERE!

SET THINGS UP WITH SUGAR? WHY, THAT LOW DOWN TWO-TIMER!

TWO-TIMER?... I GO WITH ARCHIE, TOO! REMEMBER?

HE'S A LOW-DOWN THREE-TIMER!

AFTER ALL THE TIME I'VE INVESTED IN HIM, HE DOUBLE-CROSSES ME!

RONNIE, DON'T YOU EVER LISTEN? HE'S TRIPLE-CROSSED US!

NO MATTER HOW YOU SLICE IT, BETTY--- ARCHIE'S IGNORING US!
RIGHT! LET'S INVESTIGATE!

THERE'S THE CAD!

ARE YOU COMFORTABLE, SUGAR?
2

SO HERE YOU ARE... TRIPLE-TIMING AND TRIPLE-CROSSING US!
RONNIE!?

DON'T YOU THINK YOU'RE SPREADING YOURSELF RATHER THIN?
I CAN EXPLAIN...

WELL I'M GOING TO SPREAD YOU A LITTLE THINNER!
HEY!

CRASH!
SNAP!

EEEEEEK!

HEY! WHAT ARE YOU DOING WITH MY GIRL?!

I CAN EXPLAIN...
BETTER MAKE IT FAST!

NOT FAST ENOUGH!
WHAM!

LATER:
ARCHIE KNOWS NOW, WE WON'T TAKE ANYTHING SITTING DOWN!
JUST LET HIM TRY ANYTHING ELSE!

ARCHIE!?

WAIT! GIVE A GUY A BREAK! IT'S YOUR FAULT I GOT THIS BLACK EYE!
4

YOU ALSO BROKE OUR BEACH UMBRELLA! NOW I HAVE TO GIVE SUGAR ANOTHER ONE!
"SUGAR" AGAIN ?!?

THIS TIME, BETTY, LET'S BREAK HIM!
YEAH!!

WAIT! YOU DON'T UNDERSTAND! SUGAR IS HER NAME... "SUGAR JONES!".. AND HER BOYFRIEND WALLOPED ME IN THE EYE!

THIS HAPPENS TO BE MY SUMMER JOB! I WORK FOR "JOE'S UMBRELLA RENTALS" SETTING UP UMBRELLAS!

HAH! A LIKELY STORY!
YOU'RE A PRETTY FAST TALKER, ARCHIE!

OKAY, OKAY! C'MON ALONG AND I'LL PROVE IT!
THIS WE'LL HAVE TO SEE!

WHERE DO YOU WANT THE UMBRELLA, SUGAR?
JUST ANY PLACE, ARCHIE!
5.

OKAY! RIGHT HERE!

YEOW!

I JUST HOPE YOU'VE GOT PLENTY OF MEDICAL INSURANCE!

SOCKO!

OH, ARCHIEKINS, CAN YOU EVER FORGIVE US?
YES, ARCHIE! NOW WE KNOW YOU DON'T LOOK AT OTHER FEMALES!

RIGHT, GIRLS! I ONLY HAVE EYES FOR YOU!
The End

Archie & FRIENDS in SWING TIME!
HEY! CHECK IT OUT, GUYS!
YAHOO!
Script: MIKE PELLOWSKI Pencils: BOB BOLLING Inks: JIM AMASH
HEH HEH! EVEN THOUGH THE WORLD HAS COMPUTERS AND VIDEO GAMES, SOME KIDS STILL KNOW HOW TO HAVE FUN THE OLD-FASHIONED WAY.
YIPPIE!
GO FOR IT, MARTY!

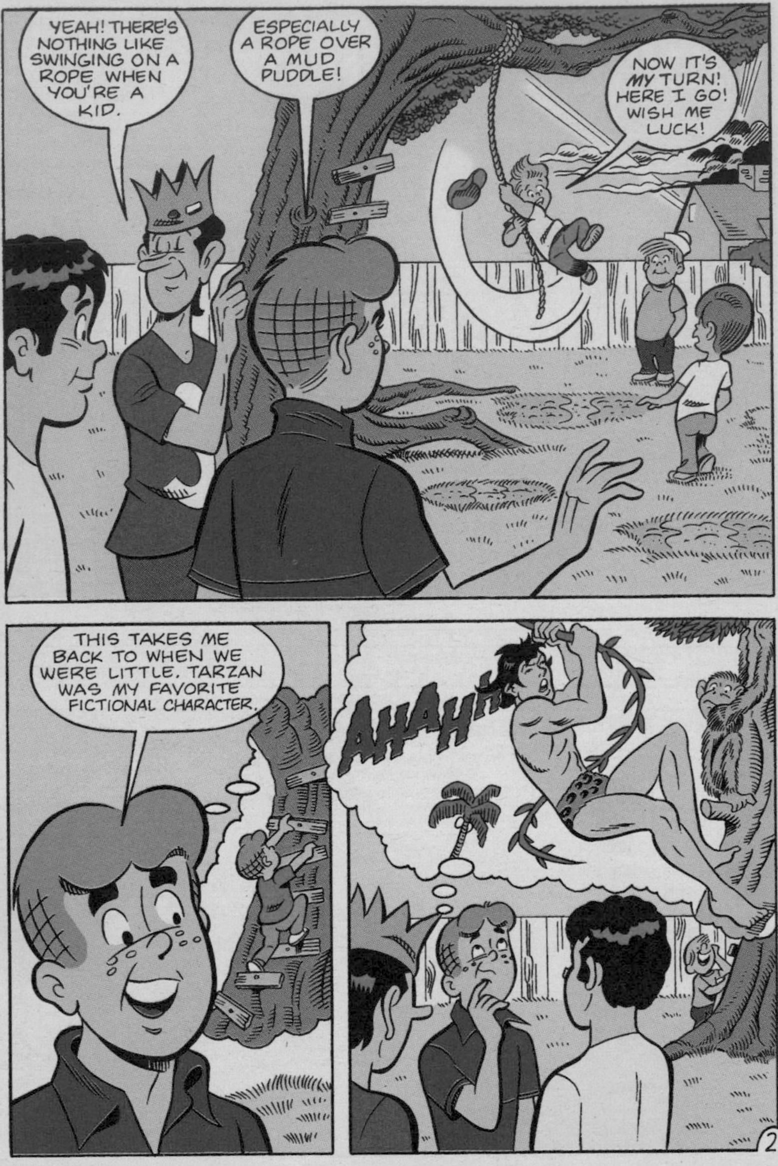

YEAH! THERE'S NOTHING LIKE SWINGING ON A ROPE WHEN YOU'RE A KID.
ESPECIALLY A ROPE OVER A MUD PUDDLE!
NOW IT'S *MY* TURN! HERE I GO! WISH ME LUCK!

REMEMBER WHEN *WE* USED TO PLAY TARZAN IN MR. WILEY'S WOODS?
THUMPA
THUMPA
ME TARZAN!
I SURE DO! THAT WAS FUN. I WAS ALWAYS KING OF THE JUNGLE!

I KNOW! I WANTED TO BE TARZAN, BUT I ALWAYS HAD TO PLAY A BIG GAME HUNTER AND JUGHEAD WAS MY GUIDE!
REGGIE! SHOOT NOW!
GULP!
POP

HEY! WAIT A MINUTE! *YOU* DIDN'T PLAY THE HUNTER! *I* DID! YOU WERE ALWAYS CHEETA, TARZAN'S PET CHIMP!

THIS IS YOUR CHANCE TO GO APE, REG!
HAR-DEE HARR-HARR.

BETTY AND VERONICA WERE ALWAYS FIGHTING ABOUT WHO GOT TO BE TARZAN'S GIRLFRIEND!
CHEETA?
LISTEN, YOU PLAIN JANE, MY JUNGLE COSTUME WAS CUSTOM MADE BY A FAMOUS DESIGNER!
Humph! WHERE DID YOU BUY IT... HOLLYWOOD AND VINE?

THE GIRLS WERE ANOTHER REASON WHY I WANTED TO BE TARZAN!
BUT ARCH WAS A GREAT APE MAN... HE HAD A COOL TARZAN YELL!

I HAVE A CONFESSION TO MAKE ABOUT THAT TARZAN YELL, GUYS. I'VE KEPT IT A SECRET ALL THESE YEARS...

MY HANDS TENDED TO SLIP AND I USUALLY GOT ROPE BURN. MY YELL WAS A SCREAM OF PAIN!
AH-OOH-EEH-AHH!

Humph! I STILL THINK I WOULD HAVE MADE THE BEST TARZAN.
LET'S GO TO MY HOUSE FOR A SNACK, GUYS!
GOOD IDEA! WHILE WE'RE THERE WE CAN PLAY SOME VIDEO GAMES!

Hmmmm...
Uh oh...

NO! DON'T EVEN THINK ABOUT IT, GUYS! YOU'RE TOO OLD FOR THAT KIND OF STUFF!

STAND ASIDE, CARROT-HEAD! THIS IS MY CHANCE TO PROVE I'M THE BETTER TARZAN!

AHHIEEAH

SNAP!
Uh oh!
SWING

YEOW!

SPLAT!

WELL, IT LOOKS LIKE TARZAN REGGIE MADE A MONKEY OUT OF HIMSELF AGAIN.
YUCK!
End

Archie in "Beddy-Bye Time"

COME ON! I'VE GOTTA GO OVER TO GRANDMA'S! SHE'S GIVING MY FOLKS HER OLD BRASS BED!

SHE AND GRANDPA GIVING UP SLEEP ALTOGETHER?

NO! THEY'RE SELLING OUT AND GOING SOUTH!

THEY'RE GOING TO LIVE IN A SWINGING SENIORS' RETIREMENT HOME!

Script: Frank Doyle / Pencils: Dan DeCarlo / Inks: Jimmy DeCarlo / Letters: Bill Yoshida

HERE WE ARE.! LET'S GET THE BED.!

IT COMES APART, YOU KNOW.!
NAH.! WE'D ONLY HAVE TO PUT IT BACK TOGETHER.!

WE'LL TAKE IT AS IS AND SAVE OURSELVES A LOT OF WORK.!

OKAY.! SHE'S BALANCED NICELY.! LET'S MOVE OUT.!

OH, NO.!! NOW THE STUPID CAR WON'T START.!!

HEY.! WE'RE NOT LICKED YET.! THIS THING'S GOT WHEELS.!

RIGHT! IT'S ONLY FIVE OR SIX BLOCKS! -- SHE ROLLS EASILY!

HEY! THIS IS GOING SO SMOOTHLY, WHY DON'T WE TAKE TURNS RIDING?
GREAT, HOP IN!

I WONDER IF YOU NEED A LICENSE FOR THIS VEHICLE?

HEY! THIS IS DOWN-HILL! HOP ABOARD!
WHY NOT?

WOW! LOOK AT ARCH AND JUG!
WAIT UP!

ARCH! WE SEEM TO BE PICKING UP HITCH-HIKERS!
HEY, YOU GUYS! THIS IS A DOUBLE BED!

I JUST REALIZED-- WE DON'T HAVE ANY CONTROLS ON THIS THING!!
WE'RE PICKING UP SPEED!

HAAALP!!

SIGH! I WISH THEY'D TRANSFER ME FROM TRAFFIC TO SOMEPLACE WHERE THERE'S A LITTLE EXCITEMENT!

ARGH!!

4

I THINK WE JUST RAN OVER A COP!
DOES ANYONE HAVE A LICENSE FOR DRIVING A BED ?

DRAG YOUR FEET, EVERYBODY.!! I THINK WE'RE GOING TO MAKE IT TO MY DRIVEWAY!

-- BRASS BED -- FULL OF KIDS-- RAN A RED LIGHT -- ALSO HIT AND RUN!
WHAT'S THE SPEED LIMIT ON BEDS ?

STAY WHERE YOU ARE, PARKER! HELP IS ON THE WAY!

EASY NOW, PARKER! THE CHIEF KNOWS WHAT HE'S DOING!
YOU'LL LIKE IT AT THIS REST HOME, PAL!
?
The END

Archie
OLD SOAKS AT HOME

HOLD FAST, YOUNG GUY! BEFORE YOU BLOW THIS TRAP, SUPPOSE YOU SPREAD A LITTLE MOISTURE ON OUR GRASS!

AW, POP!

Script: Doyle / Pencils: Lucey / Inks & Letters: Acquaviva

I'M IN THE LIVELY GENERATION! THE WORLD IS MY OYSTER! I'VE GOT TO MOVE, DAD!... *MOVE!*
SURE YOU DO, SON!
CLICK!

...SLOWLY AROUND THE HOUSE, SOAKING THE LAWN AS YOU GO!

GADZOOKS! WHAT A LACK OF UNDERSTANDING THERE IS BETWEEN GENERATIONS!

OH, OH! ...THIS IS THE MOMENT OF TRUTH!

WILL HE DESERT HIS POST? HOW WILL HE REACT WHEN HE SEES HER?

BOING!

SPUT!! I WISH I KNEW IF HE WAS AWARE OF WHAT HE WAS DOING!

MY! AREN'T YOU PERSPIRING A BIT FREELY, LORD AND MASTER?
ALL THIS AND A SMART ALEC WIFE!

IT WAS TOO ACCURATE TO BE ACCIDENTAL! THAT'S WHAT I THINK!

AHA! THE POSITION IS PERFECT!

SO HE WANTS TO PLAY "SOAK THE OLD MAN", EH?

TUM.. DEE -- DUM

WHOOPS!
EEK!
3

MARY! I'M SORRY! I'LL MOP THIS UP WHILE YOU CHANGE CLOTHES!

HMMM? I WONDER IF THAT WAS AN ACCIDENT? HE HAD A MISCHIEVOUS GLEAM IN HIS EYE!

IT'S NICE TO BE RICH AND OWN TWO HOSES!

HEY!

YIPE!
SPLAT!
4

GIVE ME THAT HOSE, ARCHIE!
HEY! WHAT'S GOING ON?

EEEK!! MR. ANDREWS!
SOAK **ALL** THE WOMEN IN THE WORLD!

COME ON, GIRLS! IT LOOKS LIKE THE MALES HAVE ISSUED A CHALLENGE!

WE'RE GONNA WASH THOSE MEN RIGHT OUT OF OUR HAIR!

SPLOOSH!
YOU GIRLS LOOK LIKE YOU'RE ALL *WASHED UP!*
WATER YOU TALKING ABOUT? YOU TWO ARE THE ONES ABOUT TO BE *HOSED!*
The End

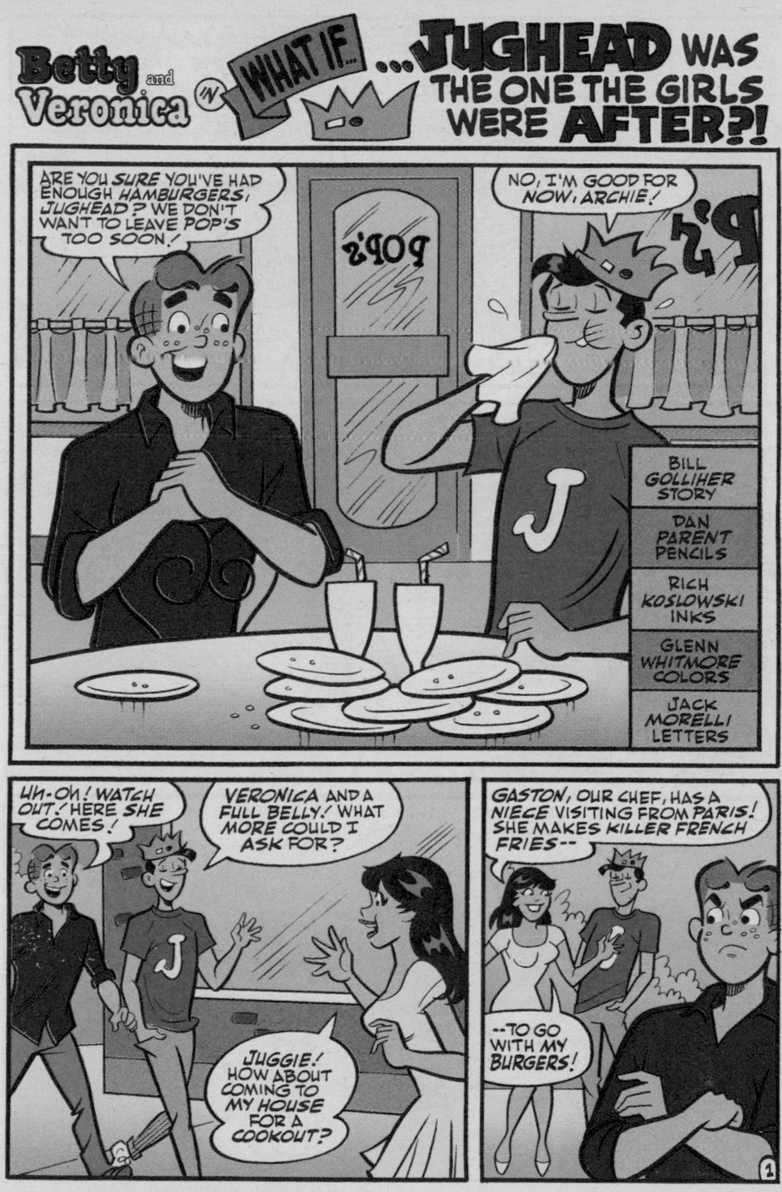

Betty and Veronica in WHAT IF... ...JUGHEAD WAS THE ONE THE GIRLS WERE AFTER?!

ARE YOU SURE YOU'VE HAD ENOUGH HAMBURGERS, JUGHEAD? WE DON'T WANT TO LEAVE POP'S TOO SOON!

NO, I'M GOOD FOR NOW, ARCHIE!

POP'S

BILL GOLLIHER STORY
DAN PARENT PENCILS
RICH KOSLOWSKI INKS
GLENN WHITMORE COLORS
JACK MORELLI LETTERS

DON'T DO IT!! I'M ON MY WAY HOME FROM THE SUPER-MARKET! I'M GOING TO MAKE YOU SOME GOURMET BURGERS!
BELIEVE IT OR NOT, BETTY, I'M ACTUALLY FULL RIGHT NOW!

MY PAL ARCHIE AND I JUST LOADED UP AT POP'S!
IT'S ALWAYS ARCHIE! YOU NEVER HAVE TIME FOR US!

THAT'S NOT TRUE! I JUST NEED SOME ME AND FOOD TIME OCCASIONALLY!
DOES HE EVER!
ZIP IT, CARROT-TOP!
JUST TO PROVE HOW I FEEL, HERE'S ONE OF MY HAT PINS FOR YOU...
...AND ONE FOR YOU!
oh, JUGGIE!

I'LL TALK TO YOU TWO LATER ABOUT THOSE BURGERS!
WINK
SWOON! THAT'S A WONDERFUL IDEA!
HE'S SMART AND CUTE!
AND I'M NAUSEOUS!

NEXT DAY...
HI, VERONICA! WE'RE HERE FOR THAT COOKOUT.!
WONDERFUL!
BUT WHY DID YOU BRING HIM?!
BELIEVE ME, I'M JUST HERE FOR THE FOOD!

VERONICA, I'M IMPRESSED! THESE BURGERS ARE DELICIOUS!
THANK YOU! GLAD TO HEAR YOU BOYS ARE ENJOYING THEM!
HELLO!
BETTY?! WHAT ARE YOU DOING HERE?!
I JUST WANTED TO DROP OFF MY BURGERS FOR JUGHEAD, SO HE CAN HAVE SOME DECENT FOOD!

IN THE MIDDLE OF MY COOK-OUT?!
CAN I HELP IT IF I'M WILLING TO DELIVER?

THESE ARE THE BEST BURGERS IN TOWN!
NO! MINE ARE!

EXCUSEZ-MOI, I HATE TO INTERRUPT, BUT I'M SURE THERE EEZ A BETTER ONE.!
WHAT DO YOU MEAN, GASTON?!

THESE EEZ MY NIECE, MONIQUE, YOU HAVE HEARD ABOUT.! YOU MUST TRY HER HAMBURGERS! THEY ARE MAGNIFIQUE.!
Oh, UNCLE! THE SWEETEST THINGS YOU SAY!

'TIS TRUE THIS! SHE WILL MAKE SOME.!
I'M WILLING TO GIVE THEM A TRY!

SOON...
MONIQUE!! THIS IS THE MOST WONDERFUL HAMBURGER I HAVE EVER HAD IN MY LIFE!
Oh, REALLY?
HOW SWEET!

YOU CAN MAKE HAMBURGERS FOR ME ANY-TIME!
GIGGLE!
WELL, IF THAT ISN'T A SLAP IN THE OLD GROUND BEEF!

HERE'S YOUR PINS BACK, JUGHEAD!
BUT, GIRLS--!
TELL IT TO YOUR NEW CHEF!
4

I THINK THIS IS THE MOST DELICIOUS ITEM!
Oh, YEAH? AND WHAT PRAY TELL ARE YOU EATING, ARCHIE?

I MADE A DOUBLE BURGER FROM BOTH OF YOUR PATTIES!
I LIKE IT MUCH BETTER THAN MONIQUE'S!

HE PREFERS BOTH OF OUR PATTIES! DID YOU HEAR THAT, BETTY?!
I DID! AND YOU KNOW, I NEVER ACTUALLY REALIZED, BUT HE'S KINDA CUTE!
YOU'RE RIGHT! HE IS CUTE!
ESPECIALLY WHEN HE'S ENJOYING OUR FOOD!

CAN WE GET YOU ANOTHER ONE OF THOSE DELICIOUS DOUBLE BURGERS, CUTIE?!
YEAH, WHAT CAN WE GET YOU, HAND-SOME?
YOU KNOW, MONIQUE, SUDDENLY EVERYTHING SEEMS JUST RIGHT!
OUI!
The END

Betty and Veronica in "CHORES"

WHAT DO YOU MEAN, YOU CAN'T GO TO THE BEACH WITH ME NOW?

WHAT'S THE MATTER, BABY?

EVERYONE IS TOO BUSY TO GO TO THE BEACH WITH ME THIS MORNING!
WHY?
SLAM

THEY SAY THEY HAVE TO DO THEIR CHORES FIRST!

Script: Jim Ruth / Pencils: Dan DeCarlo / Inks: Rudy Lapick / Letters: Bill Yoshida

CAN YOU IMAGINE THAT--CHORES!!?

THERE'S NOTHING WRONG WITH THAT, RONNIE! LOTS OF PEOPLE DO CHORES!

AND IT'S A GOOD THING TO DO... IT BUILDS CHARACTER!

YOU SHOULD TRY DOING SOME CHORES AROUND HERE, RONNIE!
DADDY!

THAT'S WHY WE HAVE A BUTLER, MAID AND GARDENER... SO I DON'T HAVE TO DO CHORES!
2

RONNIE'S RIGHT... WE HAVE A BUTLER, MAID AND GARDENER!

I WONDER HOW THEY'D LIKE THE DAY OFF!

THANK YOU VERY MUCH, MR. LODGE!
YES! THANK YOU, SIR!

WHERE ARE THEY GOING?
I'VE GIVEN THEM THE DAY OFF!

NOW YOU CAN DO SOME CHORES!
3

HERE'S YOUR LIST OF CHORES FOR THE DAY... I'LL SEE YOU LATER!

HOW AM I SUPPOSED TO GET ALL THIS DONE TODAY?
OH, YOU'LL THINK OF SOMETHING!

I'LL THINK OF SOMETHING, HE SAYS--
I'LL THINK OF SOMETHING!

HE'S RIGHT!
I DID THINK OF SOMETHING!

THANKS, DADDY!
?
4

LATER..
JUGGIE, HAVE YOU SEEN ARCHIE?
NO, I DON'T KNOW WHERE HE IS!

LET'S ASK RONNIE! MAYBE SHE KNOWS!

RONNIE... WHERE'S ARCHIE?

I DON'T UNDERSTAND WHY HE'S NOT HERE!

HE SHOULD HAVE FINISHED MY CHORES BY NOW!
?
!
END

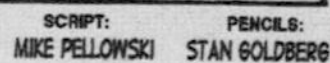

SCRIPT: MIKE PELLOWSKI PENCILS: STAN GOLDBERG INKING: JOHN LOWE LETTERING: JACK MORELLI

Betty in MY LOSS IS MY GAIN

MAYBE YOU LEFT IT HOME!
NO! I SPECIFICALLY REMEMBER TAKING IT OUT OF MY PIGGY BANK!
BUT THEN WHAT DID I DO WITH IT?
WELL, YOU OBVIOUSLY DIDN'T PUT IT IN ANY OF YOUR POCKETS!
THAT'S RIGHT! THESE SHORTS ARE KINDA SNUG! SO I PUT IT IN A BOOK!
AND THE BOOK'S AT HOME!
NOOO! THE BOOK'S AT THE LIBRARY!
I STOPPED TO RETURN IT BEFORE I CAME TO POP'S!
THEN LET'S GET MOVING!
Pant! Puff! MISS DEWEY, DID ANYONE FIND A FIVE DOLLAR BILL IN A BOOK THAT GOT TURNED IN TODAY?
NO, DEARIE!
INFORMATION

IT COULD'VE SLIPPED OUT OF THE BOOK!
LET'S RETRACE YOUR STEPS!
RIVERDALE LIBRARY EST. 1941

WAIT! I TOOK A SHORTCUT THROUGH ALLEGAHAPPENYBURGEN PARK!
THAT MUST HAVE BEEN A LONG TRIP!
ALLEGAHAPPENYBURGEN PARK

HALFWAY THROUGH, I TRIPPED OVER THAT BUSH! THE BOOK FLEW OUT OF MY HANDS!
MAYBE THE MONEY WENT FLYING, TOO!

I DON'T SEE IT HERE!
LET'S KEEP GOING... MAYBE I LOST IT CLOSER TO HOME!

HOME'S THIS WAY, ISN'T IT?
I TOOK A SIDE TRIP PAST ARCHIE'S HOUSE!
BIRCH ST.
ELM ST.

I FORGOT! TO BETTY, ALL ROADS LEAD PAST ARCHIE'S HOUSE!
YEEEK!!
ARCHIE'S MOWING HIS LAWN!!
RRRRR

THERE'S SOMETHING TERRIBLE ABOUT THAT?
HE'S GOING TO CHOP UP MY FIVE DOLLARS! STOP!
RRRRR
JUST A MINUTE-- I CAN'T HEAR--
TOO LATE!
RRRRR
RIP PIP POW

THERE! NOW, WHAT'S WRONG?
I THINK YOU JUST DESTROYED GOVERNMENT PROPERTY!

I LOST MY FIVE DOLLAR BILL ON YOUR LAWN, AND YOU JUST RAN OVER IT!
THOSE SCRAPS OF PAPER? THAT'S NOT MONEY!

JUST?!? IT MEANT AN ICE-COLD REFRESHING SODA TO ME!!
SOB!
TELL YOU WHAT...
AFTER I FINISH HERE AND DAD PAYS ME, I'LL TREAT YOU BOTH TO SODAS!
REALLY?

YOU GUYS CAUGHT ME JUST IN TIME! I WAS THINKING OF GOING OVER TO VERONICA'S!
WE SAVED YOU FROM A FATE WORSE THAN DEATH!
$ $

WHAT DO YOU SUPPOSE HAPPENED TO THAT FIVE I LOST!?
PROBABLY PICKED UP BY SOMEONE ELSE!

EVEN NOW THEY CAN'T BELIEVE THEIR GOOD FORTUNE!
UNDOUBTEDLY!

DEPENDS ON WHO WE'RE TALKING ABOUT--!
FIVE DOLLARS! HOW QUAINT! I DIDN'T KNOW THEY WERE STILL MAKING SUCH SMALL DENOMINATIONS!
$ $

HEY! I FOUND A FIVE DOLLAR BILL! ARE THEY STILL IN PRINT?
THAT'S GOTTA BE MINE!
ToDay's Specials BURGER
POP'S

HUH? ARE YOU SURE?
I'LL PROVE IT!!

THE SERIAL NUMBER IN THE UPPER LEFT IS DA226395B, IN THE LOWER RIGHT CORNER IS THE LETTER B AND THE NUMBER 25, AND IT'S A SERIES 2002 BILL!
SON OF A GUN!

HOW COME YOU CAN REMEMBER ALL THAT BUT CAN'T REMEMBER WHERE YOU LOST IT?!
THE THOUGHT OF ARCHIE WAS DRIVING ALL OTHER THOUGHTS OUT OF MY MIND!

I ALMOST DIDN'T RECOGNIZE IT AS MONEY! I RARELY CARRY ANYTHING SMALLER THAN A FIFTY!
I RARELY GET A PEEK AT OL' BEN FRANKLIN! MIND LETTING ME SEE ONE?
I GOT MY FIVE BACK AND GOT TO SHARE A SODA WITH YOU, ARCHIE! THAT'S QUITE A PROFIT IN MY BOOK!
DO TELL!
END

Betty and Veronica in "SAIL TALE"

ISN'T IT UNUSUAL FOR A GIRL TO BE ENTERING NEXT WEEK'S WIND-SURFING RACE ?

I SEE NO REASON WHY WE GIRLS CAN'T COMPETE, TOO!

THAT'S WHY I BUILT MY OWN WIND SURFER!

THAT'S VERY COMMENDABLE OF BETTY!

PRESS

Script: George Gladir / Pencils: Dan DeCarlo Jr. / Inks: Rudy Lapick / Letters: Bill Yoshida

SHE JUST WANTS TO GET PUBLICITY SO SHE CAN ATTRACT BOYS!

WELL, I'M NOT LETTING HER GET AWAY WITH IT.
--I'M GOING TO BE THE ONE WHO MAKES **THE BIG SPLASH** AT THAT RACE!
1

THE DAY OF THE RACE —
RONNIE! WHAT A SURPRISE!
I DIDN'T KNOW YOU WERE INTO WIND-SURFING!
YES! I AM!

DADDY HIRED THE GREAT JOE HAOLI TO COACH ME!

WHAT'S MORE, I HAVE THE BEST WIND-SURFER MONEY CAN BUY!

HOW DO YOU LIKE *MY* WIND-SURFER?
YAWN! NOT BAD--- FOR A HOMEMADE JOB!

I JUST HOPE YOUR SEAMS HOLD IN THIS WIND!

BOOM!
--- AND THEY'RE OFF!
LOOK AT VERONICA GO!
5
8
3

GOSH! THAT WIND IS STRONG!
RRIP

UH-OH! MY SAIL JUST TORE!
--- I'LL HAVE TO MANEUVER VERY CAREFULLY!

THINGS ARE GOING ACCORDING TO PLAN!
--- I'VE GRABBED A BIG EARLY LEAD!
3

WHAT THE--? THE WIND HAS SUDDENLY DIED DOWN!
7

BETTY! WHAT ARE YOU DOING HERE?
3
7

THAT TRICKY VICKY IS USING THE FORCE OF THE WAVES TO MOVE!
7

I'LL SHOW HER THAT TWO CAN PLAY THE SAME GAME!

I CAN TACK AND JIBE JUST AS WELL AS YOU, MS. COOPER!

OOPS!

4

BETTY COOPER WINS!

I SEE HERE, BETTY WON YESTERDAY'S RACE!
HMPF!

BUT I HAVE TO ADMIT YOU KEPT YOUR WORD!
?

YOU SAID YOU'D MAKE A BIGGER SPLASH THAN BETTY!
BETTY COOPER WINS BIG RACE
WINNER
VERONICA LODGE IN COSTLY SPILL
VERONICA LODGE IN COSTLY SPILL
END

Veronica in DEEP THINKER!

OKAY! OKAY! I GIVE UP! YOU CAN STOP PESTERING ME! YOU CAN GO DEEP SEA FISHING WITH ME!

OH, THANK YOU, DADDYKINS! USUALLY, YOU GO ALONE!

SCRIPT: MIKE PELLOWSKI
PENCILS: DAN PARENT
INKS: JIM AMASH

NOW CAN I HAVE SOME MONEY FOR SHOPPING?
MONEY? S-SHOPPING? WHAT FOR?

TO BUY A FISHING OUTFIT, OF COURSE!

YOU DON'T EXPECT ME TO GO OUT ON OUR BOAT DRESSED LIKE AN ORDINARY, UNFASHIONABLE FISHER PERSON, DO YOU? WHAT WILL THE SKIPPER THINK?
SHE'S RIGHT, HIRAM! WE DO HAVE AN IMAGE TO UPHOLD!
GROAN!

SURE! WHY NOT? HERE! GO! SHOP! IF YOU CAN'T FISH IN STYLE, WHY FISH AT ALL?!

HOW TRUE, DADDYKINS! THANKS FOR UNDER-STANDING!
I'LL GO WITH YOU, DEAR! FISHING IS TOO SMELLY FOR ME, BUT I'LL HELP YOU SELECT AN OUTFIT!

LATER, AT THE STORE...
WE'RE LOOKING FOR A STYLISH OUTFIT THAT WILL HOOK SOME MARLON BRANDOS!
THAT'S MARLIN, MOMMYKINS! YOU'RE THINKING OF AN ACTOR!

OH, PISH-POSH! BIG HAM.., BIG FISH... WHAT'S THE DIFFERENCE?

SHORTLY...
IS THIS ONE SHIP-SHAPE?
ABSOLUTELY NOT! IT HIDES YOUR FIGURE!

AFTER A QUICK CHANGE...
HOW ABOUT THIS? IS IT BETTER?
GULP! NO, NO! NOW YOU'VE GONE OVERBOARD!

FINALLY...
THAT'S PERFECT, DARLING! YOU'LL HOOK A POOR FISH FOR SURE IN THAT CUTE OUTFIT!
THANKS, MOTHER!
Brenda's Boutiq
IS SHE GOING FISHING, OR HUNTING FOR A BOYFRIEND?

LATER, BACK AT THE LODGE MANSION...
YOU TWO WERE GONE ALL AFTERNOON! DID YOU FIND SOMETHING YOU LIKE?
YES, DADDYKINS! NOW I'M ALMOST READY TO FISH!

I JUST HAVE ONE QUESTION!
SIGH! NOW WHAT?

WHAT WILL WE DO FOR LUNCH ON THE BOAT? IT'S NOT LIKE WE'LL BE TAKING OUR YACHT, WHICH HAS A GALLEY AND A CHEF!
HUH? CHEF? GALLEY?
VERONICA, WE'RE GOING ON A FISHING TRIP, NOT A CRUISE! THE SKIPPER USUALLY PACKS SOME SANDWICHES FOR LUNCH!
S-SANDWICHES-ICK!
WOULDN'T IT BE BETTER IF I ASKED THE HOUSE CHEF TO PACK US A GOURMET PICNIC BASKET FOR LUNCH?
THAT SOUNDS LIKE A WONDERFUL IDEA! YOU KNOW VERONICA HAS A SENSITIVE STOMACH, HIRAM!
FINE! JUST TERRIFIC! SOME MACHO FISHING TRIP THIS IS TURNING OUT TO BE!
IS THERE ANYTHING ELSE? SUPPOSE I TELL THE SKIPPER TO MAKE SURE THE BOAT DOESN'T ROCK TOO MUCH?!
OH, DADDYKINS! WOULD YOU? AFTER ALL, I AM USED TO RIDING ON BIGGER BOATS!
CALM DOWN, HIRAM! YOU SHOULD BE GLAD VERONICA IS FINALLY TAKING AN INTEREST IN ONE OF YOUR HOBBIES!
YOU'RE RIGHT, DEAR! I'M SORRY! I'LL TRY NOT TO LOSE MY TEMPER AGAIN!

THE NEXT DAY, AT THE DOCK...
BYE! HAVE FUN! I'LL MEET YOU HERE LATER! ENJOY YOUR GOURMET LUNCH!
BYE, MOTHER! WE WILL!
LIL LODGE II

EXCUSE ME, CAPTAIN MORGAN, BUT THIS LIFE JACKET DOESN'T MATCH MY OUTFIT! DO YOU HAVE ONE IN LAVENDER?
AH... NO, MISS LODGE! I'M SORRY!

FORGET ABOUT LAVENDER LIFE JACKETS, SKIPPER, AND GET US OUT WHERE THE BIG FISH SWIM!
YES, SIR, MR. LODGE!

LATER...
DADDYKINS, THE BOAT IS ROCKING AGAIN AND MY POLE IS HEAVY! I HOPE I DON'T BREAK A NAIL!
VERONICA, WILL YOU PLEASE BE QUIET AND LET ME FISH?
LIL LODGE II

AT THE END OF THE DAY...
YOO-HOO! HIRAM! SORRY I'M A LITTLE LATE! HOW WAS YOUR DAY?
HUMPH! DON'T ASK! IT WAS TERRIBLE!

I'M TRYING NOT TO LOSE MY TEMPER, BUT THE TRUTH IS... VERONICA SPOILED MY FISHING TRIP!
OH, MY GOSH! WHAT DID SHE DO? WAS IT HER OUTFIT? WAS IT THE GOURMET LUNCH?
NO! NO! IT WASN'T ANY OF THOSE THINGS!
WELL, THEN, WHAT WAS IT?

GRR... VERONICA CAUGHT THE BIGGEST FISH!
HI, MOMMYKINS! LOOK AT THE WHOPPER I HOOKED!

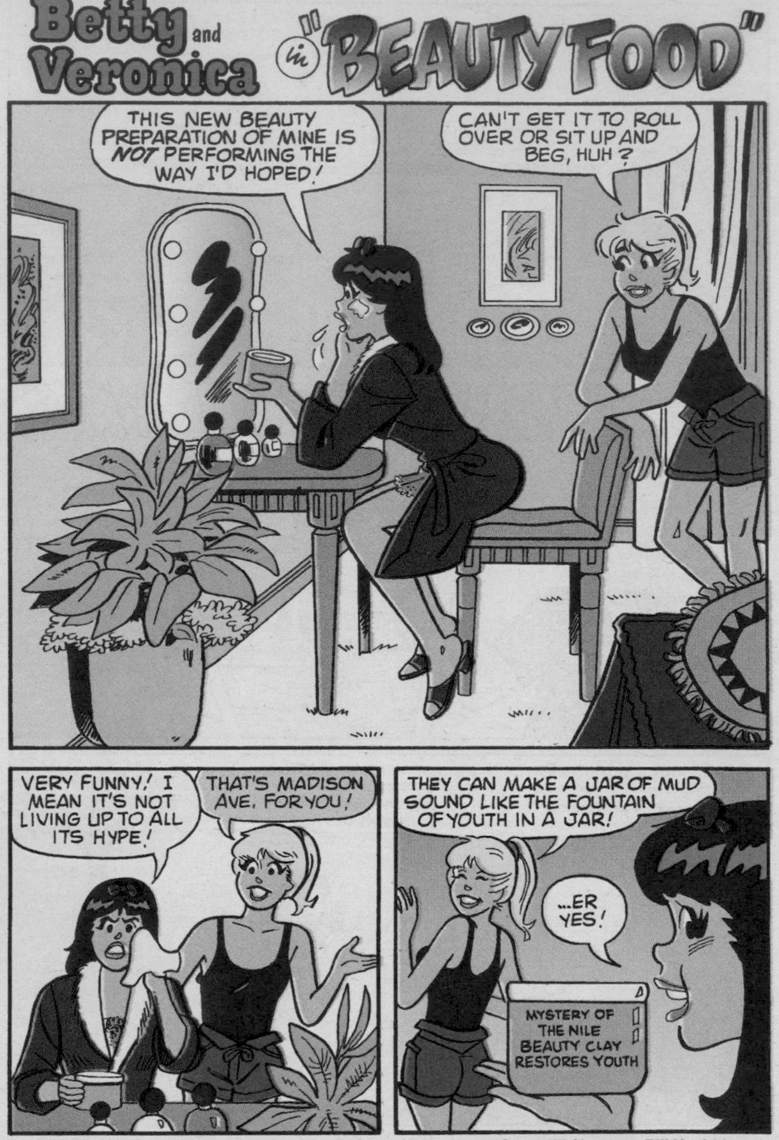

Betty and Veronica in "BEAUTY FOOD"

THIS NEW BEAUTY PREPARATION OF MINE IS *NOT* PERFORMING THE WAY I'D HOPED!

CAN'T GET IT TO ROLL OVER OR SIT UP AND BEG, HUH?

Script: Kathleen Webb / Pencils: Dan DeCarlo / Inks: Henry Scarpelli / Letters: Bill Yoshida

WELL, ANYWAY, IT WAS SUPPOSED TO MAKE A "NEW ME" IN TEN DAYS!
IT HASN'T EVEN STARTED YET!
R

GIVE IT A CHANCE!
MAYBE ON YOU IT TAKES A MONTH!

HA, HA, VERY FUNNY, BUT I WASTED $ 50 ON THIS MESS!

(SIGH) AND I'M NOT SURE DADDY'D LET ME FLY TO PARIS AGAIN SO SOON FOR SOMETHING NEW!
NO PROBLEM!

STAY HOME AND MAKE YOUR OWN BEAUTY PRODUCTS INSTEAD!
WHAT DO YOU MEAN?

I GOT A NEW BOOK THAT TELLS HOW TO MAKE BEAUTY PRODUCTS USING ALL NATURAL INGREDIENTS!
2

C'MON OVER TO MY PLACE AND WE'LL HAVE A MAKEOVER SESSION!
ALL RIGHT!

AND SO:
STRAWBERRIES ... EGGS... YOGURT... CUCUMBER... MAYONNAISE...WHEAT GERM...
GOOD! WE'VE GOT EVERYTHING WE NEED!

THE BOOK SUGGESTS WE USE WITCH HAZEL FOR TONER!
I'VE GOT SOME UPSTAIRS IN THE BATHROOM!

LET'S TAKE THE MAYONNAISE WITH US!
ARE WE GONNA MAKE SANDWICHES UPSTAIRS?

SILLY! WE'RE GOING TO USE THIS ON OUR HAIR!
YOU CALL ME SILLY, AND YOU'RE THE ONE WHO WANTS TO PUT MAYONNAISE IN YOUR HAIR?

A COUPLE OF TABLESPOONS WILL MAKE YOUR HAIR SILKY AND SOFT!
IT'LL SLIP RIGHT THROUGH ARCHIE'S FINGERS!

IF HE DOESN'T THINK I SMELL LIKE A SANDWICH!
SHUCKS... AND I FORGOT THE BOLOGNA AND CHEESE!

MEANWHILE, DOWNSTAIRS, IN THE KITCHEN...
BETTY? YOO HOO! IT'S ME, JUGHEAD!

HMM, WHAT'S THIS?
STRAWBERRIES... YOGURT... CUCUMBERS... WHEAT GERM... EGGS!

YUM! LOOKS LIKE...
LUNCH.!!
SLOBBER!
DROOL!
DRIP!

WOW! I DIDN'T THINK ANYTHING COULD MAKE MY MILLION DOLLAR TRESSES FEEL SOFTER!
THAT MAYO REALLY WORKED!

I CAN'T WAIT TO TRY THE REST OF THOSE NATURAL BEAUTY AIDES!
THEN LET'S GO DOWNSTAIRS, AND... HUH?
SNIFF!
SNIFF!
4

JUGHEAD!! YOU-YOU ATE ALL THE MAKEOVER INGREDIENTS!
IS THAT WHAT WAS SO TASTY?

AND HERE I THOUGHT IT WAS ONLY AN OMELETTE AND STRAWBERRY CREPES!
HE USED EVERY LAST CRUMB TO MAKE THEM, TOO!

OH, WELL! LET'S GO OVER TO MY PLACE! I'M SURE GASTON'S GOT EVERYTHING WE NEED IN HIS KITCHEN!
EH-HEH!

I JUST CAME FROM OVER THERE... GASTON TOSSED ME OUT FOR EATING THE REFRIGERATOR CLEAN!
AUUGH!!

SPLOOP!
MAYO

THERE! NOW YOUR SKULL IS AS BEAUTIFUL AS YOUR STOMACH!
OH, YEAH? THIS IS ONE BEAUTY PRODUCT THAT'S NOT LIVING UP TO ITS HYPE!
MAYO
END

Archie in RAINY DAY BEACH BLUES

ANOTHER RAINY DAY! I'M BEGINNING TO THINK THAT WE MIGHT NOT GET TO GO TO THE BEACH AT ALL THIS SUMMER, ARCHIE!

WELL, TRY TO LOOK ON THE BRIGHT SIDE OF THINGS, BETTY...

WHAT BRIGHT SIDE? THE SUN HASN'T COME OUT IN TWO WEEKS!

FRANCIS **BONNET** WRITER | BILL **GALVAN** PENCILS | BEN **GALVAN** INKS | GLENN **WHITMORE** COLORS | JACK **MORELLI** LETTERS

AT LEAST THE PLANTS OUTSIDE ARE GETTING PLENTY OF WATER.
PLANTS NEED SUNLIGHT, TOO!

Hmm...THAT EXPLAINS WHY THE PLANT I KEEP IN MY CLOSET IS DYING.
I JUST WISH I COULD SPEND A DAY WITH MY FEET IN THE SAND, GETTING A TAN, AND LOOKING OVER THE WATER INSTEAD OF BEING STUCK IN THE HOUSE AGAIN.

IF THAT'S ALL YOU WANT, I THINK I KNOW A WAY TO MAKE IT HAPPEN!
WHAT DO YOU MEAN, ARCHIE?

GET YOUR BATHING SUIT ON, BETTY!
TODAY IS GOING TO BE A BEACH DAY!
HOW MANY TIMES DO I NEED TO TELL HIM THAT UMBRELLAS ONLY WORK WHEN YOU OPEN THEM?

THAT SHOULD DO IT, WORKING ON THE DRAMA CLUB ART SETS REALLY PAID OFF!
JUST IN TIME, TOO... I TEXTED BETTY A WHILE AGO AND SHE SHOULD BE HERE ANY--
ARCHIE? WHAT IS ALL THIS?

SINCE WE COULDN'T GO TO THE BEACH BECAUSE OF THE LOUSY WEATHER--
--I THOUGHT I COULD MAKE OUR OWN LITTLE BEACH RIGHT HERE!

SO, DO YOU LIKE IT?
ARCHIE, I...I...

THIS IS THE MOST AMAZING THING ANYONE HAS EVER DONE FOR ME!!
WELL, THEN LET'S ENJOY IT BEFORE I PASS OUT, BECAUSE YOU JUST KNOCKED THE WIND OUT OF ME!

I'VE BEEN SHARING PHOTOS OF THE BEACH YOU MADE FOR ME ALL ACROSS SOCIAL MEDIA. YOU SHOULD SEE THE COMMENTS!
IT'S TOO BAD THAT NONE OF THOSE OTHER PEOPLE ARE ABLE TO ENJOY THE BEACH ON A RAINY DAY!

WHO *SAYS* NO ONE ELSE IS ABLE TO ENJOY THIS BEACH?
REGGIE! WHAT ARE *YOU* DOING HERE?

I SAW THE PICTURES OF YOUR BEACH THAT BETTY POSTED ONLINE. TSK, TSK, ARCHIE. WHY DIDN'T YOU THINK TO INVITE YOUR GOOD FRIEND REGGIE?
SINCE *WHEN* ARE WE GOOD FRIENDS?
IT'S OKAY, ARCHIE. LET HIM STAY FOR A WHILE. IT'S NOT LIKE WE DON'T HAVE ROOM FOR A THIRD PERSON.

BETTY, I ALWAYS KNEW YOU WERE A SMART DECISION-MAKER. WELL, EXCEPT FOR YOUR DECISION TO CONTINUE HANGING OUT WITH ARCHIE.
LISTEN, REGGIE, I DON'T HAVE TO PUT UP WITH THIS!
HEY, GUYS! I BROUGHT *HOT DOGS!*

RONNIE? JUG? YOU GUYS ARE HERE, TOO?
WHEN WE SAW THE PICTURES THAT BETTY POSTED OF YOUR BEACH, WE JUST ASSUMED THAT IT WAS AN *OVERSIGHT* THAT WE WEREN'T INVITED.
YEAH, I MEAN IT'S NOT LIKE YOU'D INVITE REGGIE HERE OVER *US!*

WELL, IT'S GETTING A LITTLE CROWDED, BUT THERE SHOULD BE ENOUGH ROOM FOR ALL OF US.
DID YOU SAY YOU BROUGHT HOT DOGS?
THEY'RE JUST FOR ME.
I GUESS WE'LL BE OKAY AS LONG AS NO ONE *ELSE* SHOWS UP...

I KNEW I'D FIND THE BEACH!
THAT'S ONLY BECAUSE I LED THE WAY!
HEY, EVERYONE!
HAVE ROOM FOR FOUR MORE?
WE, Uh, I...

THANKS, ARCHIE!
IT'S SO SWEET OF BETTY TO POST THOSE PHOTOS OF YOUR BEACH SO WE'D ALL KNOW TO COME!
WELL, THAT WASN'T EXACTLY WHAT I WAS--
YUM! I SMELL HOT DOGS!
BACK OFF, MOOSE! THEY'RE MINE!

WELL IT'S NOT LIKE THE REAL BEACH DOESN'T GET CROWDED SOMETIMES...
THIS ISN'T JUST CROWDED--THIS IS A FIRE HAZARD!

I THINK THAT THE ENTIRE TOWN SHOWED UP!
I GUESS OUR BEACH WAS FUN WHILE IT LASTED...

HEY, BETTY, I DON'T THINK WE HAVE TO GIVE UP ON OUR BEACH DAY JUST YET!
WHAT DO YOU MEAN?

THE RAIN HAS STOPPED!
AND EVERYONE IN THE GARAGE IS TOO PREOCCUPIED WITH YOUR ARTIFICIAL BEACH TO EVEN NOTICE!

ARE YOU THINKING WHAT I'M THINKING?
THAT WE SHOULD TRY AND SNEAK OUT OF HERE!

GOOD GUESS.
LET'S GO!

SOON...
WE HAVE THE ENTIRE BEACH TO OURSELVES!
NOT ONLY THAT, BUT IT'S A LOT ROOMIER HERE THAN IN YOUR GARAGE!

SO, WHEN DO YOU THINK EVERYONE WILL NOTICE THAT THE SUN CAME OUT?
HOPEFULLY NOT UNTIL SEPTEMBER!
The END

Archie in A DATE FOR ALL SEASONS

OL' PAL, YOU LOOK DOWN ABOUT SOMETHING!
I AM, JUG... I AM!

I TOOK VERONICA OUT LAST NIGHT...
...AND SHE INSISTED ON GOING TO THE MOST EXPENSIVE PLACE IN TOWN!

AFTERWARDS, SHE DID NOTHING BUT COMPLAIN ABOUT THE FOOD AND SERVICE!

WELL, AT LEAST THE WORST IS OVER!

BUT THAT'S JUST IT... IT ISN'T OVER!

WHAT DO YOU MEAN?

GLADIR * BOLLING * AMASH

I PROMISED BETTY I'D TAKE HER OUT TONIGHT...
... BUT NOW I'M BROKE AND MY CAR ISN'T WORKING!
SO POSTPONE YOUR DATE... BETTY WILL UNDERSTAND!
ELM ST

BUT I CAN'T POSTPONE IT!
IT'S HER BIRTHDAY!
YOU DO HAVE A PROBLEM!

I WAS HOPING TO... UH... MAYBE BORROW A FEW BUCKS FROM YOU!
HA!
EXCUSE ME FOR LAUGHING BUT--

--NEED I SAY MORE?

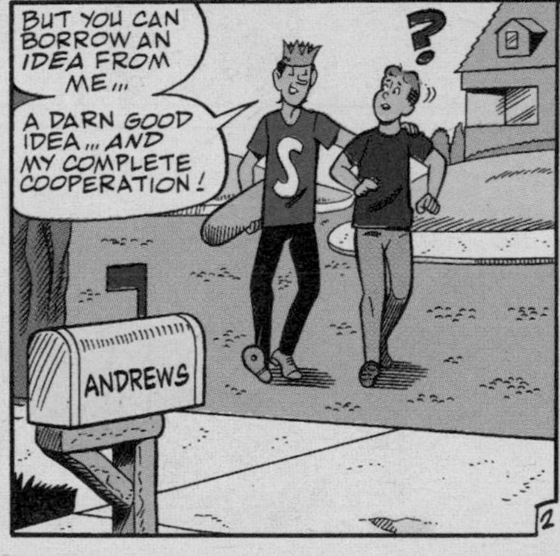
BUT YOU CAN BORROW AN IDEA FROM ME...
A DARN GOOD IDEA... AND MY COMPLETE COOPERATION!
?
ANDREWS

LET'S YOU AND I GRAB OUR SKATEBOARDS AND HEAD FOR THE NEARBY "FOOD DISCOUNT CLUB"!
BUT IF WE DON'T HAVE ANY MONEY WHAT'S THE POINT OF IT?
ANDREWS

FOOD DISCOUNT CLUB
'CAUSE THE FOOD CLUB SERVES ALL THOSE FREE YUMMY SAMPLES!

I FIND YOU USUALLY CAN CAGE TWO OR THREE SAMPLES FROM EACH OF THE DOZEN SERVERS!
SAMPLE OUR TASTY TID-BITS

OKAY, WE'VE COLLECTED ALL THESE SAMPLES! NOW WHAT?
WE TAKE IT OVER TO MY PLACE AND STORE IT IN THE FRIDGE!

IT'S TAKING ALL OF MY HUMONGOUS WILL POWER NOT TO GOBBLE THESE TREATS ON YOU!
BUT I PROMISED BETTY A DINNER!
AND A DINNER SHE WILL GET! TRUST ME!
TONIGHT, TAKE BETTY TO THE STARLUCK'S BEVERAGE SHOP... AND I'LL TAKE CARE OF THE REST!
JUST CALL ME ON YOUR CELL BEFORE YOU GET THERE!

? WE'RE NOT GOING TO DINNER IN YOUR CAR?!
WE DON'T WANT TO CONTRIBUTE TO GLOBAL WARMING, DO WE?

JUG, WE'RE LEAVING! WE SHOULD BE THERE IN FIVE MINUTES!
AND I'LL BE WAIT-ING!

BUT, ARCHIE, THIS IS A STARLUCK'S BEVERAGE STORE!
THEY DON'T SERVE DINNER AT A COFFEE SHOP!
STARLUC
THEY WILL TONIGHT ...I THINK!

AND HERE'S OUR WAITER EXTRAORDI-NAIRE!
AT YOUR SERVICE, MADAME AND MONSIEUR!
RESERVED

DOESN'T LOOK LIKE THEY DO MUCH BUSINESS HERE AT NIGHT!
WHICH IS WHY I RESERVED THIS SPECIAL TABLE JUST FOR YOU TWO!
RESERVED

YOU'RE IN LUCK, ARCH! I OPENED MY PIGGY BANK--
--AND FOUND ENOUGH TO GET YOU BOTH HOT CHOCOLATES!

HERE YOU ARE!
OUR BEST VINTAGE HOT CHOCOLATE!
STARLUCK'S

NOW ALLOW ME TO LIGHT THIS CANDLE FOR YOU!
HOW ROMANTIC!

I'LL BE RIGHT BACK WITH THE MAIN COURSE!
?HE'S LEAVING! WHERE'S HE GOING?!
TO HIS OWN PRIVATE KITCHEN, I GUESS!

?HE'S BACK SO SOON?

VOILA! THE HOUSE SPECIAL! A GOURMET BUFFET OF YUMMY TREATS... SERVED ON THE BEST PAPER PLATES I COULD GET MY HANDS ON!!

OH, ARCHIE, THIS IS THE MOST FUN MOONLIGHT DINNER I'VE EVER EXPERIENCED!

THE NEXT DAY...
I SPEND A SMALL FORTUNE ON VERONICA, AND SHE COMPLAINS IT'S THE WORST DATE SHE'S EVER BEEN ON!

MY DATE WITH BETTY DIDN'T COST A CENT ...AND SHE'S STILL RAVING ABOUT IT!

I'M SURE THERE'S A MORAL HERE SOMEWHERE... BUT I CAN'T FIGURE IT OUT!

MAYBE SOME DAY YOU WILL!
THE END

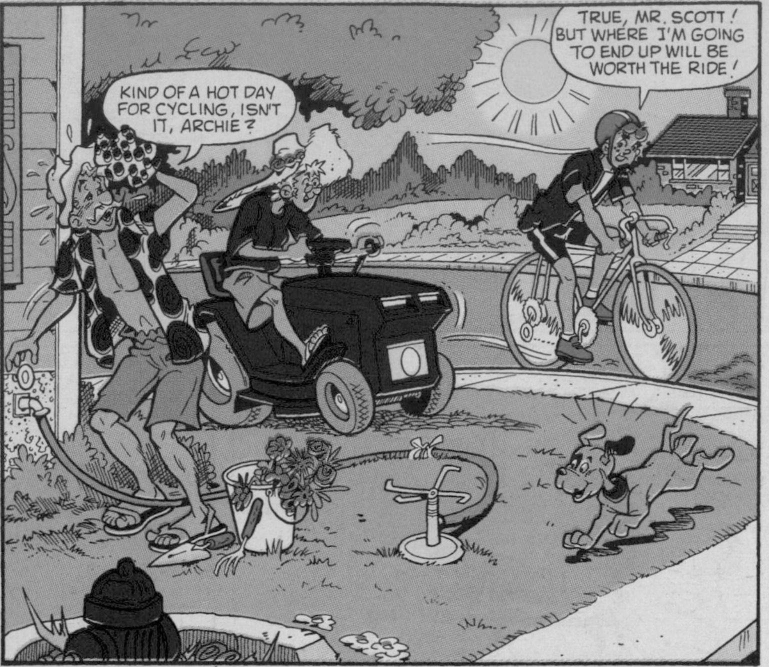

KIND OF A HOT DAY FOR CYCLING, ISN'T IT, ARCHIE?

TRUE, MR. SCOTT! BUT WHERE I'M GOING TO END UP WILL BE WORTH THE RIDE!

Script: Bob Bolling / Pencils: Doug Crane / Inks: Mike Esposito / Letters: Bill Yoshida

AAAARRRRGGH!
FWIP! FWIP! FWIP! FWIP!
GRRRRRR

OOOOOPS! ...SORRY!
S'OKAY! ...IT WASN'T YOUR FAULT...
FWIP FWIP FWIP
GRRRR

I'M SOAKED TO THE SKIN! BUT THE SUN WILL DRY ME OFF!
RIVERDALE
TOWN LIMITS

NOW THAT I'M OUT OF TOWN, THERE'S NOTHING AHEAD BUT OPEN ROAD!

I CAN'T WAIT TO GET WHERE I'M GOING!

UH-OH! IT LOOKS LIKE WE'RE IN FOR A SUDDEN SHOWER...

NO SENSE IN STOPPING! MAYBE I CAN OUTRUN THE RAIN...

RUMBLE! CRACK! BOOM!
GAHH! THANK GOODNESS THERE'S NO LIGHTNING!

HUMMMPH! THAT WAS QUICK! GOODBYE, SHOWERS! WELCOME BACK, SUN!

WHEW! EVEN THOUGH I'M DRENCHED, I'M STILL HOT!

BOY, IT REALLY MUST HAVE RAINED HERE! LOOK AT ALL THESE BIG PUDDLES!

THE SUN IS SO HOT, I'M ALMOST DRY AGAIN!

YEOW-W-W!
BLUB
BLUB
LIGHTNIN' MOVERS INC.
LIGHTNIN' MOVERS
SPLOOSH!

I DON'T BELIEVE THIS! SOAKED AGAIN!

AT LEAST I DON'T HAVE MUCH FURTHER TO GO!
4

AH-HAH! HERE'S THE TURNOFF! ... IT WON'T BE LONG NOW!

AT LAST! THE OL' SWIMMIN' HOLE SURE LOOKS GOOD!

SECONDS LATER...
EEE...YESSS! THIS IS THE MOMENT I'VE BEEN WAITING FOR...!!

YAH... HOOOOOOooo!

SPLASH!

GETTING A CHANCE TO COOL OFF IN THIS WATER WAS SURE WORTH THAT LONG RIDE!
END

Archie -in- "THE TREATMENT"

HEY, WOW! YOU LOST A LOT OF WEIGHT OVER THE SUMMER, MR. WEATHERBEE!

IT SURE MAKES YOU **LOOK YOUNGER!**

Script & Pencils: Joe Edwards / Inks: Rudy Lapick / Letters: Bill Yoshida

TSK.! ISN'T THAT DREADFUL?
DREADFUL?

HIS ANNUAL FACULTY BUTTER-UP — TO EASE HIM INTO THE NEW SEMESTER!

YOU'RE SO CYNICAL! I THOUGHT HE WAS QUITE SINCERE!

ABOUT AS SINCERE AS VERONICA PRAISING BETTY'S CLOTHES!

I WOULDN'T MIND HIS FLATTERY, IF ONLY IT WEREN'T SO OBVIOUS!

HE'S ABOUT AS SUBTLE AS A PIE IN THE FACE!
2

I THINK YOU'RE ALL WRONG! ARCHIE IS A BRIGHT LAD!

IF HE WANTED TO BUTTER US UP, I'M SURE HE'D BE SO SUBTLE, WE WOULDN'T EVEN BE AWARE OF IT!
YOU DREAMER!

MEANWHILE--
ARCHIEKINS! I'M SO GLAD YOU CAME BY!

IT'S NICE TO BE WANTED!
I WANT YOU TO DO SOMETHING FOR ME!

WE'RE REPLACING THAT CARPET IN THE UPSTAIRS HALL!
WHERE DO I COME IN?

THE DELIVERY MEN AT THE RUG COMPANY ARE ON STRIKE!
SAY NO MORE!
3

YOU'D LIKE ME TO TOOL DOWN IN OLD BETSY AND PICK IT UP!
HOW DID YOU EVER GUESS?
I'M PSYCHIC!
I SHALL RETURN!

IT'S GOOD TO BE GOOD TO RONNIE! IT GETS ME ON HER GOOD SIDE!
AND THAT'S GOOD!

LODGE? YEAH! IT'S THAT RUNNER OVER THERE!
GOTCHA!
RUG SALE

A LITTLE AWKWARD TO HANDLE, BUT NOT TOO HEAVY!

MAN! THIS IS GOING TO SCORE POINTS FOR ME WITH THE WHOLE FAMILY!

UH-OH!

OLD GIRL, YOU PICK THE DARNDEST TIMES TO QUIT ON ME!
WHAP!

SIGH! WELL, THERE'S NOTHING TO DO BUT TO HOOF IT!

NOT ONLY IS IT CLUMSY TO CARRY, BUT IT KEEPS GETTING HEAVIER!

NUTS! I COULD ASK REGGIE FOR A LIFT, BUT THEN HE'D GRAB ALL THE CREDIT!

I'M GETTING POOPED! I'LL STOP HERE AT MR. WEATHERBEE'S AND GET A COLD GLASS OF WATER, AND---

---OOPS!
CLUNK!

OUCH!

DID YOU HEAR SOMETHING OUTSIDE?
IT WAS OUTSIDE! PERHAPS SOMEBODY CALLED!

SIGH! IF THAT'S SUBTLE, MISS GRUNDY, I'D SURE HATE TO SEE HIM GET OBVIOUS!
END

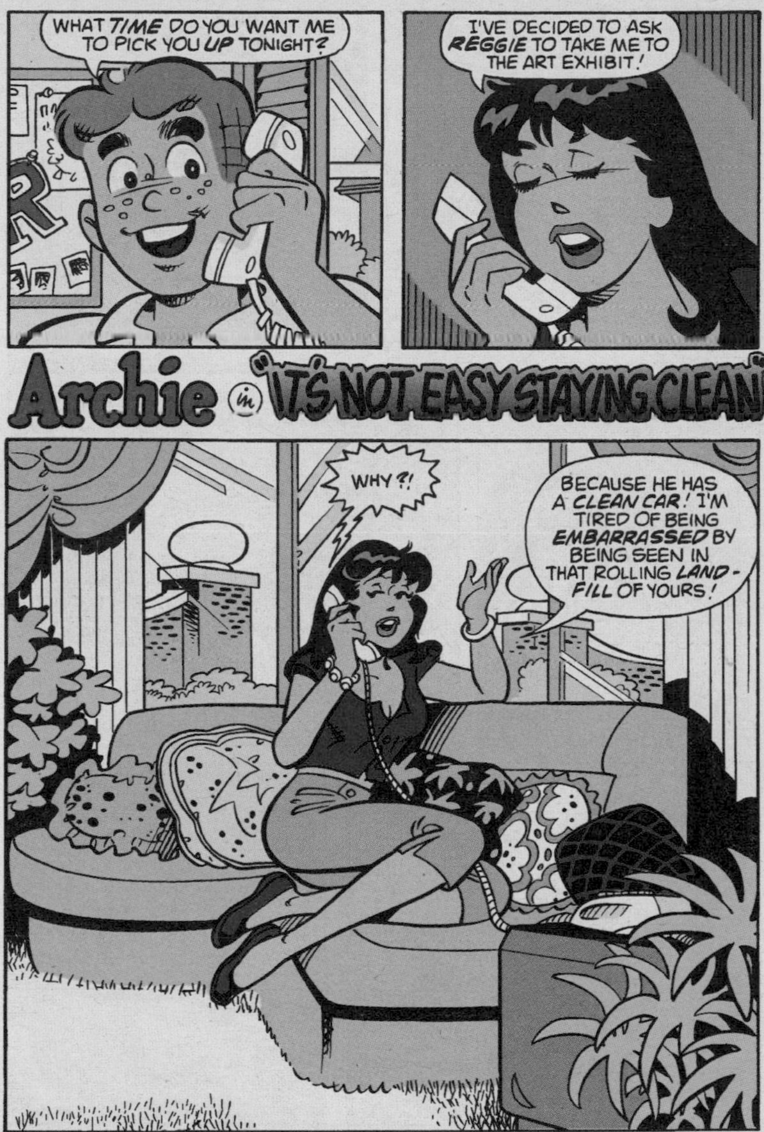

Archie in "IT'S NOT EASY STAYING CLEAN"

WHY?!

BECAUSE HE HAS A CLEAN CAR! I'M TIRED OF BEING EMBARRASSED BY BEING SEEN IN THAT ROLLING LAND-FILL OF YOURS!

Script: Hal Smith / Pencils: Stan Goldberg / Inks: Bob Smith / Letters: Bill Yoshida

I CAN CLEAN IT UP! I'LL GET RIGHT ON IT! I'LL GET JUG TO HELP ME!
DANCE
RIVERDALE

IT'LL SPARKLE LIKE A DIAMOND! IT'LL BE SO CLEAN, YOU WON'T RECOGNIZE IT!
YOU GOT THAT RIGHT...

IF IT'S CLEAN, I WON'T RECOGNIZE IT!

LATER
WHEW! WHAT A JOB!
THAT'S AMAZING!
ARCHI

WHAT'S AMAZING?
WITH ALL THAT DIRT ON IT, I NEVER KNEW WHAT COLOR IT WAS!

VERY FUNNY! DON'T LET IT GET DIRTY WHILE I GET DRESSED!
2

SHOO! SHOO! GO AWAY!

HEY!

GOTCHA!

WHA'CHA DOIN', JUG?

I JUST KEPT A *LEAF* FROM FALLING ON YOUR CAR!

..AND I *SHOOED* AWAY SOME BIRDS!
GOOD *MAN!*

ARE YOU GOING TO TAKE MAIN ST. ?
YES, IT'S THE MOST DIRECT ROUTE!
ARCHI

WHY?
THEY'RE DOING CONSTRUCTION WORK AT SIXTH AND MAIN!

OH, AND THERE'LL BE A LOT OF DUST FLYING AROUND!

THANKS, JUG, I'LL DETOUR AROUND IT!
ARCHI

UH-OH, A WATER MAIN BREAK AHEAD!
VIDEO WORLD
ARCHI

I DON'T WANT TO GET SPLASHED WITH THAT DIRTY WATER!

I'LL DETOUR AROUND THE PARK! TOO MANY LEAVES BLOWING AROUND!
RIVERDALE PARK
ONLY ONE MORE BLOCK TO GO!
ARCHIE
YOU IDIOT!
AAAGH!!
SCREECH!
THIS IS WHAT YOU CALL SPARKLING LIKE A DIAMOND? IT LOOKS WORSE THAN BEFORE!...
...HELLO, REGGIE?
The END

Script: Craig Boldman / Pencils: Rex Lindsey / Inks: Rich Koslowski / Letters: Bill Yoshida

I'LL GET IT TO HIM BEFORE HE *DRIES* UP AND *BLOWS* AWAY!
WHISH!

I'M IMPRESSED! YOU SHOWED REAL *HUSTLE*!
POP!

SPLURT!
MAYBE A LITTLE *TOO MUCH* HUSTLE THERE, HOT DOG!
MY BAD!
HOT DOG

GOTTA MAKE AMENDS! WHERE CAN I GET ANOTHER COLA?

OOH! JUST WHAT THE DOCTOR ORDERED!

HEY! WHAT THE...
WOW! NOW *THAT'S* SERVICE!
I'D ASK WHERE YOU GOT THIS, BUT WHY LOOK A GIFT HORSE IN THE...
OOPS!
FSSSTT!
I'D BETTER GET WITH IT! IT'D BE *EMBARRASSING* IF MY MASTER DIED OF THIRST!
TUMBLE!
HEY, NOW! THE PERFECT SOLUTION'S RIGHT UNDER MY...ER...*NOSE!*
3

I'VE SEEN THE BOSS DRINK OUT OF THIS THING A *ZILLION* TIMES!

NOW TO GET THE *FLOWING* GOING!

WHY DON'T THEY MAKE THESE THINGS EASIER FOR *DOGS* TO OPERATE?

HOT DOG!
OOH! I THINK I SEE WHY!
SPLOOSH!

HE'S GONNA TRADE ME IN FOR A NEW MODEL! *FORTUNATELY* I'VE GOT *ONE* MORE IDEA!

YES! THERE'S ALWAYS LOOSE CHANGE UNDER THE CUSHIONS!

AND A MACHINE ON THE CORNER!
SODA
AND I'VE SEEN JUG WORK THIS MACHINE!
CHA-KLUNK!
CHIPS
YOW! MY NOSE IS STUCK! THE IGNOMINY OF IT!
KLUNK! KLUNK!
TOLD YA! HE CAN'T GET HIS BIG FAT SNOOT OUT WITH IT WRAPPED AROUND THAT SODA!
AT EASE, H.D.!
MAN! HE'S WORN HIMSELF TO A FRAZZLE TRYING TO SCARE UP A REFRESHMENT FOR ME!
PANT! PUFF! I AM A LITTLE TUCKERED AT THAT!
ONE GOOD TURN DESERVES ANOTHER, PAL!
HE'S NO ST. BERNARD, BUT HE'S GOT A LITTLE BIT OF SAINT IN HIM!
THE END

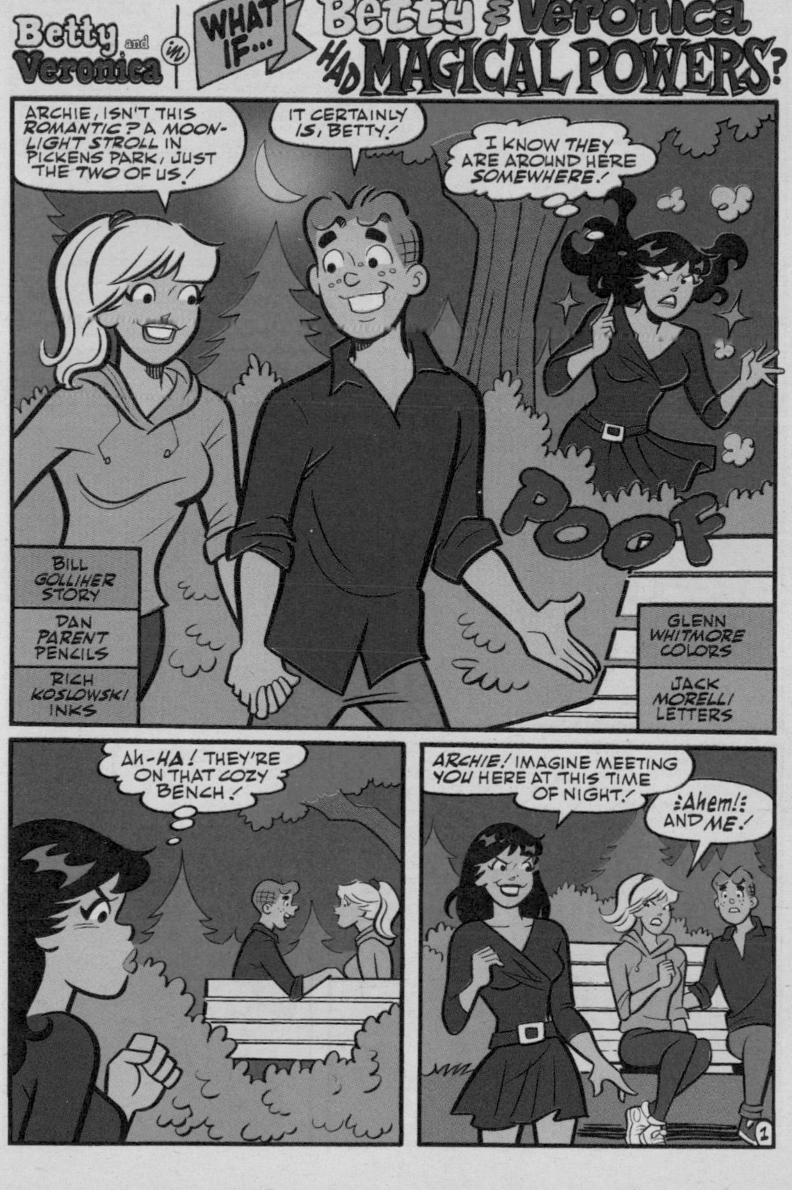

ARCHIE, ISN'T THIS *ROMANTIC*? A MOON-LIGHT *STROLL* IN PICKENS PARK, JUST THE *TWO* OF US!

IT CERTAINLY *IS*, BETTY!

I KNOW *THEY* ARE AROUND HERE *SOMEWHERE*!

POOF

BILL GOLLIHER STORY

DAN PARENT PENCILS

RICH KOSLOWSKI INKS

GLENN WHITMORE COLORS

JACK MORELLI LETTERS

HOW DID YOU FIND US?
WHAT?! I ALWAYS HANG OUT IN THE PARK IN THE MOON-LIGHT!

NOW THAT I'M HERE, LET'S ALL JUST SIT AND TALK!
HOW DOES SHE ALWAYS DO THAT?!

THE NEXT NIGHT...
VERONICA! WHY DID YOU INVITE ME TO THE MOVIES AT THE LAST MINUTE?
BECAUSE ANY TIME I MAKE PLANS WITH YOU--
--BETTY SEEMS TO FIND OUT AND BUTT IN!
ABELLA

KIND OF LIKE YOU DID WITH BETTY AND I LAST NIGHT?
THAT'S DIFFERENT!

NOW, QUICK! LET'S DODGE INTO THE THEATER!
WELL, HELLO, FELLOW MOVIE LOVERS!
POOF

KOFF! HOW DID YOU FIND US, AND WHAT'S UP WITH THE SMOKE-SCREEN?!
YOU SEEM TO HAVE A KNACK FOR THAT, TOO!

NOW LET'S ALL GO ENJOY THE MOVIE *TOGETHER*!
EASIER *SAID* THAN *DONE*!

NEXT NIGHT...
WHAT'S UP, ARCHIE? WHY THE SECRECY?!
I CAN'T GO ANYWHERE WITH EITHER *BETTY* OR *VERONICA*--
--WITHOUT THE *OTHER ONE SHOWING UP*!

I JUST WANT A *QUIET EVENING* WITHOUT THE TWO OF THEM AND ALL THEIR *DRAMA*! IT GETS **AWKWARD**!
I'VE GOT AN *IDEA*! WHY DON'T WE GO DOWN TO--
--THE *TRAMPOLINE PARK*? THAT WILL TAKE YOUR MIND OFF THINGS!

BUT...
TIME TO CHECK MY TRUSTY *CRYSTAL BALL* AND SEE WHERE ARCHIE *IS* AND BETTY HOPEFULLY *ISN'T*!
ZAP
AH! THE *TRAMPOLINE PARK*! MAYBE I'LL *JUMP* ON OVER!

MY *TEA LEAVES* ARE SPELLING OUT THAT ARCHIE IS AT THE *TRAMPOLINE PARK*! I NEED TO GET THERE TO SEE IF *VERONICA* KNOWS!
TRAMPOLINE PARK

YOU?! WHAT'RE *YOU* DOING HERE?!
RIVERDALE TRAMPOLINE PARK
I COULD SAY THE *SAME* TO YOU!
POOF
POOF

AND WHAT ABOUT THAT SMOKE TRAIL YOU LEFT BEHIND AGAIN?!
YOU DID IT, TOO!
RAMPOLINE PARK
THEN YOU'RE A WITCH AS WELL?!
YES! THAT SURE DOES EXPLAIN A LOT OVER THE YEARS!
WELL, WE'RE BOTH HERE! LET'S GET TO THE BUSINESS AT HAND!
OKAY!
ARCHIE!!
OH, BROTHER! HERE WE GO AGAIN!!
BOING
SORRY, GIRLS, BUT THIS IS GUYS' NIGHT OUT!
?
GRRRR! WHAT SHOULD I TURN HIM INTO?!
EASY, GIRL!
DON'T GIVE US AWAY! WE'LL SETTLE THIS BETWEEN US!

RIGHT! THERE'S ONLY ONE WAY TO RESOLVE OUR WAR OVER ARCHIE! A MAGIC BATTLE!
TOMORROW NIGHT, MIDNIGHT, PICKENS PARK! YOU'VE GOT YOURSELF A DUEL!

SO...
OKAY, IT'S MIDNIGHT! LET'S GET ZAPPING!
THE WINNER GETS ARCHIE! ...WAIT, SOME-ONE IS OVER THERE!
POOF

IT'S MORE THAN JUST SOMEONE! IT'S ARCHIE WITH ...SABRINA!!
WHAT COULD HE POSSIBLY SEE IN HER? LET'S GIVE THEM A PIECE OF OUR MINDS!

WELL, WELL!
ISN'T THIS COZY?!
SMOOCH
ZAP

HEY! WE'RE ON THE MOON! HOW DID WE GET HERE?!
DARN! THERE WAS A "ZAP"!
SABRINA MUST BE A WITCH, TOO!

FUNNY, I THOUGHT I HEARD BETTY AND VERONICA!
WINK
DON'T BE SILLY! I'M SURE THEY'RE SOMEWHERE FAR, FAR AWAY!
THE END

Betty and Veronica in She's ALL THAT!

WEBB
KENNEDY
D'AGOSTINO

I'M GLAD TO BE BACK AT SCHOOL!

SPEAK FOR YOURSELF!!

IT'S JUST THE SAME OLD, SAME OLD TEACHERS, CLASSROOMS, STUDENTS, SCHOOL... SAME OLD DULL BORING ROUTINE!!
SLAM

MY FABULOUS NEW SCHOOL WARDROBE IS THE ONLY THING GOOD ABOUT IT!
GLAD TO SEE YOU'VE GOT YOUR PRIORITIES STRAIGHT!
1

C'MON, RON! IT'S NOT THE "SAME OLD THING!"
WE'VE GOT TWO NEW CLASSES THIS YEAR! AND THERE'S A NEW GYM TEACHER!
Oh, WOW! ANOTHER NEW ADMINISTRATOR TO TORTURE!
NOT TO MENTION THERE ARE SOME NEW KIDS IN SCHOOL, INCLUDING THE EXCHANGE STUDENTS!
TRUE ... THAT BOY FROM ITALY IS CUTE!
AND THERE'S A WHOLE NEW CROP OF FRESHMEN TO GET TO KNOW!
YEAH!
17
A WHOLE NEW CROP OF TARGETS!
NOW, RON! NO TEASING THE FROSH!
YOU'RE TAKING AWAY THE ONLY FUN PART OF THE NEW YEAR!
NOT IN THEIR EYES!!

PEH! I DON'T SEE WHY BETTY'S SO EXCITED ABOUT THE NEW KIDS! THE FRESHMEN ARE ALL CHILDREN, AND THE OLDER NEWBIES...

...ARE JUST DOWNRIGHT WEIRD!

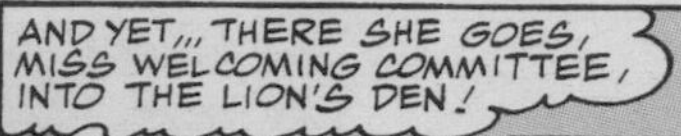
AND YET... THERE SHE GOES, MISS WELCOMING COMMITTEE, INTO THE LION'S DEN!

WELL, SHE CAN HAVE IT! I'LL STICK WITH MY OWN CROWD!
HEY, MIDGE! NANCY! WAIT UP!!

WHERE'S YOUR BUDDY, BETTY?!
OVER TALKING TO SOME OF THE NEW STUDENTS!
THEM?!

I'VE HEARD SOME RUMORS ABOUT SOME OF THOSE KIDS! THEY'RE KIND OF WEIRD!
WONDER WHY BETTY'S HANGING AROUND WITH THEM?

LATER...
BETTY'S STILL HANGING OUT WITH THE NEW KIDS?
YES! SHE JUST SNUBBED ME IN FAVOR OF EATING LUNCH WITH THEM!

AW, YOU TWO ARE ALMOST ALWAYS TOGETHER! YOU CAN STAND BEING APART FOR A LITTLE WHILE, CAN'T YOU?
I GUESS SO!

I JUST HOPE SHE REMEMBERS WHO HER REAL FRIENDS ARE!
I DOUBT SHE'S FORGOTTEN.

BUT!
BETTY'S ALREADY LEFT!!
SHE WALKED HOME WITH ONE OF THE NEW GIRLS!

SHE NEVER CALLED OR E-MAILED ME! WHAT'S SO GREAT ABOUT THOSE NEW KIDS THAT SHE'D FORGET I EVEN EXIST!?

THE NEXT DAY...
HI, RON!
YOU TALKIN' TO ME, STRANGER?

WHY DON'T YOU GO SPEND TIME WITH YOUR NEW FRIENDS, SINCE YOU SEEM TO PREFER THEM TO YOUR OLD ONES!
Huh? RON, ARE YOU CRAZY?!

YOU HARDLY TALKED TO ME YESTERDAY!
WE'RE TOGETHER SO MUCH, I JUST FIGURED YOU WOULDN'T MIND IF I SPENT TIME WITH SOMEONE ELSE!

BESIDES, THE REASON I DID WAS TO HELP MAKE THE NEW KIDS FEEL WELCOME!
SHOULDN'T HOW I FEEL MATTER MORE?!

HEY! I REMEMBER, BECAUSE OF YOUR WEALTH, HOW DIFFERENT AND OSTRACIZED YOU FELT WHEN YOU STARTED SCHOOL!!

DO YOU REMEMBER HOW WELCOME SOMEBODY TRIED TO MAKE YOU FEEL BACK THEN?!
MY NAME'S BETTY! WANNA PLAY WIF ME?

BAWL!!
BETTY TOLD YOU SHE'S BEST FRIENDS WITH THAT WEIRD GIRL?
UH-huh! PRETTY ACCEPT-ING OF ANY-BODY, ISN'T SHE?
END

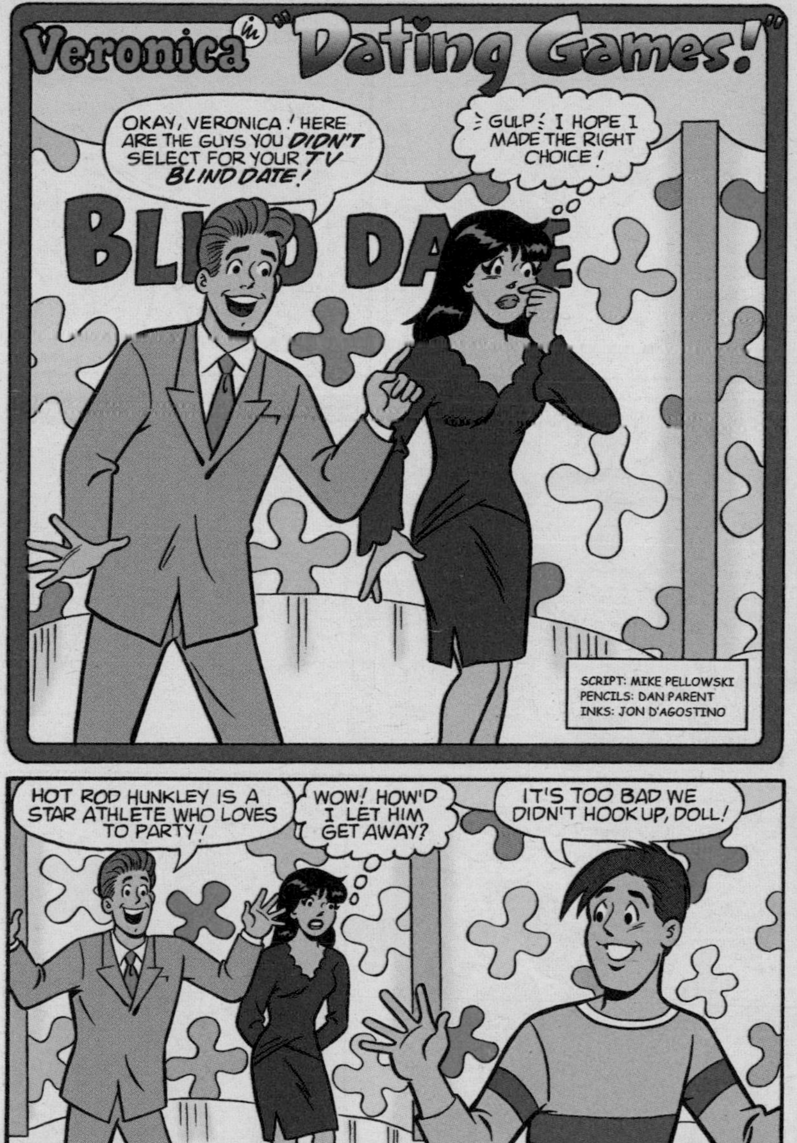

Veronica in "Dating Games!"

OKAY, VERONICA! HERE ARE THE GUYS YOU *DIDN'T* SELECT FOR YOUR *TV BLIND DATE*!

GULP! I HOPE I MADE THE RIGHT CHOICE!

BLIND DATE

SCRIPT: MIKE PELLOWSKI
PENCILS: DAN PARENT
INKS: JON D'AGOSTINO

ROCK DRUMMER IS A MUSICIAN WHO ENJOYS SKYDIVING!
YO! WHASSUP, BEAUTIFUL?

GOSH! ROCK IS REALLY CUTE, TOO!

NOW IT'S TIME TO MEET THE MAN YOU PICKED TO BE YOUR BLIND DATE TONIGHT!
I CAN'T WAIT TO SEE HIM!
BLIND DATE

PLEASE WELCOME WILBUR WATKINS, A COMPUTER EXPERT AND CHESS CHAMPION!
HI, RON! THANKS FOR SELECTING ME!

GOSH! WILBUR ISN'T THE KIND OF GUY RON NORMALLY DATES!
LET'S FACE IT! A GUY LIKE WILBUR WOULD NEVER STAND A CHANCE WITH RON IN REAL LIFE!

AND SO, OFF GO THIS WEEK'S COUPLE ON THEIR... BLIND DATE!
THAT'S A WRAP!

ARE YOU READY TO LEAVE, RON? OUR LIMO IS WAITING?
I WILL BE READY IN A MINUTE! I HAVE TO SAY GOODBYE TO SOME FRIENDS WHO CAME WITH ME!
EXIT

WELL I'M OFF ON MY DATE, GIRLS! SEE YOU BACK AT MY HOUSE! I'M GLAD YOU'RE SLEEPING OVER TONIGHT!
'BYE, RON! HAVE FUN!

EXIT
RIGHT! LIKE THERE'S ANY CHANCE OF THAT!

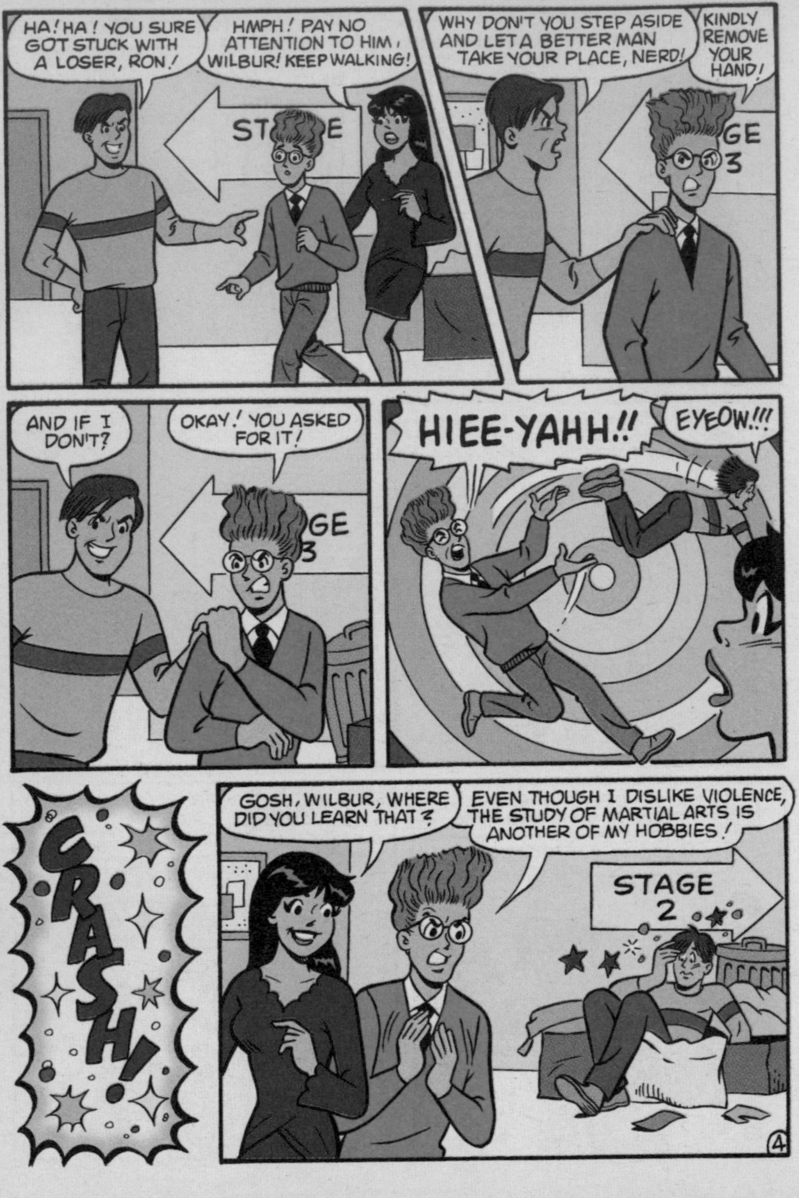

HA! HA! YOU SURE GOT STUCK WITH A LOSER, RON!
HMPH! PAY NO ATTENTION TO HIM, WILBUR! KEEP WALKING!
STAGE
WHY DON'T YOU STEP ASIDE AND LET A BETTER MAN TAKE YOUR PLACE, NERD!
KINDLY REMOVE YOUR HAND!
AND IF I DON'T?
OKAY! YOU ASKED FOR IT!
HIEE-YAHH!!
EYEOW!!!

AT DINNER...
THIS IS A NICE FRENCH RESTAURANT!
I'M GLAD YOU LIKE IT! PLEASE ALLOW ME TO ORDER FOR US!

WILBUR SPEAKS FRENCH FLUENTLY! NOW THAT'S IMPRESSIVE!
OUI!

WHEN DID YOU LEARN TO SPEAK FRENCH?
I PICKED IT UP WHILE LIVING IN EUROPE AS AN EXCHANGE STUDENT!

YOU'RE FULL OF SURPRISES! WHAT ELSE DO YOU LIKE?
ROCK MUSIC! IN FACT, I THOUGHT WE'D GO TO A TEEN DANCE CLUB AFTER WE EAT!

LATER AT THE CLUB...
YOU'RE A TERRIFIC DANCER, WILBUR!
THANKS! YOU'RE REALLY GOOD, TOO!

WHEN THE MUSIC STOPS...
YOUR ATTENTION PLEASE! JOINING THE BAND FOR THE NEXT NUMBER IS WILBUR WATKINS!
THIS IS FOR YOU, RON!

WOW! WILBUR PLAYS A MEAN GUITAR! HE REALLY ROCKS!

AT THE END OF THE DATE RON IS TAKEN HOME...
WELL, IT'S ABOUT TIME! WE THOUGHT YOU'D BE HOME A LOT SOONER! YOUR FOLKS ARE ASLEEP!
GIVE US ALL THE AWFUL DETAILS! HOW BAD WAS YOUR DATE?

HEH! HEH! I GUESS THIS WILL TEACH YOU NEVER TO GO ON A BLIND DATE AGAIN!
ACTUALLY... I HAD A WONDERFUL TIME!

AND I'VE ALREADY AGREED TO GO OUT WITH WILBUR AGAIN!
HUH? YOU DID?
THE End

Betty

WHAT TIME ARE YOU PICKING ME UP FOR THAT NEW DISCO OPENING TONIGHT, ARCHIE?

WHAT DO YOU MEAN PICK UP? I'M PLANNING ON TAKING RONNIE!

CHICKEN

Script: Dick Malmgren / Pencils: Stan Goldberg / Inks: Rudy Lapick / Letters: Bill Yoshida

BUT YOU PROMISED ME A MONTH AGO, DON'T YOU REMEMBER?
HOW DO YOU EXPECT ME TO REMEMBER THAT FAR BACK?

WELL, I WROTE IT DOWN ON MY CALENDAR IN RED MARKER AS A SPECIAL EVENT!

MAYBE SOME OTHER TIME, BETTY! I WAS JUST ABOUT TO CALL RONNIE!
HUH?
MOOSE

SNIFF! I WENT AND BOUGHT A NEW DRESS FOR THE OCCASION!
SOB!

DUH? HOW CAN YOU BACK OUT ON A DATE AFTER YOU PROMISED HER, ARCHIE?
?

DON'T YOU HAVE ANY FEELINGS? BETTY'S ALL UPSET!
BUT WE DON'T HAVE ANYTHING IN COMMON!

DUH! I THINK THAT YOU SHOULD TAKE HER TO THAT DISCO OPENING!
ME, TOO!

OKAY, OKAY! I'LL PICK YOU UP AT SEVEN-THIRTY!
2

I'LL BE READY, ARCHIE!
THAT WAS A SMART THING TO DO!
OH, HAPPY DAY! I HAVE TO GET READY FOR MY DATE!
WATCH OUT!
WHACK!
ARE YOU ALL RIGHT, BETTY?
I'M OKAY, I JUST BRUISED MY CHEEK!
YOU'RE GOING TO HAVE A BLACK AND BLUE MARK!
I'LL COVER IT UP WITH MAKE-UP!
3

NOTHING IS GOING TO MAKE ME MISS OUT ON THIS DATE!
GRUNT... THIS DOOR IS STUCK!

WHAM!

OH, GOOD GRIEF! NOW I'LL HAVE A BRUISE ON MY OTHER CHEEK!

THANK GOODNESS FOR MAKE-UP!

I'M READY, ARCHIE! HOW DO I LOOK?
GREAT, BETTY!

I HOPE YOU DON'T FEEL THAT I FORCED YOU INTO TAKING ME! WE HAVE A LOT IN COMMON, YOU'LL SEE!
4

LOOK, IF I PROMISED YOU, I PROMISED YOU! IT'S THE RIGHT THING TO DO!

WOULDN'T YOU KNOW IT, NOW IT'S STARTING TO RAIN!
ARCH I

I SHOULD HAVE BROUGHT MY UMBRELLA!
IT'S TOO LATE FOR THAT!
DISC
DANS
GRAND OPENING

WE'RE GOING TO HAVE TO MAKE A RUN FOR IT!

LET'S GO!

EEEEEK!
RIPPP!

DUH? WHERE'S BETTY? DON'T TELL ME YOU DIDN'T BRING HER?

WHERE IS SHE?
DON'T GET UPTIGHT! SHE'S RIGHT BEHIND ME!

HI, FELLOWS! FORGIVE MY APPEARANCE!
DUH!

WHAT HAPPENED?

I APPRECIATE YOU WANTING TO TAKE ME OUT AGAIN TO MAKE UP FOR IT, ARCHIE, BUT I DON'T WANT YOU TO FEEL YOU HAVE TO!
BUT I WANT TO, BETTY! WE FINALLY HAVE SOMETHING IN COMMON!
END

Betty and Veronica  BEAR FACTS

Gladir / Goldberg / Lapick / Yoshida

GOSH, BETTY! YOU'VE GOT MORE TEDDY BEARS THAN A VIDEO ARCADE HAS QUARTERS!

I GUESS AS A COLLECTOR YOU COULD SAY I'M REALLY LOADED FOR BEAR! HA! HA!

ENOUGH OF THIS BEAR TALK! I HEAR SCHLOSSMAN'S HAS A SALE ON PROM DRESSES!
OH, WOW! LET'S GO CHECK IT OUT!

BETTY, CAN WE DRAG YOU AWAY FROM YOUR URSINE FRIENDS?
OH, YES! I'M IN DESPERATE NEED OF A PROM DRESS!

OH, WOULD YOU PLEASE DROP ME OFF AT THE NEXT CORNER?
BUT I THOUGHT YOU WANTED TO COME TO THE SALE WITH US?

I DID, BUT I JUST NOTICED THE FLEA MARKET IS OPEN TODAY!
... MAYBE I CAN PICK UP MORE BEARS TO ADD TO MY COLLECTION!

I DON'T BELIEVE IT! SHE GAVE UP THE SALE TO GO SHOPPING FOR BEARS!
SALE
FLEA MARKET

COLLECTING TEDDY BEARS IS BECOMING A HANGUP WITH HER!
I'M BEGINNING TO WORRY ABOUT HER! HER BEHAVIOR IS GETTING OBSESSIVE!
VL I

THE NEXT DAY-
ETHEL, HAVE YOU SEEN BETTY?
SHE'S IN THE HOME EC CLASSROOM ALL BY HERSELF!

? BUT IT'S RECESS TIME!
SHE ALSO SPENT HER STUDY PERIOD IN THAT CLASS!
2

WELL I'M GLAD TO SEE THAT GIRL OCCUPYING HERSELF WITH SOMETHING ELSE BESIDES BEARS!

HI, GIRLS! HOW DO YOU LIKE THE OUTFITS I'M MAKING FOR MY NEW BEARS?

BETTY, I'M CONCERNED ABOUT YOU!
LATELY, ALL YOU EVER TALK ABOUT IS YOUR TEDDY BEARS!

WELL, THEY DO BRING US TEDDY BEAR OWNERS SECURITY!
...AND THEY ARE SO HUGGABLE!

THEY ALSO MAKE GREAT SCAPEGOATS! ...YOU CAN BLAME THEM FOR EVERYTHING!
...AND THEY'LL SIT PATIENTLY IN A CLOSET UNTIL THEY'RE NEEDED!

NO PUN INTENDED, BUT THAT GIRL BEARS WATCHING!
RIV

THE FOLLOWING WEEK-
I FINALLY FIGURED OUT A WAY TO GET BETTY'S MIND OFF BEARS!
HOW?

I'M GIVING A BIG PARTY AND EVERY-ONE IS INVITED!
THAT'S A FANTASTIC IDEA! THE FUN WILL DEFINITELY SNAP HER OUT OF IT!

BETTY, I'M GIVING A MASQUERADE PARTY SATURDAY AND YOU'RE INVITED!
...I EVEN BROUGHT YOU YOUR COSTUME!

THANKS, BUT I WAS PLANNING TO ATTEND A MEETING OF A TEDDY BEAR BOOSTER CLUB!

CANCEL IT! I INSIST YOU COME TO MY PARTY! EVEN ARCHIE IS GOING TO BE THERE!
DID YOU SAY 'ARCHIE'?

YES! DID YOU FORGET HE USED TO BE YOUR OBSESSION BEFORE YOU TOOK UP BEARS?
OKAY, I'LL COME! I'LL COME!
4

OH, VERONICA! I'M SO GLAD YOU INSISTED I COME TONIGHT! I'M HAVING SUCH A WONDERFUL TIME!

--AND YOU WERE SO RIGHT! MY COLLECTING MANIA WAS GETTING THE BEST OF ME!

MY PLAN WORKED! I KNEW I COULD GET THAT GIRL TO KICK HER BEAR HABIT!

UH, OH! YOU SPOKE TOO SOON!
WHAT DO YOU MEAN?

RONNIE, I THINK I'M HOOKED ON BEARS AGAIN!
END

Betty and Veronica
IN
WHEEL ZEAL
ARCHIEKINS, HOW ABOUT GOING TO THE PARK FOR A WALK?
GEE! I'D LOVE TO, RONNIE---
BUT I CAN'T STOP NOW! THERE'S A SPECIAL SKATEBOARD EXHIBITION GOING ON!
Script: Gladir / Pencils: DeCarlo / Inks: Lapick / Letters: Yoshida
HMPH! THEN I'LL JUST ASK REGGIE!

OH, REGGIEKINS---
SORRY, SUGAR!

--- A SKATEBOARD HOTSHOT IS GIVING OUT POINTERS!

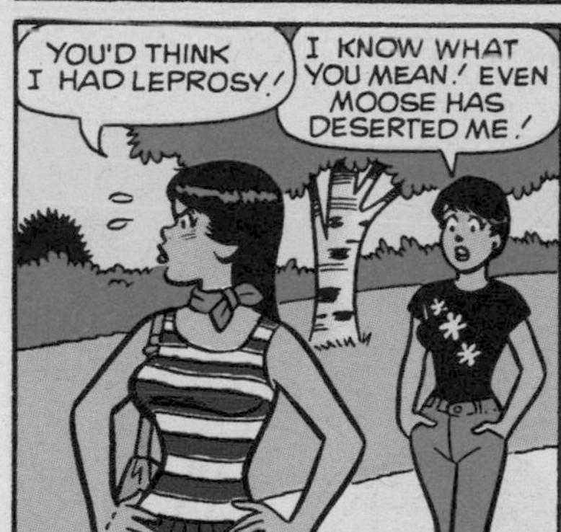
YOU'D THINK I HAD LEPROSY!
I KNOW WHAT YOU MEAN! EVEN MOOSE HAS DESERTED ME!

ALL THE BOYS IN TOWN ARE INTO SKATEBOARDS IN A BIG WAY!

I JUST DON'T KNOW WHAT WE CAN DO ABOUT IT!
I KNOW WHAT I CAN DO ABOUT IT!

I'M GOING TO DOLL MYSELF UP IN MY SHORTEST SHORTS!
I'LL JOIN YOU!
2

IF WE DON'T CATCH THEIR EYE NOW, MY NAME ISN'T VERONICA LODGE!
ZOWIE!
FANTASTIC!
SEE! WHAT DID I TELL YOU?
WOW! NOBODY CAN DO THE HIGH JUMP LIKE BETTY!
GULP!
YA HOO! LOOK AT HER DO THE SHU-FLY CHRISTIE!
HOW CAN WE WIN 'EM OVER IF THEY DON'T EVEN LOOK AT US?
LEAVE THIS TO ME!
3

OH, BETTY!
YES, RONNIE!

LOOK AT YOURSELF! ALL HOT AND SWEATY IN THOSE SHREDDED GRUBBY JEANS!
BUT I'M HAVING FUN!

I FEEL IT'S MY OBLIGATION AS A FRIEND TO POINT SOMETHING OUT!
WHAT?

GIRLS WHO ARE PART OF THE GANG DON'T GET ASKED OUT ON DATES!

GOSH! DO YOU REALLY THINK SO?
I KNOW SO!

BUT ALL THE BOYS KEEP ASKING ME FOR POINTERS!
WELL, YOU'LL BE SORRY WHEN IT'S TIME FOR FRIDAY'S DANCE!
4

RONNIE IS RIGHT.! I AM MAKING A MISTAKE BEING ONE OF THE GUYS.!
---I'LL GO HOME AND SHOWER AND LOOK MORE FEMININE.!

THERE.! NOW NO ONE CAN TREAT ME LIKE ONE OF THE GUYS.!

OH, DILTON.! HAVE YOU SEEN ARCHIE?
YES.!

VERONICA INVITED HIM TO HER PLACE.!

OH, ARCHIEKINS, SHOW ME AGAIN HOW THAT STUNT GOES.!
OH, NO.! SHE'S DONE IT AGAIN.!
END.

Archie "TRUE BLUE" PART 1

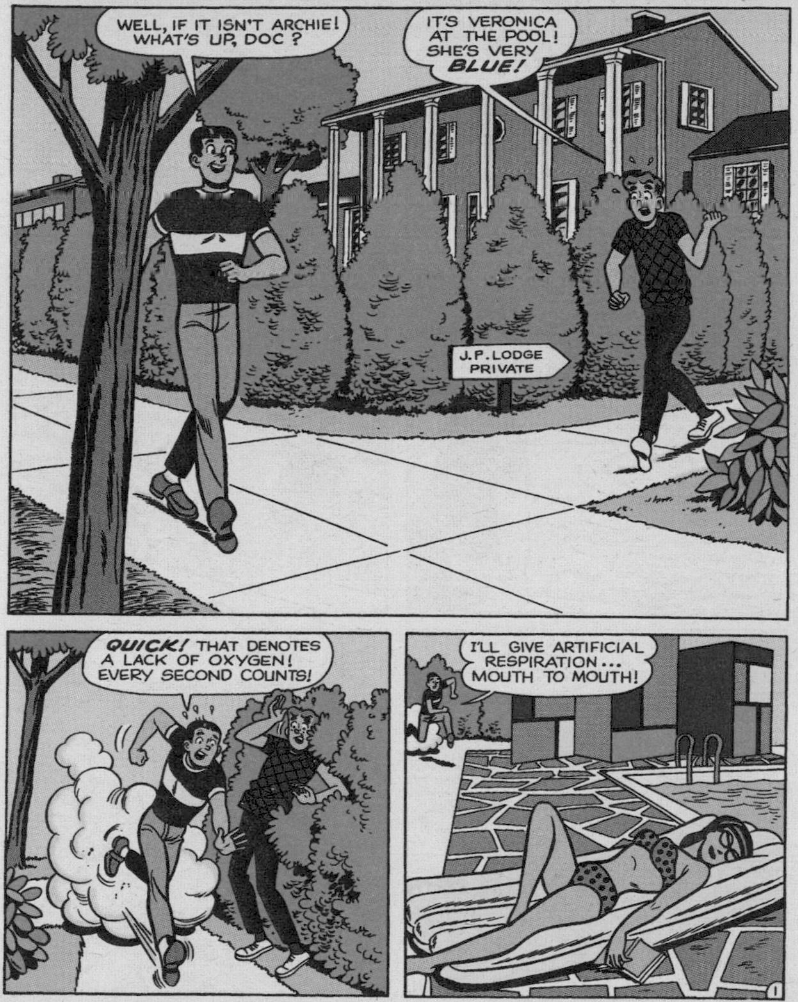

WELL, IF IT ISN'T ARCHIE! WHAT'S UP, DOC ?
IT'S VERONICA AT THE POOL! SHE'S VERY *BLUE!*
J.P. LODGE PRIVATE

Script: Frank Doyle / Pencils: Bob White / Inks & Letters: Mario Acquaviva

MMMPT!

WHAT ARE YOU DOING, KISSING MY GIRL?
SPLASH!

YOU SAID SHE WAS TURNING BLUE! I ONLY TRIED TO SAVE HER LIFE!

SAD, YOU NUT! UNHAPPY!
THAT KIND OF BLUE!
OH!

SORRY, RON! WHY ARE YOU BLUE?
WHO KNOWS NOW? YOU MADE ME FORGET!

AT THE MOMENT I'M TOO MAD TO BE SAD!

BEAT IT, YOU BLUNDERING IDIOTS, SO I CAN RECALL WHY I'M UNHAPPY!

DADDY! WHY AM I SO BLUE?
I'VE GOT EVERYTHING!
OF COURSE!
ROLEN

... INCLUDING ARCHIE!
THAT'S WHAT MAKES ME BLUE!

ARCHIE! OF COURSE!

I HEARD A RUMOR THAT HE WAS PLANNING TO DITCH ME!

LET'S THROW A PARTY! THIS CALLS FOR A CELEBRATION!

YOU MUST KNOW! WHY IS SHE SO SAD?
I'M NOT SURE!

I SUSPECT IT'S HER KIND HEART!

BECAUSE I HEARD A RUMOR SHE'S PLANNING TO DITCH ME!

IT PROBABLY MAKES HER SAD THINKING ABOUT HOW BROKEN-HEARTED *I'LL* BE!
DITCH YOU, EH?

LET'S THROW A PARTY! THIS CALLS FOR A CELEBRATION!

TRY TO FEEL THAT YOU'RE NOT LOSING A GIRL SO MUCH AS GAINING YOUR FREEDOM!
YUK! YUK!

.... BUT WHO STARTED THAT LITTLE RUMOR, BETTY? ... ANYBODY *WE* KNOW? WELL, WE'LL GO ON AHEAD AND FIND OUT!

Archie in "TRUE BLUE"

PART 2

HEY! I HEARD YOU TWO WUZ DITCHIN' EACH OTHER!

NOW WHAT SORT OF A BLEACHED BLONDE NUT WOULD START A RUMOR LIKE THAT?

"BLEACHED BLO---"?

YOU MEAN IT WAS *BETTY?*

DO YOU KNOW ANY OTHER BLEACHED BLONDE NUT?
NO!

LET'S STOP THAT RUMOR BY SHOWING THE WORLD HOW MUCH WE LOVE EACH OTHER!
LET'S DO THAT!

SMACK!

ISN'T THAT SWEET?
CHARMING!
THERE'S NOTHING SO BEAUTIFUL AS YOUNG LOVE!

THEY'RE RIGHT! I'VE BEEN A BAD GIRL!

I'LL MAKE IT UP TO THEM! CONFESSION IS GOOD FOR THE SOUL!

DARLING!
ANGEL!

HEY! GUESS WHAT! I'VE COME TO CONFESS!
BULLY!

I WAS THE EVIL ONE WHO SPREAD THAT UGLY RUMOR ABOUT YOU TWO SPLITTING!

OKAY! SO NOW WE FORGIVE YOU! NOW...
I'VE GOT TO MAKE IT UP TO YOU!

I'M GOING TO MAKE IT MY DUTY TO SHOW YOU YOUNG LOVERS A GOOD TIME!
BETTY, WE...

OKAY! NOW WHERE WOULD YOU LIKE TO GO FIRST?
AWAY!
ALONE!

WE CAN GO CANOEING! THAT'S VERY ROMANTIC!
I'LL PADDLE!

MAYBE A DRIVE IN THE COUNTRY! YOU TWO IN THE BACK WHILE I DRIVE!

COME ON! WHAT WILL IT BE? I PROMISE YOU A REAL GOOD TIME!
BETTY!

I DON'T WANT TO HAVE A GOOD TIME!

I WANT TO BE ALONE WITH VERONICA!

... DOESN'T WANT A GOOD TIME!
WANTS TO BE ALONE WI---

WELL I'VE DECIDED I DO WANT TO HAVE A GOOD TIME!
?

SO I'LL MAKE SURE I'M NOT WITH YOU!
HEY!

AH! A YOUNG LOVERS' SPAT! MAYBE I CAN TAKE YOUR MIND OFF YOUR TROUBLES!

IT'S NO USE! I'D BE BAD COMPANY! I'M TOO BLUE!

I WOULDN'T CARE IF YOU WERE GREEN!
LET'S GO!
IT DOESN'T MATTER TO HER! WHEN IT COMES TO ARCHIE, SHE'S COLOR BLIND!
THE END

Archie "DESSERT SPECIAL"

PART I

OUT! OUT! NOBODY THROWS A FIT IN **MY** SHOP!

THEY'RE NOT THROWING A FIT, POPS! THEY'RE DOING THE **JERK**!

MENU

WELL, ALL I'VE GOT TO SAY IS, YOU'VE GOT TO **BE** ONE TO **DO** ONE!
WHAT WAS THE LAST DANCE **YOU** DID, POPS?

Script: Frank Doyle / Art: Bob White / Letters: Victor Gorelick

SOMETHING THAT TOOK BRAINS! TALENT!
THE BIG APPLE!
SNAP!
SNAP!

ANYBODY CAN DO THE JERK!
SUPER SUNDAE .45¢

LOOK! IT'S THE FIRST TIME I'VE SEEN IT AND ALREADY I'M AN EXPERT!

SNAP!
OWW!

ERK! SOMEBODY HELP ME! I GOT A WHIPLASH!

I CAN'T MOVE MY NECK!

HOW AM I GOING TO WORK WITH A NECK LIKE THIS?
YOU'RE NOT!

YOU'RE GOING HOME! I'LL KEEP THE STORE GOING UNTIL YOU GET BETTER!
OW!

REGGIE, HOLD THE FORT UNTIL I GET BACK!
ROGER!

WE'LL GO ALONG AND HELP MAKE HIM COMFORTABLE!
ARE YOU SURE YOU CAN RUN THE BUSINESS?
CHOKLIT SHOPPE

HMM? NOW WHAT CAN I DO TO MAKE LIFE INTERESTING FOR DEAR OL' ARCH?

HEY! INSTANT MASHED POTATOES! JUST LIKE MOTHER USES!
FUDGE SUNDAE .30¢

WHEN WHIPPED UP REAL SMOOTH I'LL BET THEY COULD PASS FOR VANILLA ICE CREAM!
DELUXE SODAS .25¢

HYUK! YOU DEVIL, YOU!

ALL I'VE GOT TO DO IS REPLACE THE REAL VANILLA!
.25¢

WELL, WE GOT HIM HOME ALL RIGHT!
GOODY FOR YOU!

HOW ABOUT A DISH OF ICE CREAM OR A SUNDAE FOR YOUR TROUBLE?
ER- NO THANKS, PAL!

AS THE DYNAMITE SAID TO THE BURNING FUSE, I THINK I'LL BLOW!

WELL, I'LL FIX A NICE SUNDAE FOR YOU GIRLS JUST TO KEEP MY HAND IN!
I DON'T MIND!

MY, THAT LOOKS GOOD!
YOU DO FINE WORK!

AWK!
ERK!

?
IF THERE'S ANYTHING I CAN'T STAND, IT'S A PRACTICAL JOKER!
WE BETTER WARN THE KIDS TO STAY OUT OF HERE!
CONTINUED:

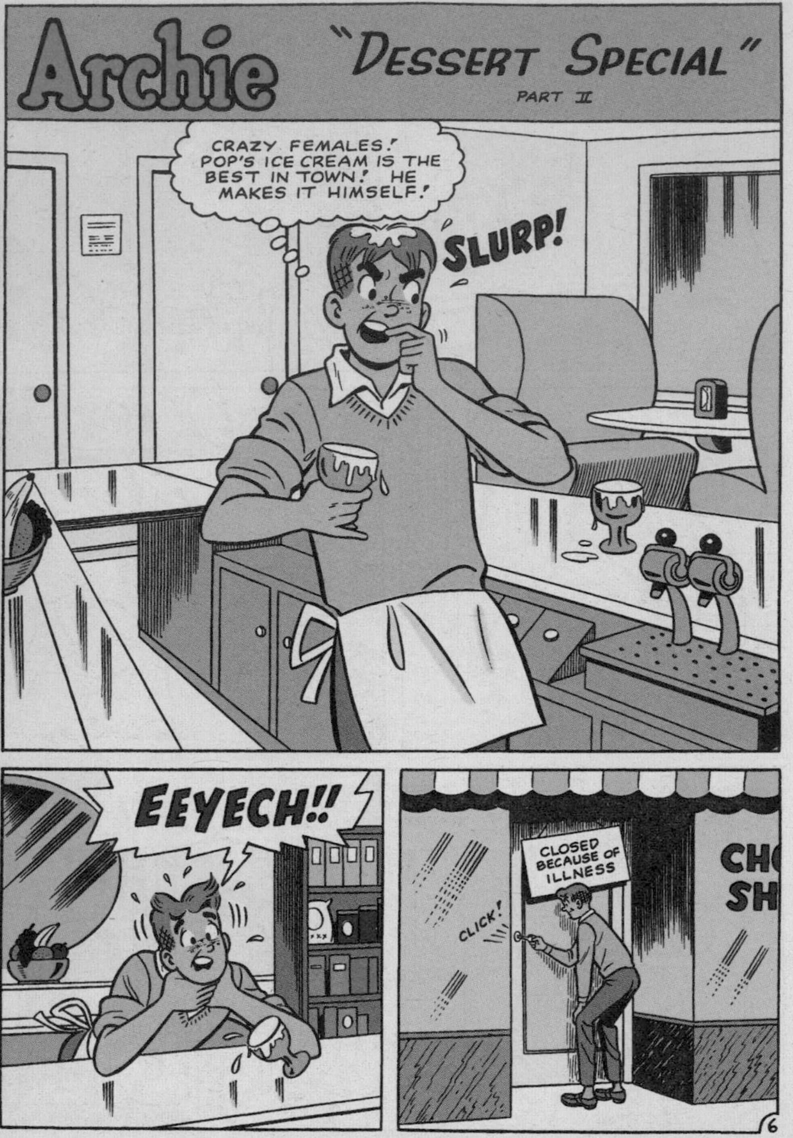

Archie "Dessert Special"

PART II

CRAZY FEMALES! POP'S ICE CREAM IS THE BEST IN TOWN! HE MAKES IT HIMSELF!

SLURP!

I COULDN'T STAY HOME, ARCHIE! HOW ARE YOU DOING?

ILLNESS? WHO'S GOT ILLNESS!
CLOSED BECAUSE OF ILLNESS

ANYONE WHO EAT'S YOUR ROTTEN ICE CREAM!
?

ROTTEN? MY ICE CREAM? ...ROTTEN?
BITE YOUR TONGUE!

THE MOST DELECTABLE ICE CREAM IN THE HISTORY OF ICE CREAM MAKING!

HMM! THAT STRAWBERRY!
MAGNIFICENT!
TRY THE VANILLA!

THE CHOCOLATE! LOOK AT THAT COLOR! THAT CONSISTENCY!

HMM! NECTAR OF THE GODS!
TRY THE VANILLA!

THE VANILLA! MY VERY FAVORITE! I'M **FAMOUS** FOR MY...

GURK!

AIEEEEE! YOU FIEND! YOU'VE BEEN SERVING MASHED POTATO SUNDAES!
WHAT?

LOOK! INSTANT POTATO BOXES! I WAS RIGHT!
REGGIE!
EXIT

HONEST, POP! I HAD NO IDEA...
MY REPUTATION! MY BUSINESS! RUINED!

I'LL NEVER GET BACK MY CUSTOMERS!
ONLY BETTY AND VERONICA TASTED IT!

IF THOSE TWO KNOW, THE WHOLE TOWN KNOWS BY NOW! I'M RUINED!
I'LL TRY TO STOP THEM!

YOU'VE **TOLD?**
OUR RUMORS ARE THE FASTEST THINGS KNOWN TO MAN!

WELL START A RUMOR THAT IT WAS ALL ONE OF REGGIE'S GAGS!
I GUESS WE OWE IT TO POPS!

ARCHIE! YOU BROUGHT THEM BACK! THEY'RE NOT ANGRY?
THEY THINK IT'S **FUNNY**!

FUNNY? NOTHING'S FUNNY ABOUT MY SPOTLESS REPUTATION IN THE ICE CREAM GAME!

HYUK! HEY POPS! HOW ABOUT A POTATO SPLIT!
EASY ON THE GRAVY!
TOP MINE WITH AN ARTICHOKE!
I'LL HAVE A TURNIP CONE WITH SPRINKLES!
ANYBODY CARE TO DO THE MASHED POTATO?
(SIGH)-IT'S LIKE I **SAID** ABOUT THE JERK! IT **TAKES** ONE TO **DO** ONE!
The END

SCRIPT: KATHLEEN WEBB
PENCILS: STAN GOLDBERG
INKING: BOB SMITH
LETTERING: JACK MORELLI

IF YOU HAVE TIME TO FLIRT, ARCHIE, YOU'D BETTER BE DONE!
ACTUALLY, DAD -- I AM!

THE WHOLE YARD IS FINISHED! FRONT, BACK AND SIDES!
GOOD! HERE YOU GO, LIKE I PROMISED!

UM... THANKS, DAD... ER... IS THAT ALL?
ALL I CAN SPARE, SPORT!

THIS WON'T GO VERY FAR ON OUR DATE TONIGHT!
I BET DADDYKINS WOULD PAY YOU MORE!

WHAT? TO GO AWAY?
NO! ONE OF OUR GARDENERS QUIT YESTERDAY AND THERE'S ALL SORTS OF YARD WORK TO BE DONE!

C'MON! IT CAN'T HURT TO ASK!
IF IT'S YOUR DAD, YES IT CAN!

YOU WANT ME TO PAY YOU TO DO YARDWORK SO YOU CAN TAKE MY DAUGHTER ON A DATE TONIGHT?
TH-THAT'S ABOUT IT, SIR--!

HOW ABOUT I JUST PAY YOU TO GO AWAY AND LEAVE HER ALONE?
WHAT'D I TELL YOU?
DADDY!

WAIT A MINUTE... I COULD GIVE HIM WORK THAT WOULD TIRE HIM OUT SO MUCH, HE'D BE IN NO SHAPE FOR A DATE! Hmmm...

I THOUGHT YOU'D BE HAPPY THAT DADDY AGREED TO HIRE YOU!
I DIDN'T LIKE THAT EVIL LEER ON HIS FACE!

PHEW! AND HE WOULD GIVE ME A TOUGH JOB TO DO! DIGGING UP THESE SHRUBS ISN'T EASY!
I'LL GO GET US SOME LEMONADE!

LIKE THAT'S GOING TO MAKE THE JOB EASIER!
WHAT I NEED IS THIS PICK-AXE!

NOW! A COUPLE OF GOOD SWINGS, AND...

WHAM
WHY DOES THE HANDLE SEEM A LOT LIGHTER ALL OF A SUDDEN?
YIKES!

URK! THE PICK CAME OFF THE HANDLE!!
ARCHIE ANDREWS, YOU IDIOT!!

YOU JUST MISSED ME AND MY BEAUTIFUL GREENHOUSE FULL OF PRIZE ORCHIDS WITH THIS THING!!
S-S-SORRY, S-SIR--!

PHOOEY!! GUESS I'LL JUST USE THIS SHORT-HANDLED SPADE INSTEAD! IT WON'T DO AS GOOD A JOB, BUT...

OOF!! WELL, WHATTAYA KNOW! I YANKED OUT THE WHOLE THING! SHRUB, DIRT AND--
YEOW!

WHOOPS! Eh-heh! SORRY, MR. LODGE!
HERE! I'M PAYING YOU FOR DIGGING UP THE BUSH! NOW, GO!-- BEFORE YOU REALLY DESTROY SOMETHING!!
YESSIR... BUT--!
I STILL DON'T HAVE ENOUGH TO TAKE VERONICA OUT ON A DATE!
Y-YOU'RE ASKING ME FOR MORE?!
WELL... YOU DID SAY YOU WERE WILLING TO PAY ME TO GO AWAY!
ROAR!!
Sheesh, WHAT A GROUCH!
NOW WHAT'LL WE DO?
GIVE ME ABOUT AN HOUR! I MAY HAVE THE SOLUTION TO OUR DILEMMA!
LODGE
?

LET ME GET THIS RIGHT... YOU WANT ME TO PAY YOU TO WASH MY WINDOWS?
YESSIR, MR. COOPER!

HOW MUCH CAN I PAY YOU TO JUST LEAVE AND NEVER COME BACK?
DA-DEEE!!

ARE YOU EARNING THAT MONEY FOR ANYTHING SPECIAL, ARCHIE?
Oh, NO... JUST A DATE TONIGHT WITH RON!

SO! NOT ONLY ARE YOU HERE WITH HER-- I'M NOTHING SPECIAL, eh?!
SO! YOU'RE WASHING MY WINDOWS TO TAKE HER OUT?!?

CLONG

Sigh! SO TELL ME, JUG... WHY AM I DOING THIS?
WELL, IT CERTAINLY ISN'T FOR YOUR LOVE LIFE!!
The END

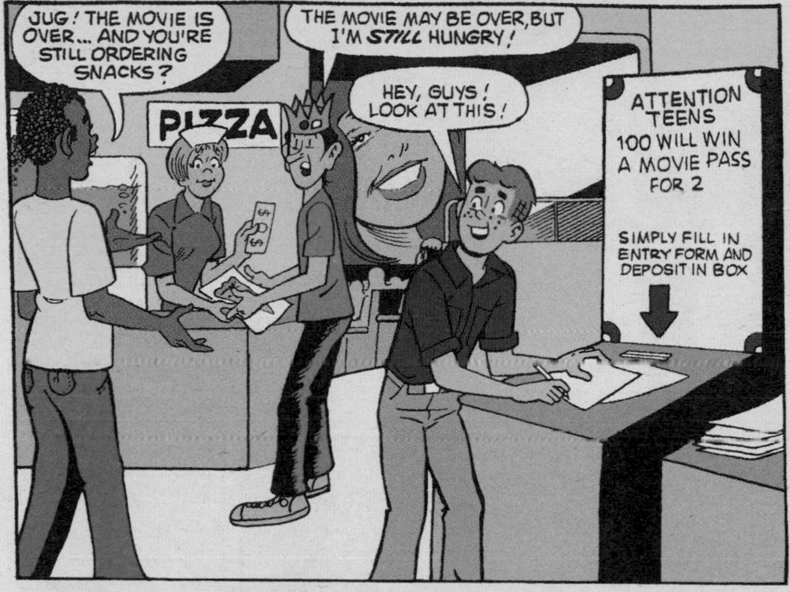

JUG! THE MOVIE IS OVER... AND YOU'RE STILL ORDERING SNACKS?
THE MOVIE MAY BE OVER, BUT I'M *STILL* HUNGRY!
PIZZA
HEY, GUYS! LOOK AT THIS!
ATTENTION TEENS
100 WILL WIN A MOVIE PASS FOR 2
SIMPLY FILL IN ENTRY FORM AND DEPOSIT IN BOX

Archie in IT'S A YOUNG, YOUNG BOY'S WORLD

Script: George Gladir / Pencils: Bob Bolling / Inks: Bob Smith / Letters: Bill Yoshida

SCENE: GLAMORAMA STUDIO...
THESE ARE ALL THE ENTRIES WE RECEIVED FROM OUR MOVIE PASS CONTEST!
AND FROM THAT PILE WE'VE CHOSEN 100 WINNERS!
WE DELIBERATELY SELECTED ONLY 13-YEAR-OLD MALES!
ZINGBAT
STAGE #5

HOW COME 13 YEAR OLD MALES?
BECAUSE THEY SEE MORE MOVIES THAN ANY OTHER AGE GROUP!

ALL 100 PASSES ARE COMPUTERIZED! WE'LL BE ABLE TO STUDY THE MOVIE HABITS OF OUR WINNERS... AND CASH IN ON IT!

BOSS, THE AGE ON THIS ONE ENTRY LOOKS LIKE 16... NOT 13!
NO, IT'S A FOOD STAIN THAT MAKES IT LOOK LIKE 16! IT IS! TRUST ME!
GLAMORAMA MOVIE PASS CONTEST
ARCHIE ANDREWS
216 OAK DRIVE
RIVERDALE

MOM! DAD!
I JUST WON A MOVIE PASS THAT'S GOOD FOR TWO MONTHS!
WONDERFUL!

TWO MONTHS LATER...
BOSS, WE HAVE THE LATEST STATISTICS ON THOSE COMPUTERIZED PASSES!
AND WHAT DO THEY SAY?

IN GENERAL, THEY CONFIRM THAT MOVIES CHOSEN BY 13-YEAR-OLD MALES BECOME HITS!

BUT THIS ONE BOY HAD A PHENOMENAL RECORD! EVERY MOVIE HE SAW BECAME A SUPER MEGAHIT!
HMM! ARCHIE ANDREWS!
MOVIE ATTENDANCE RECORD OF ARCHIE ANDREWS

GOOD! WE'LL FOCUS ON HIM!... HE'LL MAKE US HOLLYWOOD'S LEADING STUDIO!

YAHOO! I'VE JUST BEEN AWARDED A YEAR'S MOVIE PASS FOR TWO!
ANDREWS

LATER...
I JUST WON A PASS THAT'S GOOD FOR TWO!
LET'S GO TO THE MOVIES TONIGHT!
KEEN TEEN

I DON'T KNOW...
LATELY WHEN WE GO, YOU ALWAYS SELECT A VIOLENT ACTION MOVIE! WE NEVER SEE THE KIND OF MOVIE I'D LIKE TO SEE!
YOU'RE RIGHT! I'VE BEEN VERY SELFISH!
FOR THE NEXT COUPLE OF MONTHS WE'LL SEE ONLY THE MOVIES YOU WANT TO SEE!
LET'S SEE THIS ONE! THE GIRLS ARE ALL TALKING ABOUT IT!
The Love Games
with MEG SMOOCH

BOSS! I JUST GOT THE LATEST DATA ON ARCHIE ANDREWS! LAST MONTH HE SAW NOTHING BUT ROMANCE MOVIES!
VERY INTERESTING!

IT MUST BE THE GLOBAL WARMING! IT'S MATURING 13-YEAR-OLD BOYS AT AN EARLIER AGE AND MAKING THEM MORE GIRL-CONSCIOUS! SOON ALL 13-YEAR-OLDS WILL BE FLOCKING TO ROMANCE MOVIES!

THIS INFO GIVES US A TREMENDOUS ADVANTAGE OVER OUR COMPETITION!
MARK MY WORD! ... WE WILL **RULE** THE MOVIE WORLD!

IT'S THE STUDIO HEAD...
... HE WANTS US TO STOP PRODUCTION ON "THE FIGHTING TROOPERS"!
DIRECTOR
SO WHAT MOVIE WILL WE MAKE IN ITS PLACE?

"LOVERS IN LOVELAND"... IT'S ALL SET UP ON THIS NEXT SET!

SEVERAL MONTHS LATER...
BAD NEWS, BOSS! ALL OUR ROMANCE MOVIES ARE BOMBING BIG TIME! THIRTEEN-YEAR-OLD MALES ARE AVOIDING THEM LIKE THE PLAGUE!
GOOD GRIEF!

WE DID A DOUBLE CHECK ON THE KID'S AGE! ARCHIE ANDREWS IS ACTUALLY **16** AND **NOT 13**!
SOB!
THAT EXPLAINS IT! YOU KNOW WHAT TO DO!

ARCHIE! I'M FROM GLAMORAMA STUDIOS! TURN IN YOUR MOVIE PASS!
B-BUT, WHY?
ANDREWS

BECAUSE YOU'RE **NOT** 13! YOU'RE MUCH TOO OLD FOR OUR MOVIE SURVEY!

MOM!
SHHH! YOUR FATHER IS VERY DESPONDENT!

A CHANCE FOR A **BIG** PROMOTION NEVER MATERIALIZED! THEY GAVE THE POSITION TO SOMEONE WHO'S MUCH YOUNGER!

BOY! HE SURE HAS MY SYMPATHY!

I KNOW **EXACTLY** WHAT IT'S LIKE TO BE TOO OLD FOR THE JOB!
END

Betty and Me "I'M A BIG GIRL NOW!"

YOU DIDN'T FINISH YOUR LUNCH, BETTY!

I KNOW, MOM! I'M JUST NOT HUNGRY RIGHT NOW!

BUT YOU SHOULD EAT ALL YOUR FOOD, BETTY! YOU NEED ALL THE VITAMINS YOU CAN GET TO GROW BIG AND STRONG!

OH FOR GOSH SAKE'S, DADDY! I'M NOT A LITTLE BABY ANYMORE! I'M SEVENTEEN YEARS OLD!

WELL AT LEAST FINISH DRINKING YOUR MILK, SWEETHEART, IT WILL GIVE YOU STRONG BONES!
GOOD GRIEF!

Script: Frank Doyle / Pencils: Dan DeCarlo / Inks: Rudy Lapick / Letters: Bill Yoshida

WILL YOU STOP THINKING OF ME AS YOUR LITTLE GIRL, DAD? WHEN ARE YOU GOING TO REALIZE THAT I'M A YOUNG WOMAN?
SURE YOU ARE, BETTY! NOW DRINK YOUR MILK! IT'S GOOD FOR YOU!

GET OFF IT, DAD! WHY, IN THE OLD DAYS SOME GIRLS MY AGE WERE ALREADY MARRIED AND RAISING A FAMILY OF THEIR OWN!

WELL THAT WAS THE OLD DAYS, SWEETIE, THEY WERE EMOTIONALLY PREPARED TO ACCEPT RESPONSIBILITY AT AN EARLY AGE!

AS FAR AS I'M CONCERNED YOU'RE STILL MY LITTLE BABY!
I'M NOT A BABY! I'M NOT! I'M NOT! I'M A GROWN WOMAN!!
HERALD

HERE, DAD! LOOK AT THIS PHOTO ALBUM OF ME WHEN I WAS A BABY! SEE HOW SMALL I WAS?
PHOTO ALBUM
SIGH! YOU WERE SUCH A SWEET LITTLE GIRL!
WELL LOOK AT ME NOW! DO YOU SEE THE DIFFERENCE?

I'VE GROWN INTO A MATURE WOMAN! I'M NOT A BABY ANYMORE! CAN'T YOU ACCEPT THAT?
YOU'RE RIGHT, BETTY, YOU HAVE GOTTEN BIGGER, BUT DON'T FORGET TO DRINK THE REST OF THE MILK BEFORE YOU GO OUT!
PHOTO ALBUM

OH WHAT'S THE USE? YOU WON'T EVER ACCEPT ME AS A GROWN UP WOMAN UNTIL I'M MARRIED!
I'M GOING OUT, MOM!
?
SLAM!
3

I THINK YOU MADE OUR DAUGHTER A LITTLE UPSET!
NONSENSE! ALL KIDS FLAIR UP NOW AND THEN! IT'S ALL PART OF GROWING UP, DEAR!
HI, ARCHIE!
?

OH, HI, BETTY! YOU LOOK A LITTLE UPTIGHT! IS SOMETHING BUGGING YOU?
I'LL SAY!

IT'S MY DAD! HE JUST WON'T ACCEPT THE FACT I'M A GROWN WOMAN! I'VE GOT A SERIOUS PROBLEM, ARCHIE!
22

WELL IF IT'S ANY CONSOLATION TO YOU, I'VE GOT A PRETTY SERIOUS PROBLEM MYSELF!
YOU HAVE, ARCHIE? IS THERE ANYTHING I CAN DO TO HELP?
4

I DON'T KNOW, BETTY, BUT IF YOU CAN HELP ME WITH MY PROBLEM, I'LL TRY TO HELP YOU WITH YOURS!

YOU GOT YOURSELF A DEAL, ARCH! NOW LET'S HEAR YOUR PROBLEM, AND START FROM THE BEGINNING!

I THINK YOU SHOULD STOP TREATING BETTY AS A LITTLE GIRL, DEAR, AND TELL IT LIKE IT IS! AFTER ALL, SHE IS IN HER TEENS!
I KNOW! BUT WHAT IS SEVENTEEN? SHE'S STILL A BABY!
I DON'T KNOW IF I GO ALONG WITH YOUR IDEA, BETTY!
WHAT ELSE CAN WE DO, ARCHIE?

?
I MEAN IT MIGHT WORK, BETTY, BUT WHAT WILL PEOPLE THINK? THEY MAY ALL THINK IT'S A CRAZY IDEA!

IT'S NOTHING TO BE ASHAMED OF, ARCHIE! AND IF IT DOESN'T WORK, AT LEAST WE CAN SAY WE TRIED!

NOW LET'S TIE THE KNOT! IT'S THE ONLY WAY TO PUT AN END TO THIS PROBLEM!
GASP! MY BABY! SHE WOULDN'T DO A THING LIKE THAT! I'VE GOT TO STOP HER!
?

BETTY! DON'T DO IT! YOU'LL BE SORRY!
?

SEE, I TOLD YOU, BETTY! EVEN YOUR FATHER AGREES WITH ME!

WELL SOMETHING HAS TO BE DONE! IT CAN'T GO ON THE WAY IT IS!
BUT WHY CAN'T YOU GIVE IT A FEW MORE YEARS? YOU'RE BOTH SO YOUNG!
6

WHAT HAS BEING YOUNG GOT TO DO WITH IT? BOY, YOU REALLY HAVE THIS HANG UP ABOUT NOT GETTING OLD!

I KNOW AND I'M SORRY, BETTY! I ACCEPT THE FACT THAT YOU'RE A GROWN UP TEENAGE GIRL, BUT DON'T GET MARRIED TO SPITE ME!
MARRIED?

WHO'S GETTING MARRIED? I'M JUST TRYING TO TELL ARCHIE TO TIE UP THE BUMPER ON HIS CAR, BECAUSE IT KEEPS FALLING OFF!

HEE! HEE! YOU MEAN YOU WERE TALKING ABOUT TYING A KNOT IN THE ROPE TO HOLD THE BUMPER TO HIS CAR?
THAT'S ABOUT IT, DAD!

WHEW! AM I RELIEVED! I SHOULDN'T LET MY IMAGINATION RUN AWAY WITH ME! I BETTER GO CHECK AND SEE IF I'VE LOST ANY HAIR!
SOMETIMES I WONDER WHO THE BABY OF THE HOUSE IS! ME OR MY DAD?
The END
7

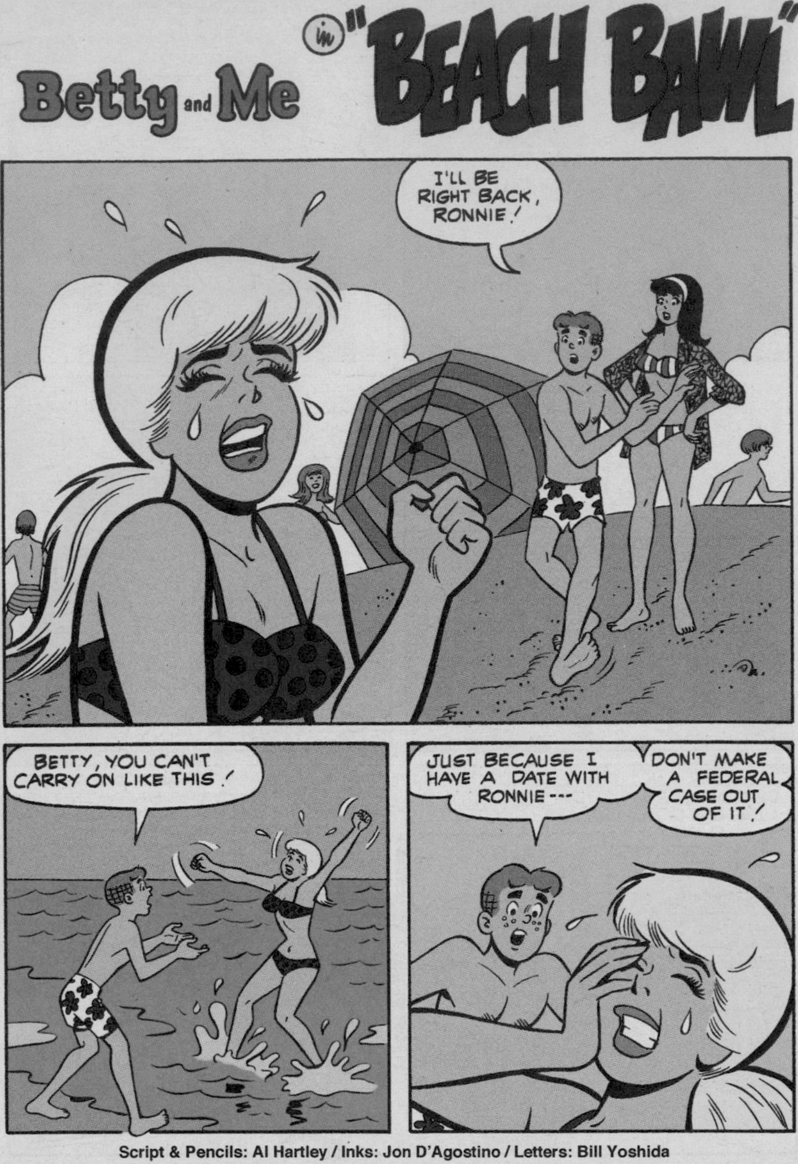

Betty and Me in "BEACH BAWL"

I'LL BE RIGHT BACK, RONNIE!

Script & Pencils: Al Hartley / Inks: Jon D'Agostino / Letters: Bill Yoshida

I KNOW YOU'RE MADLY IN LOVE WITH ME ---
BUT THIS IS RIDICULOUS!

THIS HAS NOTHING TO DO WITH YOU!

THERE'S A CRAB ON MY TOE!

HOLD STILL, BETTY!
I'LL GET HIM!
HAALP!

OKAY! YOU GOT THE CRAB OFF MY TOE---
NOW I'LL LET YOU OFF THE HOOK, ARCH!
HUH ?

YOU CAN GO BACK TO RONNIE NOW!
GO AHEAD! SHE'S WAITING!

YOU MEAN YOU'RE NOT GOING TO LIMP AND FAKE A SORE TOE AND PLAY ON MY SYMPATHY ?
WHY SHOULD I ?

VERONICA COULD WIN AN OSCAR WITH A SITUATION LIKE THIS!

I DON'T WANT TO WIN *ANYTHING* BY ACTING OR MAKING BELIEVE, ARCH!
AND THAT INCLUDES *YOU*!
3

IF I HAVE TO PLAY GAMES TO WIN YOU THEN I'M NOT PLAYING!
BUT I THOUGHT "ALL'S FAIR IN LOVE AND WAR"?

MAYBE LOVE WOULD BE MORE REAL IF PEOPLE DIDN'T GET IT MIXED UP WITH WAR!

WOW!
WHAT A STATEMENT!
THAT'S TREMENDOUS, BETTY!

I JUST REALIZED---
YOU'RE A BEAUTIFUL PERSON!
YOU CAN'T BE A BEAUTIFUL PERSON, ARCH, WITHOUT BEING AN HONEST PERSON!
OKAY, LET'S CUT OUT THE HEARTS AND FLOWERS!

ARE YOU COMING WITH ME OR ARE YOU STAYING HERE WITH DR. BROTHERS ?

JUG, I'M ALL MIXED UP!
I DON'T KNOW WHAT TO DO!

THEY'RE *BOTH* BEAUTIFUL!
RIGHT, ARCH ?
RIGHT---

--- BUT BETTY'S BEAUTIFUL ON THE *INSIDE* ---
--- AND RONNIE'S BEAUTIFUL ON THE *OUTSIDE*!
End

Betty and Me in "WHAT DO YOU PROPOSE?"

ARCHIEKINS, I'M SORRY! I REALLY, TRULY AM! BUT I'VE COME TO A DECISION! WE'RE SIMPLY TOO YOUNG TO EVEN *THINK* ABOUT SUCH A SERIOUS STEP! *MUCH* TOO YOUNG! I BELIEVE WE SHOULD CALL IT OFF RIGHT NOW, BEFORE WE BECOME TOO DEEPLY INVOLVED!
HUH?

Script & Pencils: Al Hartley / Inks: Jon D'Agostino / Letters: Bill Yoshida

NO! DON'T TRY TO CHANGE MY MIND, DARLING! I LOVE YOU, OF COURSE, BUT I JUST DON'T BELIEVE IN EARLY MARRIAGES!
B--- BUT---

MR. AND MRS. ANDREWS, I IMAGINE YOU'LL BE RELIEVED TO HEAR OF MY BIG DECISION!
WELL, WE---

OH, WE'RE NOT ALL CRAZY, HEAD-STRONG KIDS, YOU KNOW! SOME OF US HAVE A TOUCH OF SENSE! A SMIDGEN OF MATURITY! OH, YES!

NOW, LISTEN---
NO! NO! DON'T! YOU'LL ONLY MAKE IT MORE DIFFICULT FOR BOTH OF US, DARLING! MY MIND IS MADE UP! THERE'S NO TURNING BACK!
2

JUST STOP FOR A SECOND, AND---
NO! YOU STOP, SON! SHE'S RIGHT!

BUT, MOM---
NOW, DON'T BE PIGHEADED, SON!

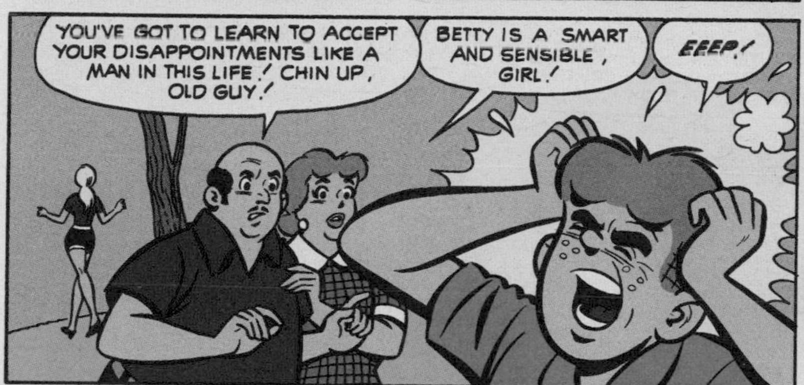
YOU'VE GOT TO LEARN TO ACCEPT YOUR DISAPPOINTMENTS LIKE A MAN IN THIS LIFE! CHIN UP, OLD GUY!
BETTY IS A SMART AND SENSIBLE, GIRL!
EEEP!

THAT GIRL--- WE NEVER--- I DIDN'T---
GROW UP, SON!

MAYBE, IN YEARS TO COME --- WHO KNOWS?
SIGH!
3

GLEEEP!

SIGH!

UH, EXCUSE ME, DILTON! LIFE HAS DEALT MY GOOD BUDDY ANOTHER CRUSHING BLOW!
IT HAPPENS THREE OR FOUR TIMES A DAY!

OKAY, ARCH! YOUR PERSONAL CHAPLAIN IS ON THE JOB!
FILL ME IN!

I'VE BEEN JILTED!

YOU DID SAY, "JILTED"?
THROWN OVER! TOSSED ASIDE LIKE AN OLD SHOE! THE HEAVE HO!
JUST A LITTLE WHILE AGO! BETTY COMES TO MY DOOR! YOU WOULDN'T BELIEVE WHAT SHE HAD TO SAY!
HARD TO BELIEVE WHAT YOU HAVEN'T HEARD!

SHE CALLED THE WHOLE THING OFF! SAID WE WERE TOO YOUNG! SHE DOESN'T BELIEVE IN EARLY MARRIAGES!
SHE SAID THAT?

SHE EVEN HAD MY MOM AND POP CONVINCED THAT IT WAS THE GREATEST IDEA SINCE SLICED BREAD!
MMMPH!

I DIDN'T EVEN GET A CHANCE TO OPEN MY MOUTH! I FELT LIKE A FISH THAT WAS THROWN BACK BECAUSE HE WAS TOO SMALL!
UH,-YOU,-YOU WANTED TO GET MARRIED, THEN?

HUH? UH---OH---ER---WELL, GEE, I DON'T KNOW.!

BUT A GUY HATES TO GET TURNED DOWN BEFORE HE EVEN ASKS.!

WHAT'S WRONG WITH ME, ANYWAY?
NOT A THING, PAL.!

MMMPH.! NOTHING WRONG WITH BETTY, EITHER.!

DROPPED ME LIKE A BAD HABIT, SHE DID.! AND AFTER ALL WE'VE MEANT TO EACH OTHER.!
WHEN THEY TALK TO THEMSELVES - THAT'S A SURE SIGN OF OLD AGE.!
MAN.! I DON'T WANT TO HANG AROUND SO LONG THAT I START CRACKIN' UP.!
6

HELLO, YOU LITTLE RED-HEADED RASCAL! WHAT'S NEW?

UH, NOT NOW, VERONICA! I'VE GOT HEAVY THOUGHTS ON MY MIND!

WELL, I *LIKE* THAT!!
YOU DON'T *REALLY*, YOU KNOW!

WELL, GOOD GRIEF, NO GIRL LIKES BEING PRACTICALLY *IGNORED*!

WOMEN! THEY DON'T KNOW THEIR OWN MINDS! IT'S STILL A MAN'S WORLD, IN SPITE OF ALL THAT WOMEN'S LIB, JAZZ!

FEMALES LIKE TO BE TOLD NOT ASKED!

THAT'S THE REASON FOR MY FAILURE! TOO KIND - TOO GENTLE - TOO POLITE!

BAM! BAM!
THAT'S ARCHIE!

I WANT TO TALK TO YOU, BETTY COOPER!

WHO DO YOU THINK YOU ARE -- TURNING ME DOWN BEFORE I EVEN ASKED?
I'M SORRY, ARCHIEKINS!

NOW LISTEN, GIRL, AND LISTEN GOOD!

WHEN THE TIME COMES, I AM NOT GOING TO ASK YOU TO MARRY ME!
YOU'RE NOT ???

NO! I AM GOING TO TELL YOU! "TELL!" GET IT ?
I - I - TH- THINK S-SO!

BETTY COOPER! YOU ARE GOING TO MARRY ME!
EEP!

OKAY! CUT! END OF SCENE! WRAP IT UP! GOOD-BYE, ARCHIE!
HUH ?
9

HOME, BOY! COLD SHOWER! COOL THE WOUNDED PRIDE!

JUGHEAD, TAKE CARE OF HIM! HE'LL BE ALL RIGHT IN A LITTLE WHILE!
OKAY, MRS. COOPER! I KNEW YOU WOULDN'T LET IT GO TOO FAR!

SIGH! I KNEW YOU'D GET AROUND TO THAT METHOD SOONER OR LATER!
HUH?

MOM! YOU'RE AMAZING!
HOW DID YOU KNOW?

HOW DO YOU THINK I GOT YOUR FATHER?
?
The End

Veronica in The Letter

WOW! LOOK AT THIS LETTER I RECEIVED TODAY!

IT'S A *WRECK!* IT LOOKS LIKE IT'S BEEN THROUGH WORLD WAR III!

SCRIPT & PENCILS: DAN PARENT
INKS: JIM AMASH

WOW! IT'S BEEN RE-ROUTED DOZENS OF TIMES DUE TO AN INCOMPLETE ADDRESS!
PLUS, THIS HAND-WRITING IS A MESS!
RE-ROUTE
INCOMPLETE

THIS LETTER'S DATED ALMOST A YEAR AGO!
IT'S FROM SOMEONE NAMED MIKE!

Dearest Veronica,
After bumping into you at the Riverdale Carnival, I fell head over heels for you! I found out your home address and have been trying to contact you ever since! If you get this, you can reach me at
xxoo
Mike
WOW! I HAVE A SECRET ADMIRER!

BUT I CAN'T READ WHERE HE CAN BE REACHED!
IT'S MESSED UP WITH A WATER STAIN!

THE RIVERDALE FALL CARNIVAL IS COMING
AGAIN NEXT WEE

MAYBE IF I SHOW UP, HE'LL BE THERE TOO! HE'LL SEE ME AND OUR LOVE WILL BLOOM!

THIS IS SO ROMANTIC!
I'VE GOT TO CALL BETTY!

SO...
HE SAID HE BUMPED INTO ME, SO I MAY RECOGNIZE HIM!
BUT CHANCES ARE YOU'LL HAVE TO HOPE HE SEES YOU!

DARLING! IT'S YOU!!
WOW! IS THAT YOU, MIKE?!

DEBBIE! THANKS FOR MEETING ME, SWEETHEART!

LET'S SIT BY THE ENTRANCE! BETTER EXPOSURE HERE!
SOUNDS LIKE A FUN NIGHT AHEAD!

2 HOURS LATER...

YEAH! YOU'RE RIGHT!
IT WAS WORTH A SHOT, THOUGH!

VERONICA! IS THAT YOU? IT'S ME-- MIKE!
MIKE! THE MIKE WHO WROTE THE LETTER?!

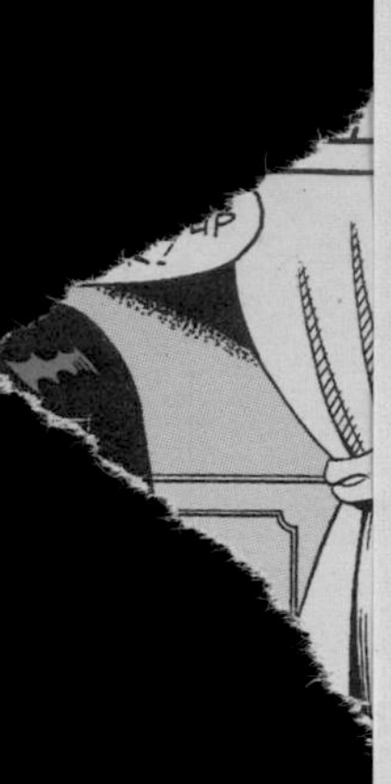

YES! DID YOU GET IT, VERONICA?
OH, HOW I'VE DREAMT OF THIS MOMENT, VERONICA!

UH... I'M NOT VERONICA! I'M BETTY!
BUT I WAS TOLD YOU WERE VERONICA!!

WHEN I ASKED THE KID WHO THE KNOCKOUT WAS, HE SAID--
OH, HER! THAT'S VERONICA LODGE!
HE MUST'VE THOUGHT I MEANT YOU! SORRY!

YOU WERE INTERESTED IN ME?!
YOU WERE INTERESTED IN HER?!
4

YES! IS THAT OKAY?
IS THAT OKAY, VERONICA?

YES! GO ON, YOU TWO!
AT LEAST I CAN HAVE ARCHIE TO MYSELF FOR AWHILE!!

SIGH!
EXCUSE ME, HOT STUFF!

GAK!
CAN I BUY YOU A SODA?

UH... NO THANKS!
CAN YOU AT LEAST TELL ME YOUR NAME?

UH... SURE!
IT'S BETTY! BETTY COOPER!!
THE END

Betty and Veronica in A Tale Of Two Diaries

EEEEEYAAARGH!!

?!

SCRIPT: KATHLEEN WEBB
PENCILS: JEFF SHULTZ
INKS: AL MILGROM

MY DIARY! I'VE *LOST* MY DIARY!!
REALLY?

WHERE DID YOU LOSE IT?
NOWHERE *YOU'LL* FIND IT!

IT'S NO USE! IT'S LONG GONE! I'LL NEVER SEE IT AGAIN!
WELL, DON'T WORRY!

CONSIDERING IT PROBABLY IS AS INTERESTING AS A CONGRESSIONAL REPORT, I DON'T THINK YOU HAVE MUCH TO WORRY ABOUT!
GEE, THANKS!

TOO BAD I COULDN'T FIND IT! I COULD USE A GOOD LAUGH!

TELEPHONE FOR YOU, MISS VERONICA! IT'S MISS BETTY!
SHE PROBABLY FOUND HER DIARY! DRAT, THE LUCK!

VERONICA, YOU'LL NEVER BELIEVE IT!!

I WON'T BE ABLE TO IF I CAN'T HEAR! TONE IT DOWN!
SORRY! BUT I'M JUST SO EXCITED!
2

YOU FOUND YOUR DIARY, RIGHT?
NO! SOMETHING EVEN BETTER HAPPENED!

A MOVIE PRODUCER FOUND AND READ IT! HE WANTS TO MAKE A MOVIE BASED ON IT!
HE'S GOING TO MAKE A COMEDY?

NO! HE SAID IT WOULD MAKE A WONDERFUL TEEN ROMANCE!
WHOOPS... GOTTA GO... THERE'RE CONTRACTS TO SIGN!
CLICK!

I CAN'T BELIEVE IT! BETTY'S DIARY... A FEATURE-LENGTH MOVIE?
I WOULDN'T HAVE THOUGHT YOU COULD MAKE A THIRTY-SECOND COMMERCIAL OUT OF IT!

RON! RON! QUICK, YOU'VE GOT TO COME OR YOU'LL MISS HIM!
HIM, WHOM?

THE ACTOR THEY'RE CASTING FOR THE PART OF ARCHIE!
THEY'RE NOT USING ARCHIE?

THEY WERE AFRAID HE'D DESTROY THE MOVIE SET!
INSTEAD, THEY HIRED BO HUNK, TEEN IDOL!
SCRIPT

OH, BO! I'M SO HONORED TO HAVE YOU STAR IN THE MOVIE ABOUT MY LIFE!
I'M HONORED TO PLAY OPPOSITE YOUR STUNNING BEAUTY, BETTY!

"PLAYING OPPOSITE--"? Y-YOU CAN'T MEAN...
YES! THEY DECIDED INSTEAD OF HIRING SOME BIG-NAME ACTRESS...

...THEY'D HAVE ME PLAY MYSELF IN THE FILM!
GULP!

BETTY... LET'S ADD SOME TORRID PAGES OF OUR OWN TO YOUR DIARY!
SIGH OH, BO!!
I CAN'T BELIEVE THIS... IT MUST BE A DREAM... IT MUST BE--!!

BOP!!
IT CAN'T... UH... WHA-?!?
OH! WHAT A RELIEF ...IT WAS A DREAM!

OH, RON! THAT IS A SILLY DREAM!
I DOUBT ANYBODY'D BE INTERESTED IN MAKING A MOVIE BASED ON MY DIARY!
NO KIDDING!

NOW, MY DIARY IS FULL OF FAR MORE INTERESTING TIDBITS!
OH? LET'S HAVE A LOOK!

HAH! AFRAID I'LL FIND OUT HOW BORING YOUR LIFE REALLY IS, EH?
NO! I JUST- YIKES!

NOW YOU'VE DONE IT, BETTY COOPER! IT'S LOST FOREVER IN THE BIG BOGANHEELA RIVER!
MAYBE IT LANDED ON THAT TOUR BOAT GOING UNDERNEATH!

WELL, IF IT DID, I'M SURE WHOEVER READS IT WILL FIND IT FAR MORE ENTERTAINING THAN YOURS IS!
I DOUBT THEY'LL WANT TO MAKE A MOVIE OUT OF IT, THOUGH!

"OH, YEAH?"
HOOHODHOOHAHAAA! B-BRUCIE BABY, I TELL YA, THIS STUFF WOULD MAKE THE GREATEST COMEDY THE WORLD HAS EVER SEEN!
AND O.O. WELLONMELLON, YOU'D BE THE DIRECTOR FOR IT- IF ANYONE COULD BELIEVE IT! HARR, HARR, HARR!
DIARY
end

LiFE WITH Archie

IN TEEVIE JEEBIES

Script: Sy Reit / Art & Letters: Bob White

ARE WE SPEAKING ABOUT "THE TWILIGHT ZONE?" NO, DEAR FRIEND! THIS ADVENTURE REALLY HAPPENED!! IN FACT, IT COULD SOME DAY, HAPPEN TO YOU!! SO- READ ON--- (IF YOU DARE!)

THE DAY BEGAN NORMALLY...
HO, HO! GREETINGS AND ALL THAT SORT OF STUFF!

YOO HOO! HELLO THERE! ANYBODY HOME??

WELL, WELL! CHOCOLATE-COVERED CHERRY CORDIALS!

KEEP YOUR GRUBBY PAWS OUT OF THE CANDY DISH, YOU CROOK!

ARCH, BOY! D-DID YOU JUST SPEAK TO ME FROM INSIDE THE TELEVISION SET?

OF COURSE NOT, JERK! FROM BEHIND THE SET! I'M TRYING TO FIX THE PICTURE TUBE!

HOW COME ALL OF A SUDDEN YOU'RE A TV MECHANIC?
I WAS AFRAID YOU'D ASK ME THAT!

YESTERDAY, DAD GAVE ME MONEY TO HAVE THE SET FIXED! BUT LAST NIGHT...

I HAD A DATE WITH VERONICA!

THE PLOT THICKENS!
WE WENT TO THE MOVIES... 'N' THEN BOWLING... 'N' THEN TWISTING...

'N' BY THE TIME WE GOT HOME, I WAS OUT OF DOUGH! SO I'VE GOTTA FIX THIS FURSHLUGGINER THING MYSELF!
TSK, TSK, TSK!

OH, WELL! LEMME SEE...
REMEMBER, DE KNEE BONE'S CONNECTED TO DE THIGH BONE! DE THIGH BONE'S CONNECTED TO...

JUGHEAD, DO ME A FAVOR! GET LOST! SCRAM! DISAPPEAR!
OKAY! I CAN TAKE A HINT!

WHAT HAVE WE HERE? WELL, WELL! IT'S A KITCHEN!

THIS LOOKS LIKE A REFRIGERATOR!

...AND THIS LOOKS VERY MUCH LIKE A YUMMY PLATTER OF FOOD!
SLAM

HEY, JUG! DO ME A FAVOR! THROW THE ELECTRIC SWITCH NEXT TO OUR FUSE BOX!
GULP ER... SURE, ARCHIE!
CHOMP!

ELECTRIC SWITCH... FUSE BOX...
OKAY, BOY!
FUSE BOX

YIPE!

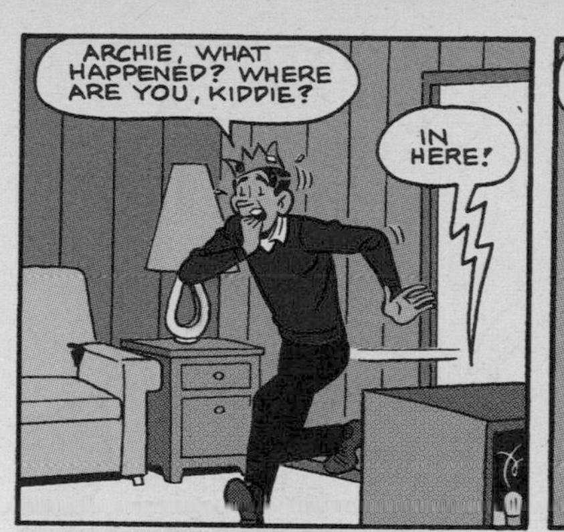
ARCHIE, WHAT HAPPENED? WHERE ARE YOU, KIDDIE?
IN HERE!

OMIGOSH! I SEE IT, B-BUT I DON'T BELIEVE IT?!
WHEN YOU THREW THE SWITCH, THERE WAS A BLINDING FLASH... AND NOW LOOK!

IT'S INCREDIBLE, ARCH! YOU'VE TURNED INTO AN IMAGE ON THE TELEVISION SCREEN!
THANKS LOADS FOR TELLING ME!
R

BUT... BUT... YOU WERE HERE JUST A MINUTE AGO!
PLEASE STOP BLABBERING AND GET ME OUT OF THIS THING!

MAYBE I OUGHTA SWITCH THE DIAL!
NO, NO! IF YOU DO THAT, I MIGHT DISAPPEAR ALTOGETHER!

OKAY! SIT TIGHT! I'LL CHECK THIS TV REPAIR GUIDE!
DON'T WORRY, BOY! UNCLE JUGGIE WILL SAVE YOU!

UH, HUH! UH, HUH! HMM... AH!
TV REPAIR GUIDE

ARCHIE, RELAX! YOU HAVE NOTHING TO WORRY ABOUT! EVERYTHING'S OKAY!
GEE, THAT'S GOOD NEWS!

YEP! ACCORDING TO THIS BOOK, WHAT JUST HAPPENED TO YOU IS ABSOLUTELY IMPOSSIBLE!
!?

YOU DOPE! GET DILTON DOILEY! HE'S THE ONLY ONE WHO CAN HELP ME NOW!

GET DILTON DOILEY! GET DILTON DOILEY!

MEANWHILE, AT THE CHOKLIT SHOPPE:

VERY QUIET AROUND HERE TODAY!

GET DILTON DOILEY! GET DILTON DOILEY!

H-HEAVENS TO BETSY!

HELLO, DOC? CAN I COME IN FOR A CHECK-UP? YES! VERY SERIOUS!

...I'M BEGINNING TO HAVE HALLUCINATIONS! I JUST THOUGHT I SAW JUGHEAD! ...AND HE WAS RUNNING!?

FIVE MINUTES LATER...

YOU SAY ARCHIE IS IN THE TV SET? BUT THAT DOESN'T MAKE ANY SENSE!
YEAH, I KNOW! EMBARRASSING, ISN'T IT?

THERE HE IS! ~SOB~ WHAT CAN WE DO?
INTERESTING! **VERRRY** INTERESTING!
HI, DIL!

AH! HUMPH! JUST AS I THOUGHT! IT'S ALL A MATTER OF RADIO WAVES!
RADIO WAVES?
OUCH! HEY! WATCH IT BACK THERE!

TELEVISION WORKS BY TRANSMITTING WAVE LENGTHS ELECTRONICALLY, LIKE A RADIO!
IF YOU SAY SO, DILL!

THE WAVES, WHICH TRAVEL THROUGH SPACE, CARRY A SUCCESSION OF IMPULSES WHICH ARE INTERCEPTED BY TV ANTENNAE...

... BUT IN THIS CASE, ARCHIE'S **OWN** WAVES GOT ENTANGLED WITH THE DEFLECTION COIL CIRCUIT OF THE CATHODE-RAY TUBE!

SO CAN YOU GET HIM **OUT** OF THERE?
OF COURSE! IT'S **EASY!** WE SHOULD HAVE HIM OUT IN TWO OR THREE MONTHS!
WHAT!

POOR ARCHIE! HOW WILL HE BE FREED FROM THE CLUTCHES OF HIS TV SET?

(OR SHOULD WE SAY **"WHEN"?**)

Archie in TUBE BE, OR NOT TUBE BE!...

DILTON GOES TO WORK, TRYING TO FREE ARCHIE'S IMAGE FROM THE GRIP OF THE..... **CATHODE-RAY TUBE!...**

THIS SHOW SURE IS DULL!

I'M GLAD MY FOLKS ARE AWAY FOR THE WEEK! THEY'D **NEVER** BE ABLE TO UNDERSTAND!

LET'S SEE! IF I MOVE THIS TUBE HERE.... SWITCH THIS WIRE HERE... AND....

DILTON! STOP! LOOK WHAT'S HAPPENING **NOW!**
HUH?

ARCHIE'S PICTURE IS **FADING!**
S-SO LONG!
GOOD HEAVENS!

:SOB: HE'S GONE!
DON'T PANIC! ARCHIE'S IMAGE IS FLOATING AROUND IN THERE **SOMEWHERE!**

LET'S TRY DIFFERENT CHANNELS! MAYBE WE'LL PICK HIM UP AGAIN!
CLICK!
CLICK!
CLICK!
2 13 12

"HAVE GUN, WILL GROVEL!" MY FAVORITE WESTERN!
HAVE GUN
WILL GROVEL

DRAW, PALADIN!
YOU FIRST, McGRAW!

OOPS!
HOLD YOUR FIRE!
HE'S NOT IN THE SCRIPT!
R

BANG!
YOU TOOK THE WORDS OUT OF MY MOUTH, SIR!
BANG!
BANG
BANG!
BANG!
R

HOW DID THAT HAPPEN?
SOMETHING'S GONE WRONG WITH ARCHIE AND HIS VISUAL MODULATION! IT'S RUNNING WILD!

LET'S TRY ANOTHER CHANNEL!
CLICK!
CLICK!

ATTENTION, MEMBERS OF THE COLONY COOKING CLASS!

IT'S TIME TO SEE HOW OUR "CHEESE SOUFLEE PARISIENNE" IS DOING!

IF WE'RE LUCKY, IT WILL BE A YUMMY GOLDEN BROWN, AND IT WILL LOOK VERY DELECT-ABLE!

???
ARE YOU T-TALKING ABOUT ME?

ARCHIE IS REALLY COOKIN' WITH GAS!
VERY FUNNY!
DO SOMETHING, DILTON! THIS IS GETTING EMBARRASSING!

HEY, DILL! HE MUST BE RUINING EVERY TV SET IN THE COUNTRY!
GEE! LET'S CHECK!

HELLO, BETTY! ANYTHING-ER-- UNUSUAL HAPPENING ON YOUR TV SET?

NO, DILTON! RONNIE AND I ARE WATCHING A COOKING CLASS! THEY JUST MADE A WONDERFUL SOUFLEE!

I THOUGHT SO! ARCHIE'S IMAGE IS MESSING UP THESE RADIO WAVES! BUT THE OTHER SETS ARE FINE!
POOR ARCH! I THOUGHT BY NOW HE'D BE ON NET-WORK!

LET'S TRY CHANNEL 18! I WANNA SEE WHAT HE DOES WITH DR. LACEY!
HOW CAN YOU BE SO CYNICAL?
CLICK

CALLING DR. LACEY! CALLING DR. LACEY! REPORT TO SURGERY!
QUIET
OPERATING RM.

THE PATIENT IS READY, DR. LACEY!
I'M NOT DR. LACEY!

I'M ARCHIE ANDREWS, OF RIVERDALE, U.S.A., AND I WANNA GET OUT OF HERE!

POOR ARCHIE!
YEAH! CHANGE THE CHANNEL... HE'LL NEVER MAKE IT THROUGH MEDICAL SCHOOL!
CLICK!

WHAT'S THIS?
"THE DEFENDANTS"! ARCHIE IS PLAYING THE LAWYER'S PART!
WHERE WERE YOU ON THE NIGHT OF APRIL 9TH?

HOW DO I KNOW? I DON'T EVEN RE-MEMBER WHERE I WAS AN HOUR AGO!

GOSH! ARCHIE'S THE LAWYER AND THE WITNESS, TOO!
HIS LIGHT MOLECULES ARE ACTING UP AGAIN!

THE WITNESS IS HEREBY ORDERED TO ANSWER THE QUESTION!
BANG!
BANG!

NOW HE'S THE JUDGE!

THE JURY IS INSTRUCTED TO DISREGARD THE WITNESS'S LAST REMARKS!
R
R
R
R

TWELVE ARCHIES! ALL AT ONCE! I CAN'T STAND IT!
HMM... I THINK WE'VE DISCOVERED SOMETHING IMPORTANT! I WISH I KNEW WHAT IT WAS!

ARCHIE IS SINKING DEEPER INTO TV-LAND!

WILL DILTON **EVER** MANAGE TO FREE HIM?

Archie in "IMAGE SCRIMMAGE!"

FOR HOURS, DILTON AND JUGHEAD HAVE BEEN TRYING TO RESCUE ARCHIE FROM VIDEOLAND...

HE'S MANAGED TO RUIN ALL MY FAVORITE PROGRAMS

JUGGIE, I'M WORRIED! WE LOST ARCHIE'S IMAGE AGAIN! I CAN'T LOCATE HIM!

CLICK! CLICK!

CLICK!

WELL, THE ONLY THING LEFT FOR HIM IS A **COMMERCIAL**!
A COMMERCIAL? DON'T BE SILLY! HE WOULD **NEVER** SINK SO LOW!
CLICK!

FRIENDS! ARE YOU TROUBLED WITH THAT DREADED AILMENT... **R.E.**? YES, I'M TALKING ABOUT **ROUGH ELBOW**!

IF SO, WHY NOT DO WHAT 36 OUT OF 4187 DOCTORS DO.... SWITCH TO SUPER-GUNK!

TESTS PROVE THAT SUPER-GUNK CORRECTS R.E. MORE EFFECTIVELY THAN ANY OF THE MORE EXPENSIVE SPREADS!

SO WHY USE THAT GREASY KID STUFF ON YOUR ELBOWS? RUSH OUT AND STOCK UP ON SUPER-GUNK! OUR SPECIAL FOR TODAY: THE 23 GALLON FAMILY SIZE FOR ONLY $1.98!

TO THINK THAT MY PAL ARCHIE SHOULD WIND UP A TV HUCKSTER!
STOP SNIVELING AND START THINKING! WE'VE GOT TO SAVE HIM BEFORE....

RING! RING! RING!
OMIGOSH! ANSWER IT, DILTON!
N-NO! YOU ANSWER IT!

IF YOU ANSWER IT, I'LL GIVE YOU A PENNY!
QUIT STALLING! MAYBE IT'S IMPORTANT!
MAKE IT A NICKEL!
H-HOW ABOUT A DIME?

HELLO, JUGHEAD! THIS IS MR. ANDREWS!
ANDREWS? ANDREWS? ER... UM... **WHICH** MR. ANDREWS, EXACTLY?

WHAT ARE YOU TALKING ABOUT? THIS IS ARCHIE'S **FATHER!** IS ARCHIE THERE?
UH... NO, SIR! HE'S... ER AUDITIONING FOR A **TV SHOW!**
WELL, GIVE HIM A MESSAGE! TELL HIM HIS MOTHER AND I WILL BE HOME AT 8 P.M. TONIGHT!
TONIGHT?

B-BUT, MR. ANDREWS! LISTEN! YOU CAN'T.... ER.... I MEAN, I MEAN, IT MIGHT NOT BE....
SO LONG, JUGHEAD!
CLICK!

WHAT ARE WE GONNA DO NOW?
I DUNNO! I CAN'T DECIDE BETWEEN FAINTING AND SCREAMING!

POOR ARCHIE! WAIT TILL HIS DAD FINDS OUT!
WE **MUST** STICK BY ARCHIE IN HIS HOUR OF NEED! THINK, JUGHEAD, **THINK!**

I'VE GOT IT! THE **PERFECT SOLUTION!** WE SHOULD HAVE DONE THIS **LONG** AGO!
SNAP!

GOOD BOY! WHAT'S YOUR SOLUTION?
LET'S GET OUTA TOWN!

NO YOU DON'T! YOU'RE NOT CHICKENING OUT ON ME NOW!
CRASH!

HEY, WILL YOU GUYS STOP FIGHTING AND DO SOMETHING ABOUT ME!
GOOD GOSH! HIS IMAGE HAS TURNED UPSIDE-DOWN!
I **KNEW** ARCHIE WOULD FLIP SOME DAY!

DOES THIS MEAN MORE TROUBLE?

CAN THE BOYS RESCUE ARCHIE BEFORE HIS FOLKS RETURN?

"WELCOME HOME!"

A BRIEF REVIEW OF THE INCREDIBLE EVENTS THAT HAVE TAKEN PLACE SO FAR....

IT ALL STARTED WHEN ARCHIE TRIED TO FIX THE FAMILY TV SET, BY HIMSELF...

RIGHT IN THE MIDDLE OF THINGS, JUGHEAD THREW AN ELECTRIC FUSE BOX SWITCH.....

WHEN THE SMOKE CLEARED, ARCHIE'S IMAGE WAS TRAPPED **INSIDE** THE CATHODE-RAY TUBE......

DILTON AND JUGHEAD HAVE BEEN TRYING DESPERATELY TO RESCUE HIM....

MEANWHILE, ARCHIE'S FOLKS ARE ON THEIR WAY HOME UNEXPECTEDLY, FROM A SOUTHERN VACATION..... SO...

THIS TV ENGINEERING BOOK SHOULD GIVE ME SOME HELP!
HURRY, MAN! ARCHIE'S FOLKS WILL BE HOME IN LESS THAN AN HOUR!
TV REPAIR GUIDE

I'VE GOT IT! I'VE GOT IT! HOORAY!
TV REPAIR

GOOD OLD DILLY! I KNEW YOU'D FIND THE ANSWER!
UNPLUG THE SET--QUICK!

FIRST I MOVE THIS SYNCHRONIZING TUBE HERE-- NOW THESE MODULATING UNITS GO HERE-- UH--SWITCH THESE WIRES SO
NEXT I PUT TH!!!......

TWENTY MINUTES LATER...
ALL SET, JUGGIE! YOU CAN PLUG THE SET IN AGAIN!
AYE, AYE, SIR EINSTEIN!

HELLO! HELLO! WHY IS IT SO DARK HERE? SOMEBODY TURN ON THE LIGHTS!
OMIGOSH! WE STILL HAVE HIS VOICE, BUT HIS IMAGE IS GONE!
GULP!

YOO HOO! JUGGIE? DILTON? WHERE IS EVERY ONE?
POOR MR. AND MRS. ANDREWS! THEIR ONLY SON HAS TURNED INTO A TV SET!

OF COURSE, IT DOES HAVE ADVANTAGES! THEY CAN TURN HIM OFF WHEN-EVER THEY WANT, AND—
BE SERIOUS, JUG! THERE'S ONLY HALF AN HOUR TO GO!

SO MAKE WITH THE BOOK, DILL! THE BOOK IS OUR ONLY CHANCE!
OKAY! I'LL GO THROUGH IT AGAIN!
TV REPAIR GUIDE

MEANWHILE, AT THE AIRPORT...
FASTEN YOUR SAFETY BELTS, PLEASE!
MARY, ANOTHER FEW MINUTES AND WE'LL BE HOME!

HMM--THIS WHOLE THING STARTED WHEN I CAME INTO THE KITCHEN AND THREW THAT DURN ELECTRIC SWITCH!

WHAT WOULD HAPPEN IF I THREW THAT SWITCH AGAIN?
FUSES

PHOOEY! THIS BOOK IS NO HELP ANYMORE!
KLUNK!

BZZZZZZZZZ...
POOF!

WHAT HAPPENED?
WHAT HAPPENED?

WHAT I WANT TO KNOW IS-- WHERE AM I?
ARCHIE! YOU'RE BACK!
THE BOOK FINALLY HELPED!
4

HEY! SOMEBODY'S AT THE FRONT DOOR!

SURPRISE!!
MOM! DAD! YOU'RE HOME FROM YOUR VACATION!
BROTHER! HOW'S THAT FOR TIMING?

DID YOU BEHAVE YOURSELF WHILE WE WERE AWAY?
SURE, MOM! I-ER-HARDLY EVEN MOVED!

YES! LIFE JUST FLOWED ALONG IN THE USUAL CHANNELS!
WELL, ARCHIE. WE HAVE ANOTHER SURPRISE! WE DECIDED TO Bzz Bzz Bzz!
HUH!

ARCHIE FAINTED!
I CAN'T UNDERSTAND! ALL I SAID WAS THAT WE WERE GOING TO BUY HIM HIS VERY OWN PERSONAL TV SET!
HOT STUFF!
THE END

WORLD OF Archie Vid:ot's Delight

DILTON, WHAT EXACTLY ARE THESE VIDEO GAMES YOU'VE DESIGNED AND HOPE TO SELL?

WELL, HEALTH EXPERTS SAY TODAY'S EXERCISE-ORIENTED VIDEO GAMES DON'T GO FAR ENOUGH...

... THE EXERCISE HAS TO BE MUCH MORE VIGOROUS TO DO ANY GOOD.

MY IMAGINATION HAS HELPED ME DESIGN 3-D VIDEO GAMES THAT ENCOURAGE THE PLAYER TO EXPEND MORE ENERGY...
...AND I'D LIKE YOU ALL TO HELP ME DEMONSTRATE THESE GAMES.
SCRIPT: GEORGE GLADIR
PENCILS: PAT KENNEDY
INKS: JIM AMASH
LETTERS: TERESA DAVIDSON

GENTLEMEN, I'VE DESIGNED SEVERAL 3-D EXERCISE GAMES THAT GIVE THE PLAYERS A *REAL* WORKOUT!
MY FRIENDS HERE WILL HELP ME DEMONSTRATE THESE GAMES.

BETTY AND NANCY WILL PLAY THE FIRST GAME IN WHICH GIRL SHOPPERS HAVE TO SIMULATE FIGHTING THROUGH A MOB TO OBTAIN THEIR BARGAINS.

GIRLS, I'LL PLACE THESE 3-D GLASSES ON YOU AS YOU HOLD ONTO YOUR CONTROLS.

NOW I WANT YOU BOTH TO MAKE WILD PUSHING AND SHOVING MOTIONS AS YOU LUNGE FOR YOUR BARGAINS!

DILTON! WE RESENT THE SEXIST AND DEMEANING WAYS YOU IMPLY GIRLS GET THEIR BARGAINS!
WE REFUSE TO PLAY THIS SILLY GAME!

EVERYONE KNOWS WE GET OUR BARGAINS BY SHOWING UP *BEFORE* THE STORE OPENS!
WE'LL MEET YOU BOYS LATER AT POP TATE'S.

I MAY HAVE MISCALCULATED MY 3-D EXERCISE GAME FOR GIRLS...

...BUT THE *OTHER* GAMES I'VE CREATED ARE RIGHT ON TARGET!
PROCEED.

THIS NEXT 3-D GAME IS DESIGNED FOR THOSE WHO DRAW A LOT...
...AND WHO NORMALLY ARE NOT VERY ACTIVE.

AFTER CHUCK PUTS ON HIS 3-D GLASSES, I ATTACH A CONTROL GADGET TO HIS DRAWING HAND...
3

...AND THEN ASK HIM TO GO THROUGH THE MOTIONS OF SKETCHING A FOOD FIGHT IN THE SCHOOL CAFETERIA.

ALL OF A SUDDEN CHUCK HAS TO DUCK AND WEAVE TO AVOID 3-D IMAGES BEING HURLED AT HIM!

YAAAA!

AND MIRACLE OF MIRACLES, CHUCK DOESN'T APPEAR TO HAVE BEEN HIT *ONCE* DURING THE STORMY TEN-MINUTE FOOD BATTLE!
BUT HE APPEARS TO HAVE GOTTEN MORE THAN HIS SHARE OF EXERCISE.

I'M SURE NOW WE'LL HAVE EVEN *MORE* SUCCESS WITH THIS NEXT GAME TO BE PLAYED BY ARCHIE!
IT'S DESIGNED FOR BOYS WHO ASPIRE TO MAKE IT BIG AS ROCK STARS!
ROCKIN' IN ♫ROCK N'ROLL TOWN! ♪

OUR PLAYER HAS TO GYRATE AND MAKE ALL SORTS OF LEAPING MOTIONS.
♪YEAH YEAH♫ YEAH!

BUT THE *REAL* EXERCISE COMES INTO PLAY...

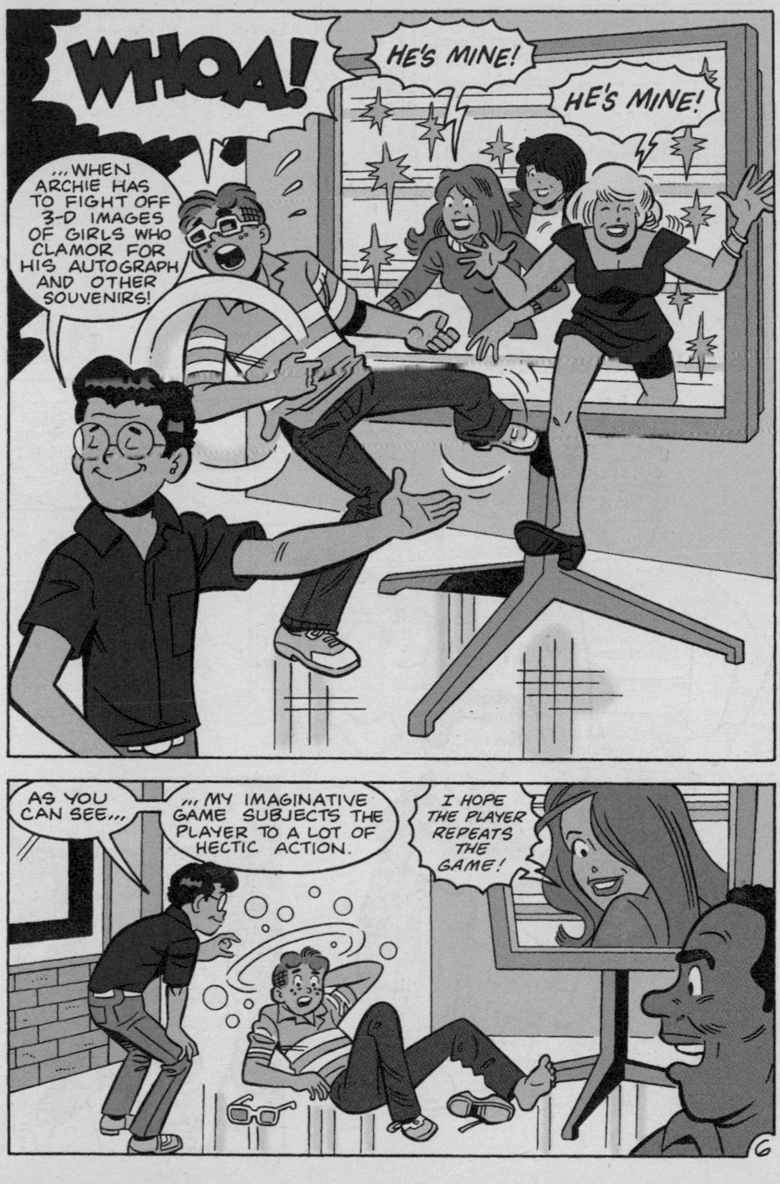

WHOA!

HE'S MINE!

HE'S MINE!

...WHEN ARCHIE HAS TO FIGHT OFF 3-D IMAGES OF GIRLS WHO CLAMOR FOR HIS AUTOGRAPH AND OTHER SOUVENIRS!

AND NOW THE FINAL 3-D GAME IS DESIGNED FOR BOYS AND GIRLS WHO HAVE HEALTHY APPETITES!

THAT'S *ME!*

IN THIS GAME THE PLAYER MOUNTS A TREADMILL, WHICH YOU GENTLEMEN WERE KIND ENOUGH TO SUPPLY.

I THEN ATTACH A CONTROL GADGET TO EACH OF HIS LEGS.

THE OBJECT OF THE GAME IS TO CATCH UP TO THE ICE CREAM TRUCK BEFORE IT CAN LEAVE THE NEIGHBORHOOD...
...THE FASTER OUR TEEN MOVES THE CLOSER HE COMES TO THE TRUCK!
YES, BUT WHERE DOES THE 3-D ASPECT COME INTO PLAY?

YOU MEAN THEY WANT TO RUN THE COUNTRY?

THINK BIG, GIRL!

THE WORLD!

BUT, THEY HAVE NO EXPERIENCE!

BAH! EXPERIENCE IS HIGHLY OVERRATED!

LOVE IS EVERYTHING! YOU'VE GOT TO LOVE! THE REST TAKES CARE OF ITSELF!

WHY... THAT'S BEAUTIFUL!

NO WAR! NO POVERTY! NO CRIME! NO COPS! NO ARMY!

GOLLY!

WHY- THAT'S REAL GROOVY! IT WILL BE A UTOPIA!... I CAN JUST PICTURE IT NOW!

GO AHEAD! LAY IT ON ME!

TO BRING ABOUT THE MAXIMUM EFFORT ON OUR PLAYER'S PART...

...THE SCREEN OCCASIONALLY FLASHES 3-D IMAGES OF THE YUMMY TREATS ABOARD THE TRUCK.

AND TO REWARD OUR EXHAUSTED PLAYER FOR HIS EFFORT HE SHOULD BE GIVEN A FEW *REAL* GOODIES!

SO, GENTLEMEN, WHAT DO YOU THINK OF MY COMBINING EXERCISE GAMES WITH 3-D IMAGERY?
IT SHOWED *AMAZING* IMAGINATION!
BUT UNFORTUNATELY, THERE WAS JUST TOO MUCH STRESS ON THE PLAYERS.

YES, IN SOME CASES IT COULD CAUSE HARMFUL PHYSICAL CONSEQUENCES!

LATER...
WELL... THEY TURNED DOWN DILTON'S GAMES.
OH, THAT'S TOO BAD.
POP'

MAYBE YOUR NEXT VIDEO GAMES SHOULD HAVE A LITTLE LESS ACTION...
...AND A *WHOLE LOT* LESS IMAGINATION!
End

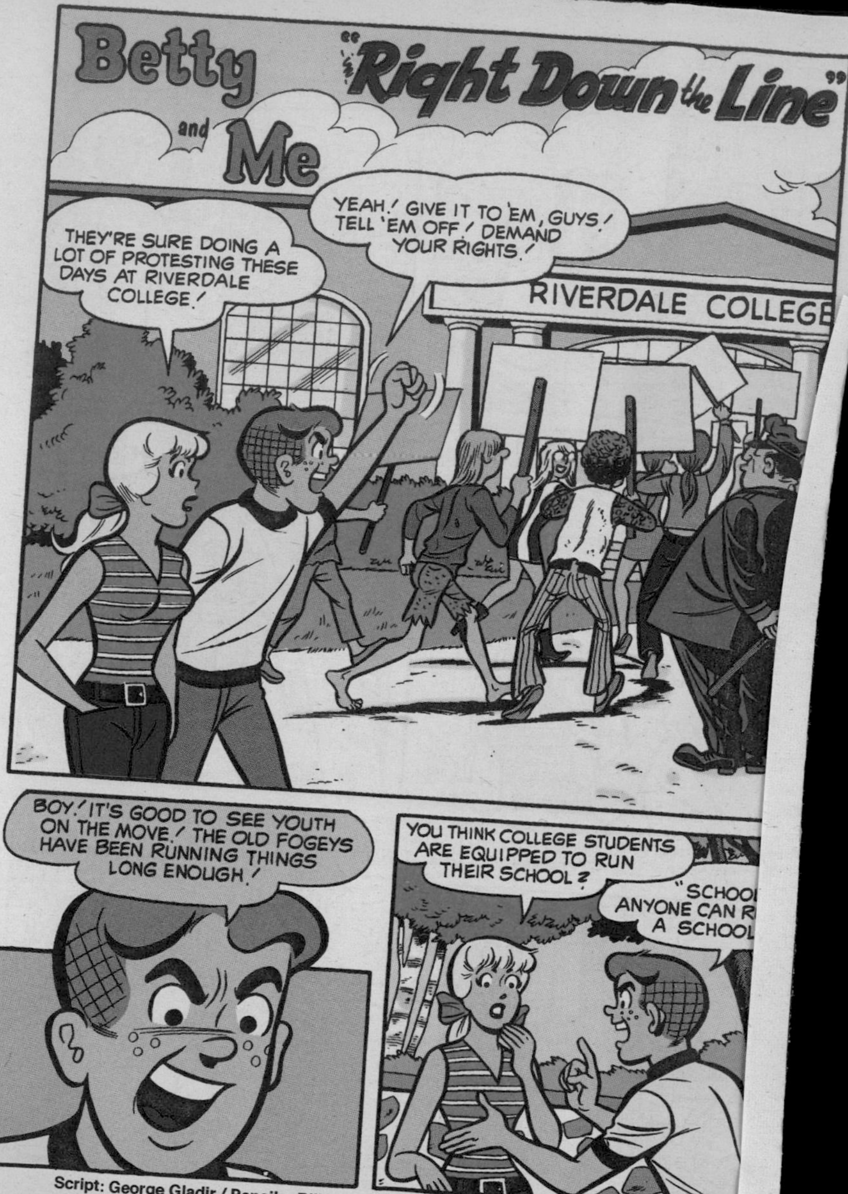

Betty and Me

"Right Down the Line"

THEY'RE SURE DOING A LOT OF PROTESTING THESE DAYS AT RIVERDALE COLLEGE!

YEAH! GIVE IT TO 'EM, GUYS! TELL 'EM OFF! DEMAND YOUR RIGHTS!

RIVERDALE COLLEGE

BOY! IT'S GOOD TO SEE YOUTH ON THE MOVE! THE OLD FOGEYS HAVE BEEN RUNNING THINGS LONG ENOUGH!

YOU THINK COLLEGE STUDENTS ARE EQUIPPED TO RUN THEIR SCHOOL?

"SCHOO

ANYONE CAN R

A SCHOOL

Script: George Gladir / Pencils: Bill Vigoda / Inks: Rudy Lapick / Letters: Bill Yoshida

WHEN NOT IN CLASS THE COLLEGE KIDS ARE RUNNING THE COUNTRY!

DOWN TO D.C. AGAIN, LARRY?
GOT TO STRAIGHTEN OUT THE BUDGET BEFORE LATE CLASS, AL!

NEW BLOOD BRINGS NEW METHODS!

WE NEED LOTS MORE MONEY, MR. PRESIDENT! NOBODY'S WORKING! OUR WELFARE BUDGET IS OUTASIGHT!
PRINT MORE MONEY!
LOVE
PRESIDENT

WE'VE GOT MILLIONS OF SERVICE MEN AND NO WAR! WHAT'LL THEY DO?
THEIR OWN THING, MAN! THEIR OWN THING!
PRESIDENT
LOVE

NOW, SPLIT MAN! DON'T BOTHER YOUR PRESIDENT WITH DETAILS!

ISN'T THAT A GREAT PICTURE? I WONDER WHY THE ESTABLISH-MENT NEVER THOUGHT OF IT?

NOW, THE WAY I SEE IT - THESE COLLEGE STUDENTS ARE GOING TO BE VERY BUSY RUNNING THE COUNTRY!
THE WORLD!
THEN OF COURSE, IT WILL BE UP TO US HIGH SCHOOL KIDS TO RUN THE COLLEGES!
HUH?
WELL- WE'VE GOT TO BE LOGICAL ABOUT THIS, RIGHT?
OH, YES! LOGICAL!
IF COLLEGE KIDS CAN RUN THE WORLD BETTER THAN THE ESTABLISHMENT- WHY SHOULDN'T HIGH SCHOOL KIDS RUN THE COLLEGES BETTER THAN THEIR ELDERS? DIG?
HEY, TEACH! WE LEARNED ALL THIS STUFF BACK IN THE OLD DAYS WHEN THE ESTABLISHMENT WAS IN POWER!
WHAT DO YOU KNOW ABOUT ANYTHING? YOU MUST BE ABOUT TWENTY ALREADY!

IT'S NOT OUR HANGUP, BABY! YOU GUYS STARTED THIS FAD OF THE YOUNG PEOPLE MOVING UP THE LADDER!

YOU'RE RUNNING THE COUNTRY AND WE'RE RUNNING THE COLLEGES!

BUT I'LL HAVE TO SPLIT! BECAUSE I'M OFF TO CLASS! I HAVE SHOW 'N' TELL TODAY!
SHOW'N' TELL? IN HIGH SCHOOL? BUT THAT'S GRAMMAR SCHOOL STUFF!

OF COURSE IT IS! WE'RE MERELY FOLLOWING THE LOGICAL TREND! COME! I'LL SHOW YOU!
RIVERDALE HIGH

SO WHO DO YOU THINK IS RUNNING THE HIGH SCHOOLS?
HI! I'M THE PWINCIPAL OF WIVERDALE HIGH!
PRINCIPAL
2
5

YOU LEFT YOUR SLEEPING MAT HOME YESTERDAY! HOW ARE YOU EVER GOING TO PASS REST PERIOD?
(GULP) SORRY, TEACH!
I'VE GOT AN EXTRA MILK AND COOKIES BREAK TODAY! TRADE YOU ONE FOR A LATE PASS!
YOU GOT A DEAL!

OKAY! OKAY! STOP, BETTY! I GET THE PICTURE!

"PICTURE"? WHAT PICTURE?

WHY DON'T YOU GO BACK TO YOUR CLASSES? YOU DING-A-LINGS! YOU'RE CREATING A MONSTER!
WHAT'S WITH THE TEENAGER?
WHO KNOWS WHAT'S WITH TEENAGERS?
END
6

Betty and Me in "PLEASANT DREAMS"

I WENT AND BOUGHT TICKETS FOR RONNIE AND I TO SEE A STAGE SHOW TONIGHT AND NOW SHE SAYS SHE CAN'T MAKE IT! I WAS WONDERING IF YOU WOULD LIKE TO TAKE HER PLACE!

I'D LOVE TO, ARCHIE! WHAT TIME DO I HAVE TO BE READY?

?

SEVEN O'CLOCK! I KNEW I COULD COUNT ON YOU BETTY, YOU'RE TOPS!

FOR A WHILE, I THOUGHT I WAS GOING TO BE STUCK WITH TWO TICKETS!
NOT AS LONG AS I'M AROUND!
1

Script: Dick Malmgren / Pencils: Dan DeCarlo / Inks: Rudy Lapick / Letters: Bill Yoshida

I WOULD NEVER DO A THING LIKE THAT TO YOU, ARCHIE!
WELL, I WASN'T QUITE SURE HOW YOU WOULD REACT TO BEING RONNIE'S REPLACEMENT! BUT YOU'RE AS DEPENDABLE AS THE TIDE, BETTY! I CAN ALWAYS COUNT ON YOU!

I'LL PICK YOU UP IN A LITTLE WHILE!
I'LL BE READY AND WAITING, ARCHIE!

YA-HOO!
ARCHIE AND I ARE GOING OUT TOGETHER! ISN'T THAT GREAT?
?

AREN'T YOU BEING A LITTLE EAGER JUST TO BE SECOND CHOICE, BETTY?
NONSENSE, MOM! IT'S ME ARCHIE REALLY LOVES, NOT RONNIE! HE JUST HASN'T FACED UP TO THE FACTS YET!
2

THE WAY HE ACTS COULD CERTAINLY FOOL ME! WHAT MAKES YOU SO SURE OF YOURSELF?

WELL THERE WAS THIS TIME WHEN ARCHIE HAD AMNESIA, THAT'S WHEN HIS TRUE FEELINGS CAME OUT!

HE CHOSE ME OVER RONNIE, AND HE SAID I WAS BEAUTIFUL AND SWEET AND UNASSUMING! I MELTED LIKE PUTTY IN THE HOT SUN! IT WAS ONE OF THE MOST HAPPIEST DAYS OF MY LIFE, MOM!
THAT'S ALL WELL AND GOOD, BETTY! BUT HE DOESN'T HAVE AMNESIA ANYMORE AND YOU'RE STILL SECOND FIDDLE!

BUT THAT PROVED HE DID LOVE ME, AND HE'S BOUND TO COME AROUND TO HIS SENSES AGAIN ONE OF THESE DAYS!

MAYBE TONIGHT HE MAY TELL ME HOW HE FEELS ABOUT ME! AFTER THE WAY RONNIE LEFT HIM STUCK WITH TWO TICKETS TO A SHOW THAT SHE TOLD HIM TO BUY!
3

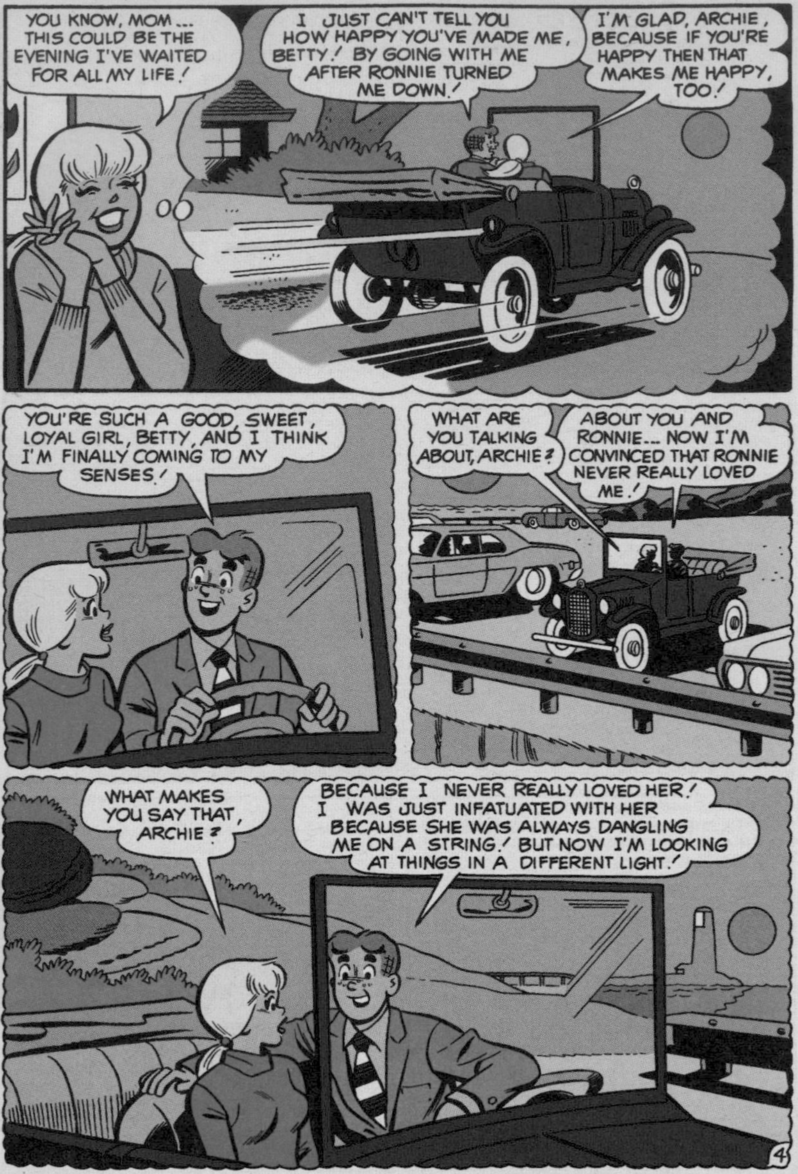

YOU KNOW, MOM ... THIS COULD BE THE EVENING I'VE WAITED FOR ALL MY LIFE!

I JUST CAN'T TELL YOU HOW HAPPY YOU'VE MADE ME, BETTY! BY GOING WITH ME AFTER RONNIE TURNED ME DOWN!

I'M GLAD, ARCHIE, BECAUSE IF YOU'RE HAPPY THEN THAT MAKES ME HAPPY, TOO!

YOU'RE SUCH A GOOD, SWEET, LOYAL GIRL, BETTY, AND I THINK I'M FINALLY COMING TO MY SENSES!

WHAT ARE YOU TALKING ABOUT, ARCHIE?

ABOUT YOU AND RONNIE... NOW I'M CONVINCED THAT RONNIE NEVER REALLY LOVED ME!

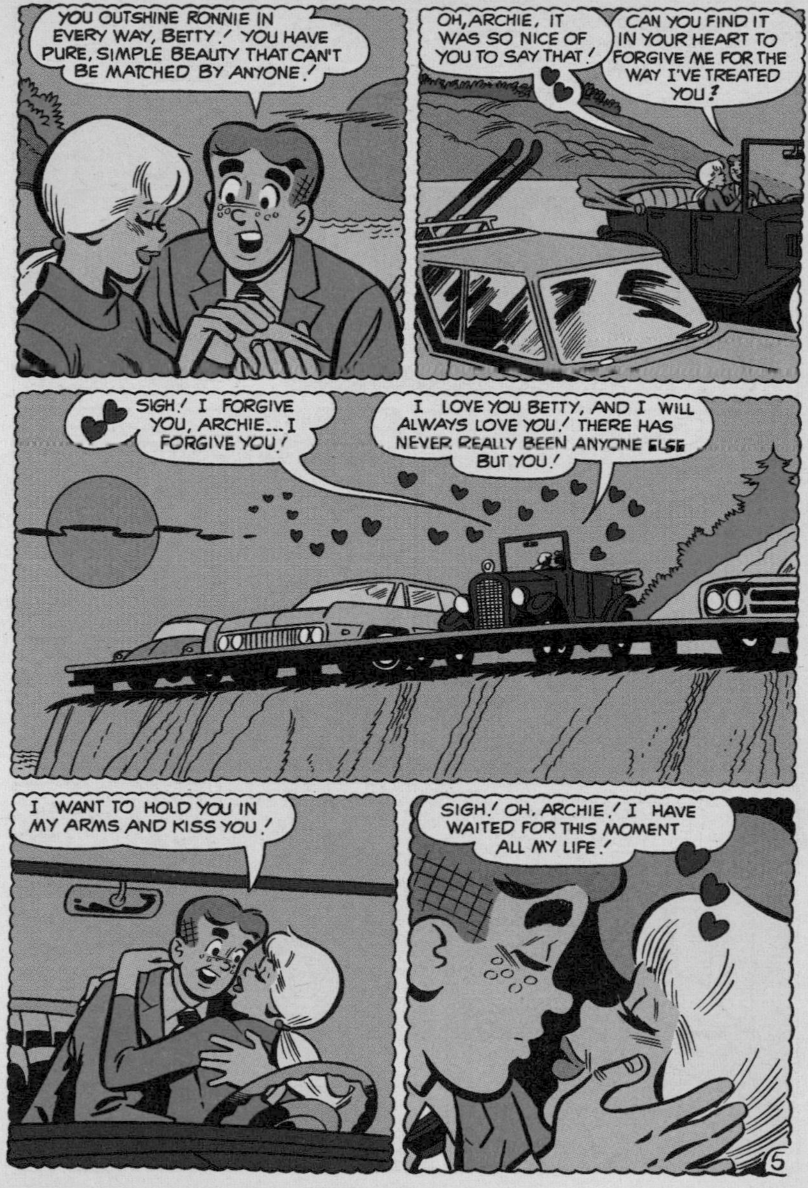

YOU OUTSHINE RONNIE IN EVERY WAY, BETTY! YOU HAVE PURE, SIMPLE BEAUTY THAT CAN'T BE MATCHED BY ANYONE!

OH, ARCHIE, IT WAS SO NICE OF YOU TO SAY THAT!

CAN YOU FIND IT IN YOUR HEART TO FORGIVE ME FOR THE WAY I'VE TREATED YOU?

SIGH! I FORGIVE YOU, ARCHIE... I FORGIVE YOU!

I LOVE YOU BETTY, AND I WILL ALWAYS LOVE YOU! THERE HAS NEVER REALLY BEEN ANYONE ELSE BUT YOU!

ARCHIE ... WHEN YOU KISS ME I HEAR BELLS
IT'S FOR YOU, BETTY! IT'S LOVER BOY!

BETTY, THE FUNNIEST THING HAPPENED...

... RONNIE JUST CALLED AND SAID SHE COULD MAKE IT AFTER ALL!
I HOPE YOU WON'T MIND TAKING A RAIN CHECK FOR SOME OTHER NIGHT!
?
!

: SOB : RONNIE MAY BE ABLE TO TAKE ARCHIE AWAY FROM ME, BUT ONE THING SHE CAN'T TAKE IS MY DREAMS!!
6
The End

Betty and Me

I CRIED FOR YOU

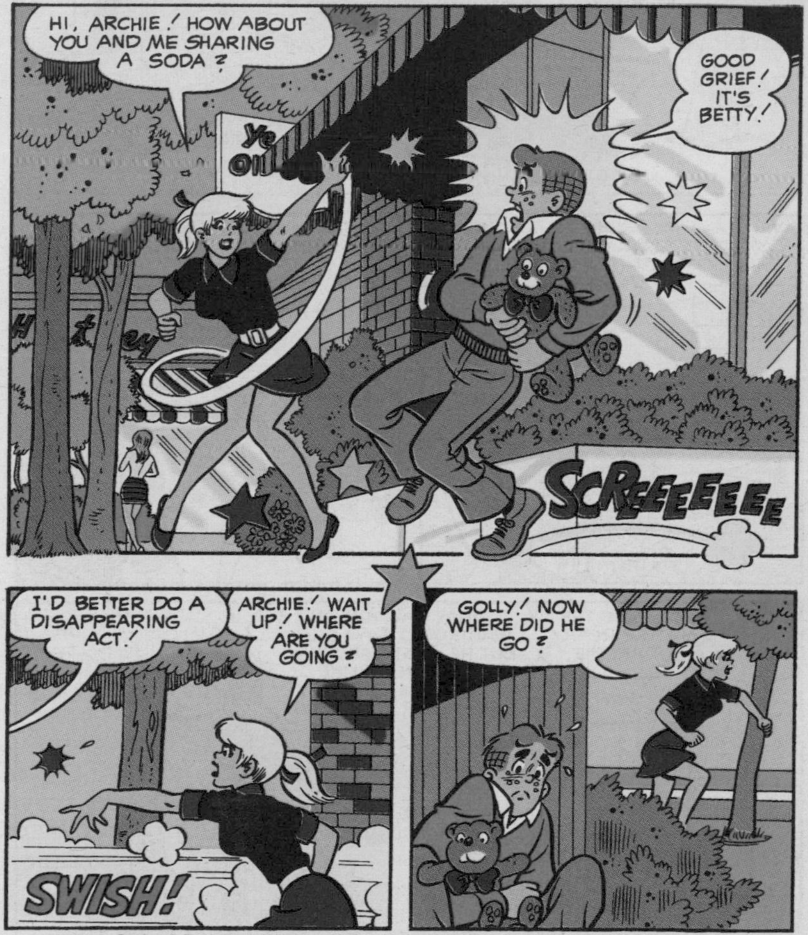

HI, ARCHIE! HOW ABOUT YOU AND ME SHARING A SODA?
GOOD GRIEF! IT'S BETTY!
SCREEEEEEEE

Script & Pencils: Al Hartley / Inks: Jon D'Agostino / Letters: Bill Yoshida

ARCHIE!
COME ON OUT!
I KNOW YOU'RE SOMEWHERE AROUND!
I SAW YOU!
NOW STOP FOOLING AROUND!

WHAT A FINK ARCHIE IS TURNING OUT TO BE! I'M CERTAINLY NOT THAT UGLY THAT HE HAS TO HIDE FROM ME!

WHAT A LOUSY THING TO DO! SNIFF! SNIFF!
D-UH!--- WHAT'S THE MATTER, BETTY? WHY ARE YOU CRYING?

OH, HI, MOOSE!
NOTHING'S THE MATTER REALLY BUT ARCHIE!
SNIFF! SNIFF!
I JUST SAW HIM AND I WANTED TO SAY HELLO BUT HE JUST RAN AWAY AND HID ON ME LIKE I WAS SOME SORT OF A FREAK OR SOMETHING!
D-UH!
2

D-UH, WELL I WOULDN'T CRY ABOUT HIM! HE'S NOT WORTH IT!
SNIFF! SNIFF! MAYBE YOU'RE RIGHT, MOOSE!

BUT I JUST THOUGHT THAT MAYBE TODAY HE WOULD SHOW ME A LITTLE KINDNESS AND UNDERSTANDING!
SNIFF!

SOB! BUT I GUESS THAT'S ASKING TOO MUCH! MAYBE I SHOULDN'T HAVE CALLED HIM LAST NIGHT LIKE I DID!
BOO HOO!
WHY THAT CREEP! HOW COULD HE TREAT SUCH A NICE GIRL LIKE YOU! LIKE YOU WERE A PIECE OF DIRT! D-UH! IT MAKES ME SEE GREEN!

I'M GOING TO TEACH THAT LITTLE LUNKHEAD A LESSON IN MANNERS ONCE AND FOR ALL!
?

D-UH, HEY, JUGHEAD! DID YOU SEE THAT CREEPY BUDDY OF YOURS ANYWHERE?

ER--- ER --- NO, MOOSE! I HAVEN'T! WHAT DID HE DO?
RUGS
IT DOESN'T MATTER WHAT HE DID! I'M JUST GOING TO MAKE SURE HE DOESN'T DO IT AGAIN!

HOLY TOLEDO! I HOPE I CAN FIND ARCHIE BEFORE MOOSE'S FIST DOES!
FOOOOM!

ARCHIE, ARE YOU LUCKY I FOUND YOU FIRST! IF I WERE YOU, I'D GO STOW AWAY ON THE FIRST TRAMP STEAMER SAILING TO SHANGRILA!

I DON'T KNOW WHAT YOU DID TO MOOSE, BUT I WOULDN'T WANT TO BE IN YOUR SHOES!
HE LOOKED SO MEAN THAT IF YOU KICKED HIM IN THE HEART, YOU'D BREAK YOUR TOE!
WHY?
I DIDN'T DO ANYTHING TO HIM!

WHO ARE YOU KIDDING, ARCH?
YOU CAN LEVEL WITH ME! I'M YOUR BUDDY!
WHATEVER YOU DID TO HIM MUST HAVE BEEN OUT OF SIGHT! HE'S FUMING!

I HAVEN'T EVEN LAID EYES ON HIM TODAY!
WELL, IF I WERE YOU I'D PRETEND NOT TO SEE HIM NOW EITHER, BECAUSE---
HERE HE COMES!

SO LONG, OL' BUDDY! I'LL VISIT YOU AT THE HOSPITAL! I CAN'T STAND THE SIGHT OF BLOOD!
BUT! BUT!
D-UH! SO THERE YOU ARE, ARCHIE! I WANT SOME WORDS WITH YOU!

GASP! TRY CALLING ME ON THE PHONE! I'M GOING HOME!
OH, NO YOU DON'T!

D-UH, COME BACK HERE, ARCH!
WATCH WHERE YOU'RE GOING!
GULP!

D-UH!
WHOOA! EEYOW! OUCH! OW!
THUMP!
KLOP!
BUMP!
KLUMP!
BONK!

D-UH! ARE YOU ALL RIGHT, ARCHIE? THAT WAS SOME FALL!
GAK!

I WASN'T GOING TO HIT YOU, BUDDY! I JUST WANTED TO KNOW WHY YOU RAN AWAY FROM A NICE GIRL LIKE BETTY!
? YEESH!

LATER ---
D-UH! ARCHIE ASKED ME TO GIVE YOU THIS PRESENT HE DIDN'T WANT YOU TO SEE BEFORE AND SAY HAPPY BIRTHDAY! HE WANTED TO SURPRISE YOU BUT HE GOT SURPRISED FIRST!
WHEN WILL I LEARN NOT TO GET SO EMOTIONAL?
End

Betty and Veronica in "SEER SUCKER"

HOW COME YOU WERE SO ANXIOUS TO BE THE FORTUNE TELLER AT OUR TOWN FAIR, RONNIE?
IT'S SELF-EXPLANATORY!
KOSALEE FORTUNE TELLER
1.00 1.00
KISSES KISSES
$1.00 A KISS
HOMEC
PIE

IT IS?
THE NAME ISN'T FORTUNE **READING**, OR FORTUNE **ASKING**!
IT'S FORTUNE **TELLING**!

YOU KNOW ME, KID! I'M ALWAYS HAPPIEST WHEN I'M **TELLING** SOMEBODY SOMETHING! **ANYTHING!**
TRUE!

Script: Frank Doyle / Pencils: Dan DeCarlo / Inks: Rudy Lapick / Letters: Victor Gorelick

I LOVE TO LEAD PEOPLE BY THE NOSE, DANGLE THEM LIKE PUPPETS!
YOU CAN'T **REALLY** LEAD THEM WITH **THIS** JAZZ!

LOOK! YOU BE MY SHILL! LISTEN IN! I'LL SHOW YOU MY POWER!
OKAY! IF YOU COULD JUST ANSWER ONE QUESTION!
ROSALEE FORTUNE TELLER

WHAT IS A **SHILL**?
A **SALESMAN**!
BINGO
CO
CA

YOU LURE THE SUCKERS IN! TELL THEM HOW GOOD I AM!
OH, **THAT**!

WOW! IS THAT FORTUNE TELLER GOOD! MAN! SHE KNOWS EVERYTHING! JUST **EVERYTHING**!
D-UH! SHE DOES?

WHY DON'T YOU TRY HER, MOOSE?
WHY NOT? THERE'S **SOME** THINGS **I** DON'T KNOW!
1.00
KISSES
FORTU

BEWARE OF A DARK-HAIRED GIRL WHOSE INITIAL IS "M!"
D-UH! THAT'S MY GURL, MIDGE!

SHE WILL BRING YOU BAD LUCK TODAY! PROTECT YOUR FEET WHEN YOU THINK OF THIS GIRL!
MY FEET?

D-UH! WHAT KINDA PHONEY BALONEY IS **THAT**? PERTECT MY **FEET**! HAH!

THIS IS DANGLING PEOPLE LIKE PUPPETS? EVEN **MOOSE** YOU CAN'T FOOL!
WATCH!

EEYOW!
WHACK!

D-UH! GO AWAY! DON'T COME NEAR ME, MIDGE! YOU'RE BAD LUCK FER MY FEET TODAY!!
?

SEE? A SLIGHT WHACK ON THE TOE AND HE'LL SPREAD MY FAME ALL OVER!

NOW GET ME THAT GLORIA GIMBER WHO'S BEEN GETTING SO COZY WITH MY ARCHIE!
COMING UP, CHIEF!

REALLY, GLORIA! SHE'S VERY GOOD!
I DID HEAR MOOSE RAVING ABOUT HER!

I SEE A REDHEAD IN YOUR LIFE! A FRECKLE-FACED REDHEAD!
HMM?

YOU HAVE NOTHING TO FEAR FROM THIS BOY UNLESS HE CARRIES A **GREEN HANDKERCHIEF**!
TSK! WHAT UTTER NONSENSE!

SO WHAT GOOD IS THAT? EVEN IF ARCHIE DOES HAVE A GREEN HANDKERCHIEF, IT'S NOT GOING TO SCARE HER OFF!
WATCH!

I THINK I FIGURED OUT WHO THE FORTUNE TELLER IS, ARCHIE! LET'S SEE YOUR HANDKERCHIEF!
HOT DOGS

HANDKERCHIEF??
AIEEEE!!

GO AWAY! DON'T EVER COME NEAR ME AGAIN! YOU'RE THE ONE WITH THE KISS OF DEATH!
?
HOT DOGS

GOOD GRIEF! WHAT HAPPENED?
I SAW ARCHIE **BEFORE**!

I TOLD HIM TO BEWARE OF ANYONE WHO QUESTIONED HIM ABOUT HIS HANDKERCHIEF, FOR SHE WOULD POSSESS THE KISS OF DEATH!
THAT SOUNDS SILLY!

SURE! THAT'S WHAT MAKES IT SO CONVINCING WHEN IT **ACTUALLY HAPPENS**!
?

HOW IS THE FORTUNE TELLING BOOTH GOING, GIRLS?
FINE, MR. WEATHERBEE!

WE MUST BE CAREFUL THAT NO ONE IS ACTUALLY FOOLED BY THIS HOKUM!
WE MUST?

YES! THAT'S WHY I PUT THIS TAPE RECORDER UNDER THE TABLE!

I WANT TO PLAY IT OVER THE PUBLIC ADDRESS SYSTEM SO THEY MIGHT ALL HEAR HOW FOOLISH IT ALL SOUNDS!

BETTY, I ACTUALLY **CAN** SEE THE FUTURE IN THIS CRYSTAL BALL!
REALLY? WHAT DO YOU SEE?
6

I SEE THAT I'M GOING ON A LONG TRIP, AS OF **NOW**!
HOT
The END

NANCY & CHUCK IN THINGS IN COMMON!
SCHOOL LIBRARY
WOW!
CHUCK, YOU'RE REALLY GOING HOT AND HEAVY AT THIS NEW GAME!
I'VE GOT TO NAIL THIS SUCKER!
BETTY, WITH ARCHIE YOU HAVE ONLY ONE RIVAL TO CONTEND WITH... AND THAT'S VERONICA!
BUT WITH CHUCK, I HAVE TO PUT UP WITH TWO RIVALS...
...CARTOONING AND VIDEO GAMES!
NANCY
I'M BEGINNING TO HATE BOTH OF HIS PASSIONS WITH A PASSION!
POOR NANCY! I CAN'T SAY THAT I BLAME HER!
NEITHER CAN I!
RIVERDALE HIGH SCHOOL EST. 1941
SCRIPT: GEORGE GLADIR
PENCILS: STAN GOLDBERG
INKS: BOB SMITH
LETTERS: JACK MORELLI
1

WAIT UP, NANCY! I'VE BEEN LOOKING ALL OVER FOR YOU!
YOU'D NEVER KNOW IT!
WHAT'S UP?

I NEED A GIRL'S ADVICE ON SOME-THING I'M WORKING ON!
...IT COULD HELP ME LAND AN INTERNSHIP WITH A GREAT OUTFIT THIS SUMMER!
WHAT ARE YOU WORKING ON?

DRAWING UP CARTOON IDEAS FOR A VIDEO GAME COMPANY!
Oh, NO! CHUCK, I'M ABSOLUTELY THE LAST ONE YOU WANT TO CONSULT ON THAT!

NANCY, YOU DON'T UNDER-STAND!
THE COMPANY WANTS ME TO HELP DESIGN A GAME FOR TEEN GIRLS!
YOU MEAN A GAME THAT DOESN'T HAVE ZOMBIES, WEREWOLVES OR SPACE ALIENS?
RIVERDALE PARK

SO I THOUGHT OF DOING A GAME ABOUT TWO TEEN GIRLS WHO COMPETE FIERCELY FOR A CERTAIN BOY'S AFFECTION!
HAHA!
WHOM CAN YOU POSSIBLY BE THINKING OF?!
2

OF COURSE! IT'S BETTY, VERONICA AND ARCHIE!
BUT IN MY GAME THEY'RE CALLED JILL, JEZEBEL AND JACK!

IN THE GAME JILL AND JEZEBEL SCORE POINTS AGAINST ONE ANOTHER... THE WINNER GETS TO GO TO THE PROM WITH JACK!

YOUR BASIC CONCEPT ISN'T BAD... BUT YOU NEED TO JAZZ YOUR IDEA UP A BIT!

LET'S GO TO POP'S FOR A MILKSHAKE WHERE YOU AND I CAN TALK IT OVER!
IT'S BEEN A WHILE SINCE HE'S INVITED ME TO ANYTHING!
POP'S
PARK

SO! HOW DO I JAZZ UP THE GAME?
BY MAKING YOUR JILL A GOOD TEEN WITCH, AND JEZEBEL A BAD TEEN WITCH!
...AND JACK IS JUST AN AVERAGE JOE WHO CAN'T DECIDE BETWEEN THE TWO!

"JEZEBEL, THE BAD TEEN WITCH, CONCOCTS A PERFUME THAT MAKES JACK DO HER EVERY BIDDING.

"JEZEBEL MAKES JACK TAKE HER TO A VERY POSH RESTAURANT...

"...WHERE HE ENDS UP SPENDING EVERY LAST CENT IN HIS WALLET... AND *THEN SOME*!
CHECK

"WHICH LEAVES JACK NO MONEY TO TAKE JILL ON A PROMISED DATE!
EMPTY

"SCORE 50 POINTS FOR THE EVIL TEEN WITCH!"
4

BUT THE GOOD TEEN WITCH ISN'T THWARTED BY JEZEBEL'S EVIL SCHEME!
WHAT DOES SHE DO?

"SHE USES MAGIC TO INSERT A SPECIAL MOVIE PASS INTO JACK'S POCKET!
SUPER PASS FOR 2

"NOW, NOT ONLY IS JACK ABLE TO TAKE JILL TO THE MOVIES IN STYLE...
SUPER PASS FOR 2
NOW PLAYING

"BUT THE PASS ALSO ENTITLES THEM TO ANY GOODIES AT THE SNACK COUNTER, INCLUDING A SUPER-DUPER BUCKET OF POP CORN!"
POP CORN

AND YOU SHOULD ALSO BRING A WICKED PRINCIPAL INTO THE GAME!

"ONE WHO LOVES SENDING POOR JACK INTO A SNAKE-FILLED DETENTION DUNGEON!

"BUT GOOD WITCH JILL MANAGES TO FREE HIM, SCORING AN ADDITIONAL 200 POINTS! THAT WINS HER THE GAME...

"... AND THE PRIZE OF BEING JACK'S PROM DATE!"
PROM

AND THAT, CHUCKY-BOY, IS HOW I THINK YOUR GAME SHOULD GO!
WOW! WHAT A WILD AND FANTASTIC IMAGINATION YOU HAVE! I'M FLABBERGASTED!!

YOUR VERSION IS EXACTLY WHAT THE GAME PEOPLE ARE LOOKING FOR!
I CAN'T WAIT TO DRAW IT UP!!

I LOVE THE WAY YOU'VE DRAWN UP THESE CHARACTERS AND SITUATIONS FOR THIS GAME, CHUCK!
THANK YOU, MR. ROCKMORE!
VIDEO GAMES

THEY DEFINITELY ENTITLE YOU TO BE AN ARTIST INTERN WITH OUR COMPANY NEXT SUMMER!
WOW!

BUT I LOVE YOUR IMAGINATIVE IDEAS EVEN MORE!
YOU COULD ALSO INTERN AS A GAME DESIGNER!

UH... MOST OF THOSE IDEAS COME FROM MY GIRL-FRIEND, NANCY!
WELL, TELL HER IF SHE WOULD LIKE TO HAVE AN INTERNSHIP AS A GAME DESIGNER, THEN SHE'S GOT THE JOB!

NANCY! YOU'RE NOT GOING TO BELIEVE THIS!
...I NOT ONLY WON THE SUMMER INTERN-SHIP...

...BUT THE COMPANY WOULD ALSO LIKE YOU TO INTERN-- RIGHT ALONGSIDE OF ME!
MY CUP RUNNETH OVER!

NANCY, WE COULDN'T HELP BUT NOTICE HOW WELL YOU AND CHUCK ARE HITTING IT OFF LATELY!
RIVERDALE HIGH SCHO

YOU AND HE ARE A CONSTANT TWOSOME EVERYWHERE!

THAT'S BECAUSE WE BOTH DISCOVERED WE SHARE SOME VERY STRONG COMMON INTERESTS!
LIKE WHAT?

NANCY!
LIKE CARTOONING AND VIDEO GAMES!
?!!
NANCY
END

EEEYOOW! HEADS UP!

Archie in "SCENTS OF JUSTICE"

WHOOSH!

THAT WAS CLOSE! THERE'S A SKUNK IN THOSE WOODS!
HYUK! NOT ANY MORE!

Script: Frank Doyle / Pencils: Bob White / Inks & Letters: Marty Epp

I DON'T LIKE YOUR INSINUATION, GREASE TOP!

HOLD IT, TIGER! RELAX!
YOU TOO, MUSCLES!

DADDY BROUGHT US UP TO HIS RIVER LODGE FOR FUN AND FROLIC!

PUNCHING HIM IN THE NOSE IS FUN AND FROLIC FOR ME!
JUST TRY IT!

WHAT WE NEED IS SOME THERAPY TO KEEP THEM OUT OF EACH OTHERS HAIR!

YOU'RE RIGHT! WE'VE GOT TO KEEP THEM TOO BUSY TO FIGHT!

I'VE GOT A REAL FUN IDEA! COME UP TO THE CABIN WITH ME, BETTY!

YOU TWO STAY THERE AND DON'T FIGHT!

I WONDER WHAT THEY'RE UP TO NOW ?
WHATEVER IT IS, I WON'T LIKE IT!

COME ON, GIRLS! WHAT'S TAKING YOU SO LONG ?

HMM? NO ANSWER!
THAT'S FUNNY!

HEY, BETTY! VERONICA! WE'RE COMING IN!
WHY DON'T YOU ANSWER?

A NOTE?
THEY'VE GONE INTO THE WOODS AND WANT US TO TRY AND TRAIL THEM!

SHUCKS, I CAN READ A TRAIL LIKE THE PALM OF MY HAND!
NOW IF YOU COULD ONLY READ THE PALM OF YOUR HAND!

C'MON, DANIEL BOONE! WHICH WAY DID THEY GO?
THIS WAY!

TRAMPLED LEAVES! BROKEN BRANCHES! THEY LEFT AN EASY TRAIL!
--IF IT WASN'T A BEAR OR A DEER OR A FOX!

(GIGGLE) WON'T THEY GET LOST?
IT'S AN OLD TRAIL DADDY BLAZED FOR ME YEARS AGO! IT WILL LEAD THEM BACK TO THE CABIN EVENTUALLY!
4

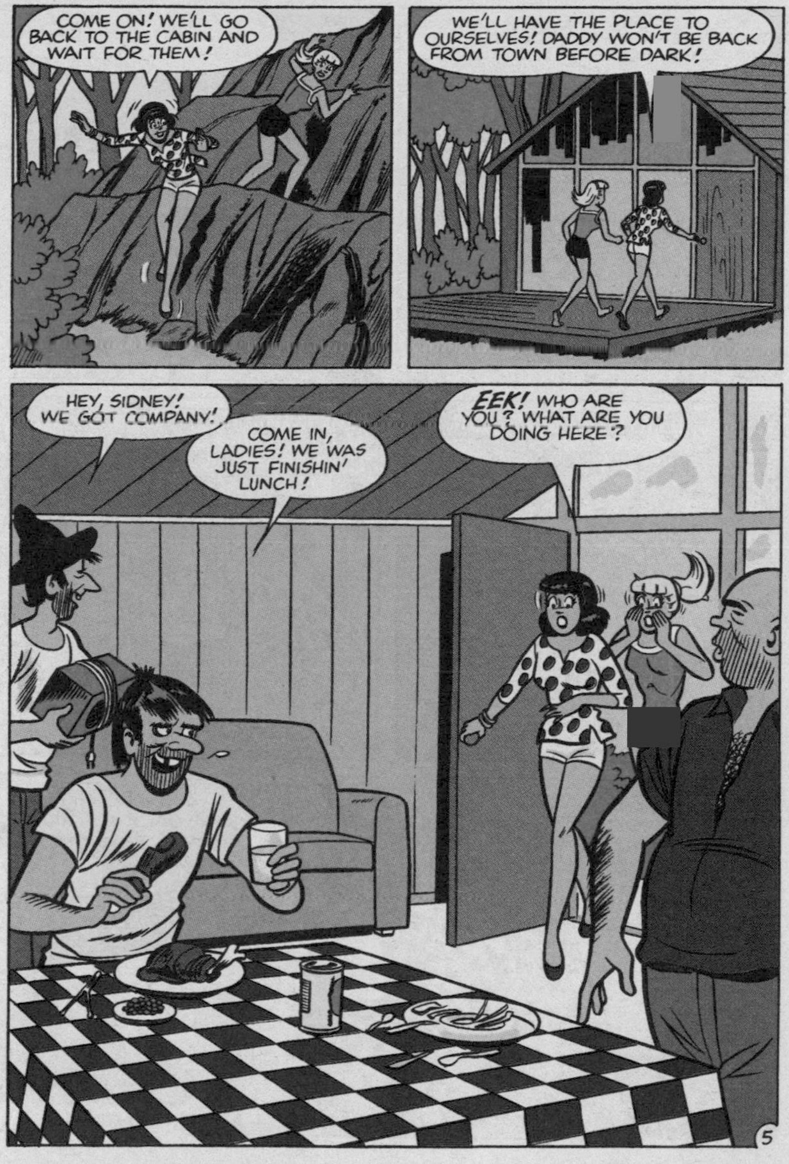

HEY, SIDNEY! WE GOT COMPANY!

COME IN, LADIES! WE WAS JUST FINISHIN' LUNCH!

EEK! WHO ARE YOU? WHAT ARE YOU DOING HERE?

YOU MIGHT SAY WE'RE CLEANING UP THE PLACE, GIRLIE!
HAW! YOU MEAN "CLEANIN' OUT," DON'T YOU, MOUSE?

WE MAKE A HOBBY OF VISITING THE EMPTY CABINS ALONG THE RIVERSIDE!
THIS ONE ISN'T EMPTY!

HYOK! IT WILL BE WHEN WE LEAVE!

WE'LL TELL THE POLICE! THEY'LL PICK YOU UP!
OH! DIDN'T WE TELL YOU?

WE DECIDED TO TAKE YOU GIRLS ALONG FOR THE RIDE!
OH, NO! PLEASE!
NOTHING LIKE A JAUNT DOWN THE RIVER ON A RAFT TO PUT THE COLOR BACK IN YOUR CHEEKS!

CONTINUED!

I DON'T SEE ANY RAFT!

WE-ER--DON'T EXACTLY ADVERTISE IT!
BRING IT AROUND, LUNK!

A TRUCK IS GOING TO MEET US AT CALEB'S LANDING TO PICK UP OUR LOOT!
...AND US!!

WE'LL TURN YOU LOOSE AS SOON AS THE TRUCK'S LOADED!

WATCH THE RAFT, LUNK, WHILE WE LOAD THESE GIRLS UP FOR ONE LAST HAUL!
RIGHT, STONEY!

... THE ONLY LOOT THE LOOTERS HAVE LEFT IS OUR LOVELY LASSIES! OUR LADS HAVE LATCHED ON TO A LOAD OF LARCENY! LOOK AND LEARN

Archie in "SCENTS OF JUSTICE"

PART TWO

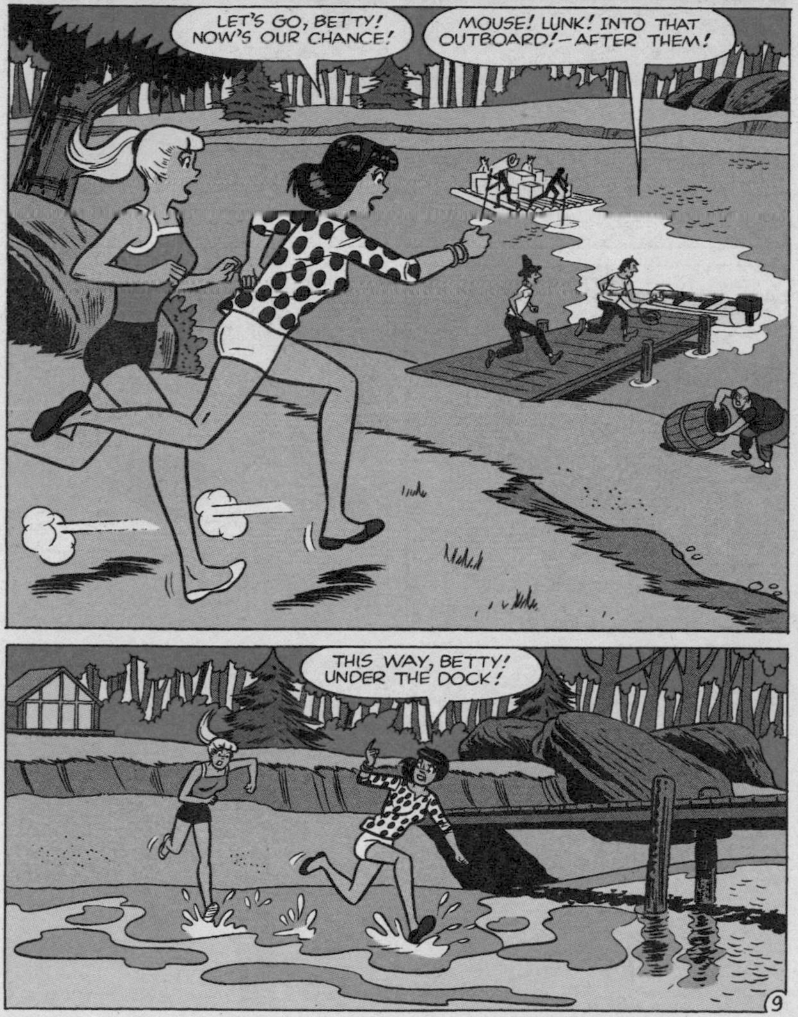

LET'S GO, BETTY! NOW'S OUR CHANCE!

MOUSE! LUNK! INTO THAT OUTBOARD!—AFTER THEM!

OKAY! I'VE CAST OFF! GET THAT MOTOR GOING!

BRROOAR!

BEAUTIFUL!
SPRONG!

I CAN'T SWIM!
NEITHER CAN WE! GRAB THIS ROPE!
IT'S THOSE GIRLS! AFTER THEM!
SPUTTER!

TIE UP AGAINST THE BANK HERE! WE'VE GOT TO HELP THE GIRLS!

WHOOPS! LOOK WHO'S COMING ABOARD!

LET'S GET OUT OF HERE!

AIEEEE!
THAT'S BETTY SCREAMING!

YOO HOO! GIRLS!!
HEY! THOSE CROOKS WILL HEAR YOU!

HOLD IT! THAT MUST BE THOSE PUNKS WHO STOLE OUR RAFT!

I WAS RIGHT! THERE IT IS!

THE HECK WITH THOSE KIDS! LET'S GET---WHOOPS!!

TURN 'EM LOOSE, ARCH!

YIPES! IT'S A SKUNK!!
I DIDN'T THINK IT WAS A GERANIUM!
12

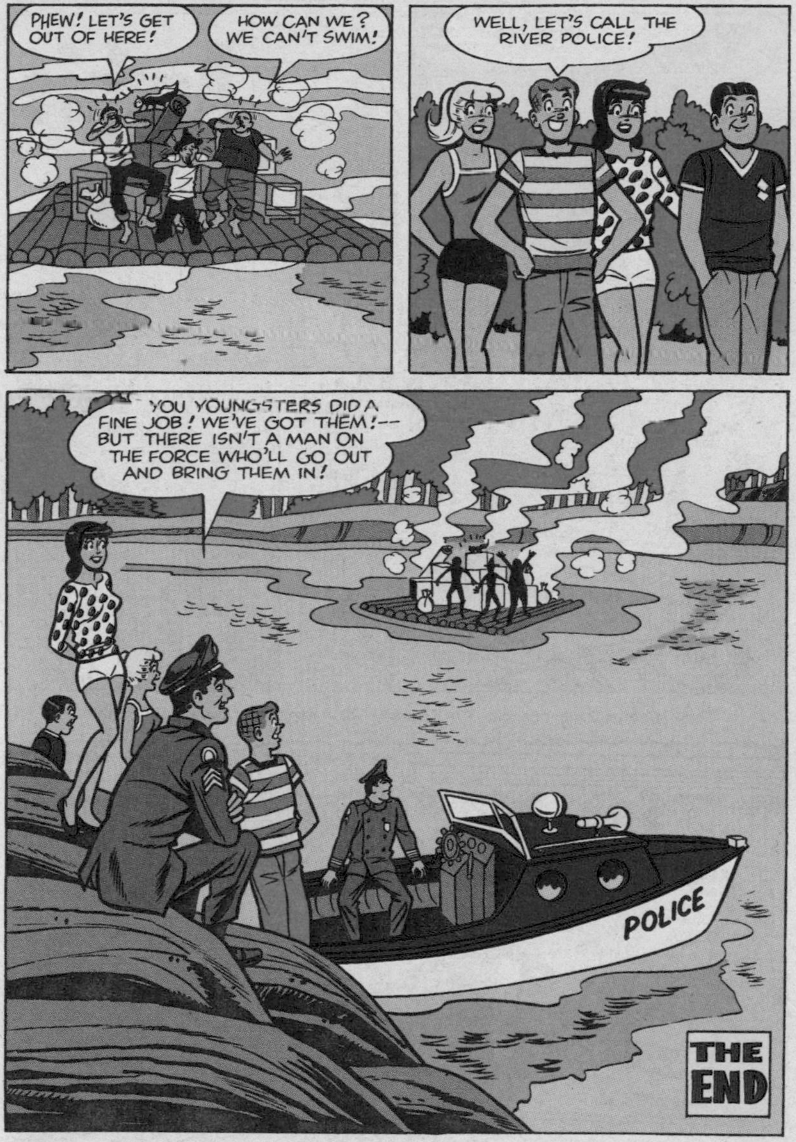

YOU YOUNGSTERS DID A FINE JOB! WE'VE GOT THEM!-- BUT THERE ISN'T A MAN ON THE FORCE WHO'LL GO OUT AND BRING THEM IN!

POLICE

THE END

MY PARENTS ARE ALWAYS TELLING ME TO *ACT MY AGE*!

WOULDN'T IT BE GREAT IF A SPECIAL DAY WAS SET ASIDE WHEN WE *DIDN'T* HAVE TO ACT OUR AGE?

ME TOO!

Archie

in

"SPECIAL DAZE"

YEAH, I CAN JUST SEE IT NOW...

Script: George Gladir / Pencils: Tim Kennedy / Inks: Ken Selig / Letters: Bill Yoshida

SPLASH
LET THEM BE! IT'S ALL RIGHT!
TODAY IS "*DON'T ACT YOUR AGE*" DAY!
1

WE HONOR SENIOR CITIZENS...
HOW ABOUT SETTING ASIDE A SPECIAL DAY TO HONOR US JUNIOR CITIZENS?
"...ON THAT DAY EVERYTHING WOULD BE HALF PRICE FOR US TEENAGERS..."
TWO JUNIOR CITIZEN TICKETS!
TODAY, OUR SNACK COUNTER IS ALSO HALF PRICE FOR JUNIOR CITIZENS!
SNACK BAR

LET BETTY GO TO THE HEAD OF THE LINE... IT'S "JUNIOR CITIZEN DAY"!
10 ITEMS OR LESS

WHILE WE'RE DECLARING SPECIAL DAYS, HOW ABOUT DOING AWAY WITH MONDAYS?
YES! THE LEAST WE COULD DO IS MAKE THE FIRST MONDAY OF EVERY MONTH AN "UNMONDAY"!... ON "UNMONDAYS," STUDENTS ARE FREE TO DO ANYTHING THEY WANT TO DO!
2

DO YOU KNOW HOW LATE IT IS ?
CHILL OUT, MOTHER! TODAY IS "UNMONDAY"!

SCHOOL IS SO EMPTY ON "UNMONDAYS"!
SIGH! I WISH WE TEACHERS COULD CELEBRATE "UNMONDAYS"!

BUT WHAT WE REALLY NEED IS A "GLUTTON DAY"!
A DAY ON WHICH WE CAN ALL PIG OUT TO OUR HEART'S CONTENT!

...LIKE TODAY, FOR EXAMPLE!

YOU CELEBRATE "GLUTTON DAY" EVERY DAY, YOU CHOWHOUND!
SLAP!
3

YOU BOYS ARE ALWAYS SHOWING OFF FOR US GIRLS...

WHAT IF WE HAD A SPECIAL DAY WHEN WE GIRLS COULD SHOW OFF FOR YOU GUYS? LOOK AT ME, ARCHIE!

HEY! YOU GIRLS ALREADY SHOW OFF FOR US WITH YOUR BIKINIS!

WOW! SPEAKING OF BIKINIS, LOOK AT THESE TWO HEADED OUR WAY!
ARCHIE!!

HA! GIRLS SURE DON'T LIKE IT WHEN GUYS LOOK AT OTHER GIRLS!

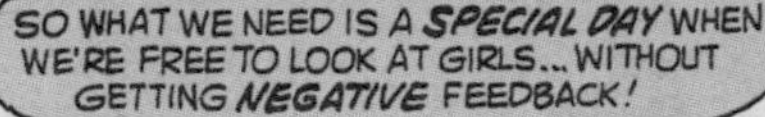
SO WHAT WE NEED IS A SPECIAL DAY WHEN WE'RE FREE TO LOOK AT GIRLS... WITHOUT GETTING NEGATIVE FEEDBACK!

4

BETTY! VERONICA! DON'T YOU AGREE... "LOOK AT GIRLS DAY" IS A GREAT IDEA?
BETTY? VERONICA?
WHERE DID THOSE TWO GO?
I THINK THEY DECIDED TO CELEBRATE "LOOK AT GUYS" DAY!
?
END.

SCRIPT: MIKE PELLOWSKI PENCILS: FERNANDO RUIZ INKS: RUDY LAPICK
LETTERS: VICKIE WILLIAMS

SITCOMS NEVER PORTRAY REAL PEOPLE.
HA! HA! KEEP AWAY! MARTIN IN THE MIDDLE! MARTIN IN THE MIDDLE!
GRRR!
YOU GUYS ARE TEASING ME JUST BECAUSE I'M SMART.
DUH...! THAT'S RIGHT, BRO.
STOP TEASING YOUR BROTHER OR YOU'LL BE SO SORRY.
OUCH!
NAME ONE SITCOM THAT PORTRAYS A REALISTIC FAMILY.
WELL... I CAN'T OFF THE TOP OF MY HEAD.
SEE!
ADMIT IT! HAVE YOU EVER BUMPED INTO ANYONE WHO REMINDED YOU OF A CHARACTER ON A SITCOM?
LET ME THINK.
2

LATER, FRIENDS... I HAVE AN AUDITION FOR A PLAY.
COFFEE CLUTCH
GOOD LUCK, JOE!
COFFEE CLUTCH
Humm...
GEE, I GUESS NOT.
I TOLD YOU SO. PEOPLE LIKE THAT JUST DON'T EXIST.
I MEAN, WHERE DO T.V. WRITERS COME UP WITH THOSE BIZARRE CHARACTERS? WELL, WHERE?
GULP!
YOU GOT ME, ARCH. I'M NOT A WRITER.
McBEAL LA
GOOD LUCK AT YOUR NEW JOB IN OHIO, ANDREW!
MUCH LOUDER
DEPARTMENT STORE
3

YOU SHOULD ASK CHUCK CLAYTON, ARCH. HE'S ALWAYS DRAWING CARTOONS.
CARTOONS ARE NOT REAL PEOPLE!
DOH! BRENT! DON'T DO THAT!
YO, DUDE!
DON'T HAVE A COW, BOY!
I AM NOT A COWBOY! I'M YOUR FATHER!
THERE ARE REAL WORLD SHOWS, JUG, BUT NO REAL SITCOMS!
PHASER, MUST YOU ANALYZE EVERYTHING?
I'M SORRY, STYLES, I'LL TRY NOT TO IN THE FUTURE.
CAFE
HEAR THAT, ARCH? THAT'S YOUR PROBLEM. YOU ALWAYS WANT TO ANALYZE THINGS.
HEY! THE TRUTH IS THE TRUTH, JUG.

TELEVISION PROGRAMMERS SHOULD GET IN TOUCH WITH WHAT'S REALLY HAPPENING.
HOW DO YOU MEAN?
JUST ONCE I'D LIKE TO SEE A SIT-COM ABOUT AN EVERY DAY ORDINARY TEEN.
OH, REALLY?
DO YOU HAVE ANYONE IN MIND?
OF COURSE, I DO. ME!
THE TRIALS AND TRIBULATIONS OF TEEN-AGER ARCHIE ANDREWS WOULD MAKE A TERRIFIC SITCOM!
FACE IT, ARCH...
DO YOU LIKE EDMOND?
SURE! EVERYONE LOVES EDMOND!
YOUR LIFE ISN'T A T.V. SITCOM. IT'S MORE LIKE... WELL, LIKE A COMIC BOOK STORY.
HUMPH! NOT HARDLY!
THE END

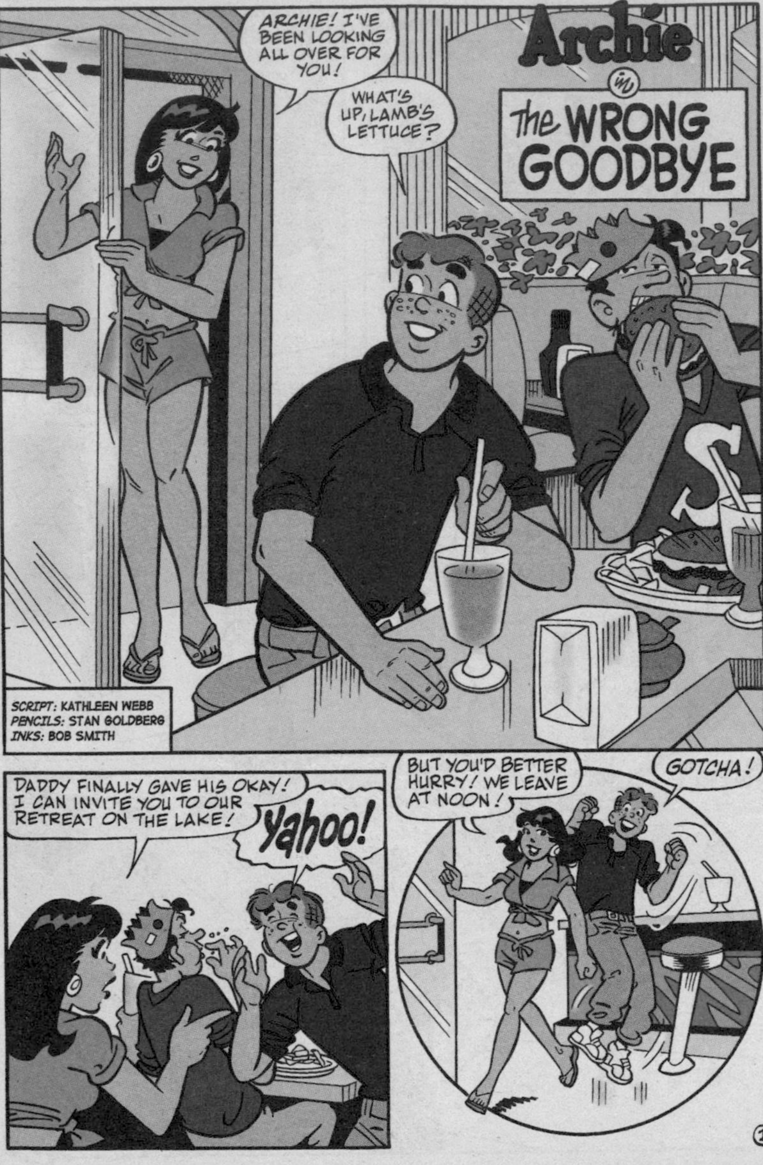

ARCHIE! I'VE BEEN LOOKING ALL OVER FOR YOU!

WHAT'S UP, LAMB'S LETTUCE?

Archie in The WRONG GOODBYE

SCRIPT: KATHLEEN WEBB
PENCILS: STAN GOLDBERG
INKS: BOB SMITH

MOM! WHERE'S MY DUFFLE BAG? AND MY FISHING GEAR? DID YOU WASH MY JEANS?
BANG

HEAVENS, ARCHIE! WHAT'RE YOU SO FIRED UP ABOUT?!
VERONICA'S INVITED ME TO THE LODGE'S RETREAT ON THE LAKE!

BUT I'VE GOT TO HURRY IF I WANT TO GO!
BRING

I HEAR YOU'RE HEADED OUT OF TOWN WITH THE LODGES!
NEWS TRAVELS FAST!

I'M JUST ABOUT PACKED!
CAN YOU STOP OVER HERE ON YOUR WAY OVER TO VERONICA'S?!

I'VE GOT SOMETHING FOR YOU TO TAKE!
OKAY! BUT ONLY FOR A MINUTE!

ARE THOSE YOUR CHOCOLATE COOKIES I SMELL?
I THOUGHT SOME MIGHT BE GOOD FOR YOUR TRIP!
COOPER

I JUST PUT THEM IN THE OVEN! THEY'LL ONLY BE A FEW MINUTES!
GOOD! I CAN'T STAY LONG!

WHILE WE'RE WAITING, CHECK OUT THE NEW BIKINI I ORDERED!
PRETTY CUTE!

I TRACKED THE SHIPPING ONLINE! IT'LL ARRIVE TWO DAYS FROM NOW!
I'LL STILL BE UP AT THE LAKE!
TEEN Fashion CATALOG

YES, TOO BAD YOU WON'T BE THERE WITH THE OTHER BOYS WHEN I DEBUT IT AT THE BEACH!
YESSS... TOO BAD!

WHILE YOU'RE WITH THE LODGES, YOU'LL ALSO MISS THE CLASSIC CAR SHOW AT THE FAIRGROUNDS!
I-IS THAT *THIS* WEEK?!
RIVERDALE STAR TRIBUNE

WE HAD SO MUCH FUN LAST YEAR WHEN WE WENT!
YOU WON THE RAFFLE FOR A NEW SET OF TIRES!
YEAH!

I MIGHT GET FREE PASSES THIS YEAR! MY DAD'S COMPANY IS SPONSORING IT!
NO KIDDING!?

UM... WELL, I'D BETTER GO! RON'S WAITING!
DON'T FORGET YOUR COOKIES!

AND I'LL TAKE A GOODBYE KISS AS WELL! I WON'T BE SEEING YOU FOR A WHILE!

SMOOCH!

'BYE, ARCHIE! DON'T FORGET ME!
A-AFTER THAT, WHO COULD?!

IT'S PAST NOON! WHERE IS THAT IMBECILE??
ARCHIE SAID HE'D BE HERE, DADDY!

THERE'S HIS CAR!
FINALLY!

SORRY I'M LATE, LOVE BUG! I GOT HELD UP!
I CAN SEE THAT! WELL, I HAVE A SOLUTION FOR THAT!!

REGGIE! PULL A SUITCASE TOGETHER AND BE HERE IN TEN MINUTES!
ROGER, DOLL!

B-B-BUT, LAMB'S LETTUCE! WHAT'S WRONG WITH MY BEING A FEW MINUTES LATE?!?
SHOWING UP DECORATED WITH BETTY'S LIPSTICK AND STINKING OF HER COOKIES, FOR STARTERS!!

YOU PLANNED IT ALL ALONG, DIDN'T YOU?
WHY, DARLING! HOW COULD YOU THINK SUCH A THING?!

END

Archie in "WOMEN'S RIGHTS"

WHAT ARE YOU DOING HERE ? I THOUGHT YOU WERE GOING TO THAT NEW STAGE PLAY WITH RONNIE !

I WAS, BUT NOT NOW !

BOY, THAT RONNIE MAKES ME MAD !
WHAT HAPPENED ?

SHE DECIDED THAT SHE WANTED REGGIE TO TAKE HER INSTEAD OF ME !

Script & Art: Dick Malmgren / Letters: Bill Yoshida

WHEN DID SHE DECIDE THIS?
JUST A WHILE AGO!

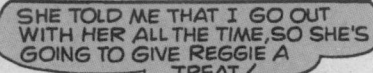

SHE TOLD ME THAT I GO OUT WITH HER ALL THE TIME, SO SHE'S GOING TO GIVE REGGIE A TREAT!

I WAS DEEPLY HURT! IT WAS LIKE BEING STABBED IN THE BACK!

I WAS LOOKING FORWARD TO SEEING THAT STAGE PLAY, BUT NOW I'M A SHATTERED PERSON!

SHE CAN'T DO THIS TO YOU, ARCHIE! SHE MADE A COMMITMENT TO YOU!
WELL, SHE DID!

BUT SHE INVITED YOU FIRST, ARCH! SHE CAN'T CHANGE HER MIND AT THE LAST MINUTE!
2

LOOK, JUST BECAUSE HER FATHER GAVE HER THE TICKETS FOR FREE DOESN'T MEAN SHE CAN DUMP YOU LIKE THAT!

YOU STILL HAVE SOME RIGHTS, ARCHIE!
I DO?

SURE YOU DO! A PROMISE IS A PROMISE AND SHE PROMISED YOU THAT YOU COULD TAKE HER!

I'D GO BACK TO HER AND DEMAND MY RIGHTS!

YOU WERE PLANNING ALL WEEK TO SEE THAT PLAY! SHE OWES IT TO YOU!

YOU'RE RIGHT! SHE CAN'T PUSH ME AROUND LIKE SOME DUMMY!
NOW YOU'RE TALKING!
SMACK!

YOU'VE GIVEN ME NEW COURAGE, PAL.!
LET HER KNOW WHAT THE SCORE IS.!

ALL HE NEEDED WAS A LITTLE GOOD ADVICE.!

ARCHIE.! WHAT ARE YOU DOING BACK HERE ?

DIDN'T YOU DEMAND YOUR RIGHTS?
I SURE DID.!

SHE ALSO GAVE ME A FEW LEFTS TO GO WITH THEM.!
END

Script & Pencils: Dan Parent / Inks: Jim Amash / Letters: Bill Yoshida

HEY! WHAT'S THIS? "MUSIC EXPRESS" IS HAVING A CONTEST FOR A CUB REPORTER!
MEET THE SUGAR POPZ
THE WINNER GETS TO TRAVEL ACROSS THE COUNTRY WITH THE BAND AND CHRONICLE THEIR ADVENTURES FOR THE MAGAZINE!
MUSIC

ALL I HAVE TO DO IS WRITE AN ESSAY ABOUT WHY IT WOULD BE IMPORTANT TO WRITE THIS ARTICLE!

THAT'S EASY! FOR THE FAME AND THE GLORY!! PLUS, IT COULD LAND ME ON LOTS OF COOL TALK SHOWS!

THAT WAS EASY!
I'LL LET BETTY READ IT OVER!!

SOON...
SO, HOW MUCH DO YOU LOVE IT?
WELL, RON!! IT'S...UH...

IT'S A BIT SELF-ABSORBED!
IT'S MORE ABOUT YOUR FAME AND GLORY THAN ABOUT THE MUSIC!

LET'S REWORK THIS A BIT!!
OKAY, WORK YOUR LITERARY MAGIC!

"... MUSIC IS THE BRIDGE THAT CONNECTS SO MANY SOULS AND GENERATIONS! TO WITNESS THIS FIRSTHAND WOULD BE A ONCE IN A LIFETIME EXPERIENCE ..."
THAT'S GREAT!

I'M SENDING IT OFF TO THE MAGAZINE...
U.S. MAIL

SEVERAL DAYS LATER...
MUSIC X-PRESS
SOB! THIS LETTER HAS ME IN TEARS!
THIS VERONICA LODGE IS WISE BEYOND HER YEARS...
I THINK WE HAVE A WINNER...
U.S. MAIL
U.S. MAIL

A FEW DAYS LATER...
WHAT? I WON! HOORAY! THIS IS MY LUCKY DAY!!

YOU'LL BE SENDING OVER THE PAPERS FOR MY PARENTS TO SIGN? OH, SURE!! THEY'RE EXPECTING THEM!!

I GUESS THIS IS A GOOD TIME TO TELL THEM...

WHAT?! NO WAY!!
NO DAUGHTER OF MINE IS TRAVELING WITH A ROCK BAND ON THE ROAD!!

BUT IT'S DURING MY SCHOOL VACATION!
I DON'T CARE!

WAH!! THIS IS MY CHANCE TO SHOW MY LITERARY TALENTS! THIS ARTICLE I WRITE COULD GET ME A SCHOLARSHIP!
4

SCHOLARSHIP!
SURE! HOW MANY TEENS ARE PUBLISHED IN A NATIONAL MAGAZINE?

YOU KNOW, DEAR, I'M PROUD OF VERONICA!!
MAYBE WE COULD MAKE THIS WORK!!

WHAT IF WE GET A CHAPERONE?
SOMEONE WE TRUST STRONGLY!

I KNOW! MY SISTER GLADYS!
OH, BROTHER! MAYBE THERE'S ANOTHER WAY!

YOU WILL BE CHAPERONED, OR YOU WON'T GO AT ALL...
OKAY! BRING ON MY WACKY TRUCKER AUNT...

ON THE BIG DAY...
LOOK! IT'S THE "SUGAR POPZ" TOUR BUS HERE TO PICK US UP!!
5

DON'T WORRY, HERMOINE, I'LL TAKE GOOD CARE OF VERONICA !!
`BYE, SWEETHEART! WRITE A GREAT STORY !!

HEY, FOLKS! WE'RE THE SUGAR POPZ !! WE'LL TAKE GOOD CARE OF YOUR LITTLE GIRL !!

HOW *REASSURING* COMING FROM YOU!
ROCK 'N' ROLL FOREVER, MAN !!

YEAH, RIGHT, MAN !!
WHAT ARE WE GETTING OURSELVES INTO ?!

ON THE ROAD...
OH, I'M NOT FEELING SO GOOD !!
I THINK IT WAS THAT BURRITO I ATE!

OOPS! THAT BURRITO WAS A MONTH OLD!
GET ME TO AN EMERGENCY ROOM...
6

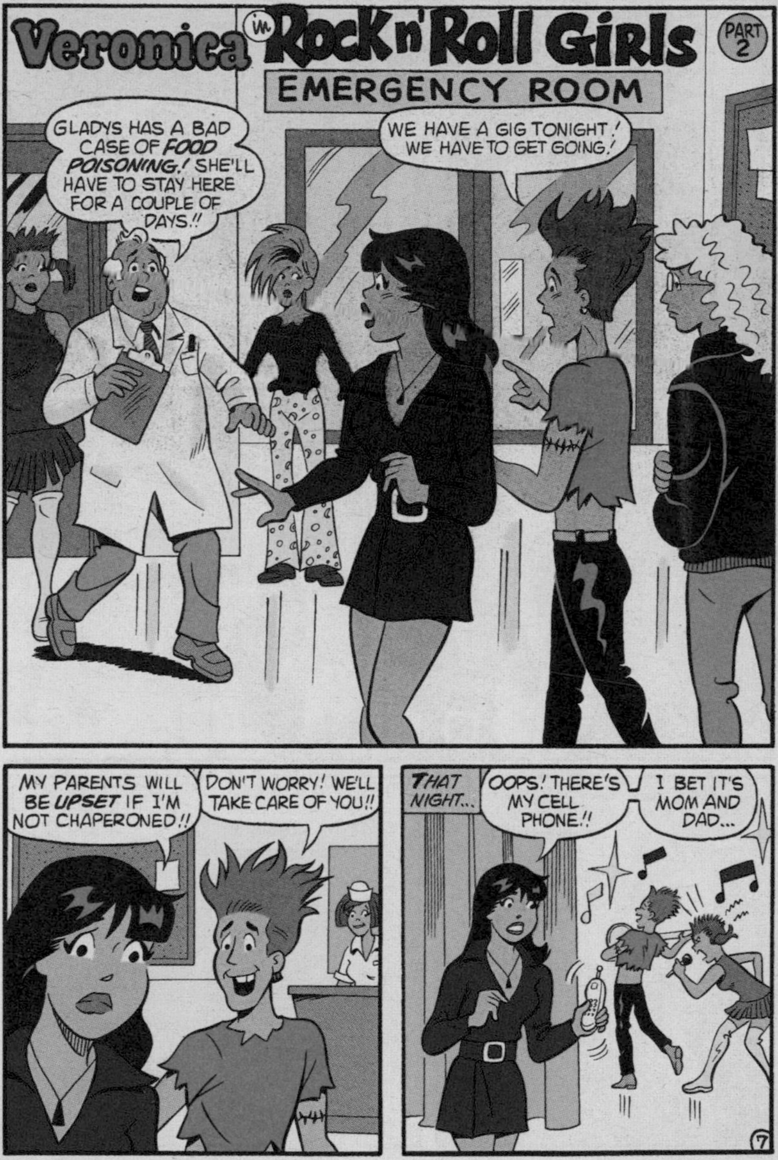

Veronica in Rock n' Roll Girls

PART 2

EMERGENCY ROOM

GLADYS HAS A BAD CASE OF *FOOD POISONING!* SHE'LL HAVE TO STAY HERE FOR A COUPLE OF DAYS!!

WE HAVE A GIG TONIGHT! WE HAVE TO GET GOING!

MY PARENTS WILL BE *UPSET* IF I'M NOT CHAPERONED!!
DON'T WORRY! WE'LL TAKE CARE OF YOU!!

THAT NIGHT...
OOPS! THERE'S MY CELL PHONE!!
I BET IT'S MOM AND DAD...

HI, HONEY!! ARE YOU HAVING FUN!! HOW'S GLADYS?!
WELL, SHE SORT OF HAD A PROBLEM! SHE'S AT A HOSPITAL IN GLENVILLE!

WHAT? YOU'RE UNCHAPERONED?!
UN-CHAPERONED!?

TELL ME WHERE YOU ARE!
I'M AT LANGLEY STADIUM IN LAMBERTVILLE!!

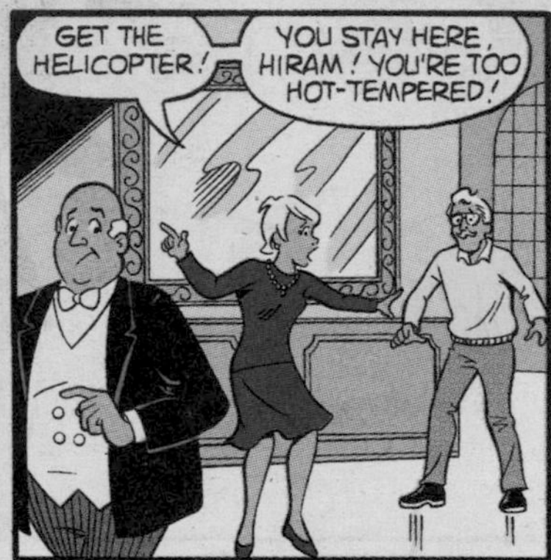
GET THE HELICOPTER!
YOU STAY HERE, HIRAM! YOU'RE TOO HOT-TEMPERED!

I'LL TAKE CARE OF THIS!
LAMBERTVILLE! PRONTO!!

THERE! A SMOOTH LANDING RIGHT ON TOP OF THE STADIUM!!
WOW! MOM GOT HERE VERY QUICKLY!

MOM'S HERE TO SAVE THE DAY!!
MOM! PLEASE DON'T EMBARRASS ME!!
SORRY! I GUESS THAT'S NOT VERY "GROOVY" OF ME!!
MOM! THIS ISN'T 1970!!
I THINK YOUR MOM IS COOL!!
WELL, THANK YOU, YOUNG LADY!!
MOM! THAT'S A BOY!!
OOPS!
SOON...
THIS BOOK ON THE "ROLLING ROCKS" IS GREAT! THEY'RE MY FAVORITE BAND!!
YES! I LOVED THEIR "PURPLE HOTPANTS" ALBUM!!
YOU KNOW "PURPLE HOTPANTS"? THAT'S ONE OF THE MOST UNDERRATED ALBUMS OF ALL TIME!!
I SAW THE ROLLING ROCKS PERFORM IT LIVE!!

VERONICA! WHY DIDN'T YOU TELL US YOUR MOM IS A ROCK GODDESS?
I WASN'T AWARE OF IT MYSELF!!

I WAS YOUNG ONCE MYSELF, VERONICA! ROCK MUSIC WAS A PART OF MY YOUTH, TOO!
WELL, I NEED TO INTERVIEW THE BAND FOR MY ARTICLE!!

ROSEBUD, SLASH, HOW ABOUT AN INTERVIEW NOW...
LATER! WE WANT TO KNOW MORE ABOUT WHAT MAKES YOUR MOM TICK!

HMPH! I NEVER THOUGHT MY MOM WOULD HORN IN ON MY TURF!
PURPLE HOTPANTS, MAKES MY SOUL DANCE...

I HAVEN'T BEEN ABLE TO GET ANY WRITING DONE WITH MOM AROUND!
GANG! WE HAVE A PROBLEM! WE CAN'T GO ON TONIGHT!

WHY?
SMITHVILLE ARENA FORGOT TO SECURE PERMITS! WE HAVE TO CANCEL!
ALL OUR POOR FANS!

WE CAN'T LET THIS HAPPEN TO ALL THOSE POOR FANS...
I HAVE AN IDEA!
HIRAM! DON'T WE OWN JACKSON STADIUM 10 MILES FROM HERE?
YES!

CAN YOU PULL SOME STRINGS!? WE NEED THAT STADIUM TONIGHT!
I THINK I CAN DO SOMETHING...

SOON...
GOOD NEWS! THE CONCERT IS ON AT JACKSON STADIUM!!
ROCK 'N' ROLL LIVES! THANKS TO MRS. LODGE!

VERONICA, YOUR MOM ROCKS!
YOU KNOW, I BELIEVE YOU'RE RIGHT!
IN FACT, I HAVE A GREAT ANGLE FOR MY STORY...
"THE DAY MY MOM SAVED ROCK 'N' ROLL..."
SUGAR POPZ
END

Betty and Veronica in "FOR THE BENEFIT of MR. KITE"

HI, BETTY!

VERONICA! HAVE YOU SEEN MY NEW KITE?

Script: Kathleen Webb / Art: Dan DeCarlo / Letters: Bill Yoshida

WOW! THAT'S A BEAUTY! IT MUST'VE SET YOU BACK A BIT!
YUP! BUT IT WAS WORTH IT!

IT'S A DREAM TO FLY!
HOW DO YOU GET IT TO DO ALL THOSE DIVES?
1

I JUST TUG ON THE HANDLES! IT'S EASY!
LET ME GIVE IT A TRY!

OOPS! I FORGOT... I'VE GOT MY SKATES ON!
NO PROBLEM!

I'LL COME UP TO THE BOARDWALK!
THANKS, BETTY!

NOW, HERE! HOLD ONTO THESE HANDLES, AND DON'T LET GO!
OKAY! MY, BUT THE WIND IS...

...STROOOONNG!!!
OMIGOSH! I SHOULD'VE HAD HER TAKE THOSE SKATES OFF!
2

LOOK OUT!

VERONICA! HANG ON.! I'M RIGHT BEHIND YOU!

YIPE!!
?

WHAM!

RON! RON!! DON'T LET GO! HANG ON! I'M COMING!!

HANG ON?!? ARE YOU KIDDING?? I'VE GOT TO LET GO BEFORE MY ARMS ARE YANKED OUT OF THEIR SOCKETS!
3

RON! THAT KITE COST ME A FORTUNE! DON'T LET GO.!!
I'LL BUY YOU A NEW ONE, FOR HEAVEN'S SAKE!

THERE! LET THE WIND HAVE IT! AT LAST I'M...

OMIGOSH... I'VE GOT TOO MUCH MOMENTUM... I CAN'T STOP.!!

...AND THIS IS THE END OF THE BOARDWALK!
GOODBYE, CRUEL WORLD!

RON.!!!
AIEEEEEEE

RONNIE! VERONICA.!! SPEAK TO ME! ARE YOU ALL RIGHT??

JUST FINE, DARLING!
OH, FOR GOODNESS SAKE!

NEXT DAY...
THANKS FOR THE NEW KITE, RON!
BUT YOU DIDN'T HAVE TO GET SUCH AN EXPENSIVE ONE!

IT'S BECAUSE OF YOU AND YOUR KITE THAT I GOT TO MEET FREDDY!
HE AND I HAVE A DATE TODAY!
OH?

WHAT ARE YOU GOING TO DO?
I DON'T KNOW YET! HE WANTED TO MEET ME HERE AT THE BEACH, AND...
HEY, VERONICA!!

READY TO TRY SOMETHING DIFFERENT WITH ME?

WHAT DID SHE MEAN, "GO FLY A KITE"?
END.

Betty IN SHELL BELLE
GIRLS, FOR TODAY'S BROWNIE MEETING, WE'RE GOING TO COLLECT SEASHELLS!
I'D LIKE EVERYONE TO FILL UP THEIR BUCKETS WITH A VARIETY OF SHELLS!
WHITE SHELLS...
BROWN SHELLS...
PINK AND BLUE SHELLS...
CONCH SHELLS...
CRAB SHELLS...
BIG SHELLS, LITTLE SHELLS...
AND MORE!!
Script: John Rose
Pencils: Pat Kennedy
Inks: Mike DeCarlo
Letters: Jack Morelli
Colors: Digikore Studios

SHELLO, BROWNIES! AND MS. BROWNIE LEADER!
HI, JUGGIE!

WOULD YOU LIKE TO HELP US COLLECT SEASHELLS?

SURE!
WHAT ARE YOU PLANNING ON DOING WITH THE SHELLS AFTER YOU COLLECT THEM?

WE'RE GOING TO MAKE SOME REALLY COOL CRAFTS WITH THEM AT NEXT WEEK'S BROWNIE MEETING!

THAT SOUNDS LIKE A LOT OF FUN!

SINCE YOU'RE HELPING US COLLECT THE SHELLS, WOULD YOU LIKE TO COME TO NEXT WEEK'S MEETING TO SEE WHAT WE CREATE?
SURE!!
2

AT THE FOLLOWING WEEK'S BROWNIE MEETING...
WELCOME, EVERYONE!
TODAY WE'RE GOING TO MAKE SEASHELL CRAFTS WITH THE SHELLS WE COLLECTED LAST WEEK!
FIRST, WE'LL BUILD FUNNY LITTLE SEA-SHELL CREATURES...
I'VE PURCHASED SETS OF CRAZY PLASTIC EYES...
...PAINTS AND GLITTER!
I'D LIKE EACH OF YOU TO SELECT A SHELL AND THEN GLUE THE CRAZY EYES AND GLITTER TO IT!
THEN PAINT A FACE ON IT, AND YOU'LL HAVE YOUR OWN LITTLE SEASHELL CREATURE!
COOL!
AWESOME!
I'M GONNA NAME MINE SHELLY!!

I KNOW YOU ALL HAVE BABY BROTHERS AND SISTERS!
SO, WHILE WE WAIT FOR THE GLUE TO DRY ON OUR FIRST PROJECT...
...LET'S MAKE SOME-THING FOR THEM!
WHAT ARE WE GOING TO MAKE, BETTY?
A SEASHELL MOBILE FOR CRIBS!
FOR THIS CRAFT WE NEED STRING...
...TWO TWELVE INCH DOWEL RODS... GLUE AND SEA-SHELLS!
WE USE THE STRING TO MAKE THE TWO DOWEL RODS INTO AN "X"...
AND THEN TIE THE STRING INTO A KNOT ALL AROUND THE DOWEL RODS...
"GLUE THE SHELLS ONTO DIFFERENT LENGTHS OF PIECES OF STRING..."
4

AFTER THE GLUE DRIES, TIE THE STRINGS WITH THE SHELLS TO THE DOWEL RODS AT ALL FOUR CORNERS, AND SOME IN BETWEEN, TOO!
LIKE SO!
OKAY, GIRLS...
...LET'S CLEAN UP OUR MESS!
HEY, JUG! WHILE WE'RE CLEANING UP--
--CAN YOU HANG UP THIS MOBILE SO THAT I CAN SHOW THE GIRLS HOW IT WORKS?
COMMUNITY CENTER
OKAY, BETTY!
5

A FEW MINUTES LATER...
BETTY!
CAN I SHOW YOU SOME-THING?
SURE, MACEY!
SKYNXX
MY MOBILE ACTUALLY WORKS! IT PUT JUGHEAD TO SLEEP, JUST LIKE A BABY.!!
END

Veronica in "HEIR STYLE"

Script & Pencils: Fernando Ruiz
Inks: Rudy Lapick / Letters: Bill Yoshida

WHOOPS!!

THUMP!

CRASH!

GOSH, MR. LODGE! I'M REALLY SORRY!
ARCHIE, LIKE YOU KIDS TODAY SAY... APOLOGY ACCEPTED...
...NOT!!
1

AND STAY OUT!

DAA-DEEE! WHY MUST YOU ALWAYS KICK ARCHIE OUT THAT WAY?!
IF YOU LIKE, NEXT TIME I'LL USE MY RIGHT FOOT!!
DADDY, I'M SERIOUS! YOU ARE A SIGNIFICANT ROLE MODEL IN ARCHIE'S LIFE! YOU SHOULD TRY TO MAKE AN IMPRESSION ON HIM!

I'M JUST SAYING YOU TWO SHOULD COMMUNICATE MORE!
I'D LIKE TO MAKE AN IMPRESSION ON HIS HEAD!

FINE! TELL HIM TO E-MAIL ME... FROM ANTARCTICA!
2

OOO! YOU'RE IMPOSSIBLE, DADDY!
IMAGINE! DELIBERATELY SEEKING OUT THAT REDHEADED NUT CASE!
SIR, IF I MAY BE SO BOLD...

THERE MAY BE SOMETHING TO WHAT MISS VERONICA SAYS...
WHAT?
JUST HOW TIGHT ARE YOU TYING THAT BOW TIE THESE DAYS, SMITHERS, OLD BOY?

YOU'RE ALWAYS CLEANING UP THAT IDIOT'S MESSES!
THERE ARE BIGGER ISSUES TO CONSIDER HERE, SIR!

OF ALL THE YOUNG GENTLEMEN MISS VERONICA HAS HAD CALL ON HER, ARCHIE APPEARS TO BE THE MOST PERSISTENT...
YEAH... LIKE A RASH!

IT MAY WELL BE THAT ONE DAY IN THE FUTURE, ARCHIE AND MISS VERONICA WILL MARRY!!
EGAD, MAN!!

...AND THEREFORE IT MAY ONE DAY FALL UPON ARCHIE'S SHOULDERS TO RUN LODGE ENTERPRISES!
WHAT?!? ARCHIE?! RUN MY COMPANY?!
GOOD GRIEF, MEN! LODGE ENTERPRISES' STOCK IS TANKING BIGTIME!
WHAT ARE WE GOING TO DO?
WHERE'S YOUR PRESIDENT, MR. ANDREWS?
LODGE ENTERPRISES
LODGE E SINKING FAST

WHOOPS!!
MY GOSH, MAN! NO! WHAT CAN I DO, SMITHERS? WHAT CAN I DO?
IT'S NOT TOO LATE, SIR! YOU CAN STILL TAKE THE BOY UNDER YOUR WING!
ENTERPRISE

YES! THAT'S IT! I'LL MAKE ARCHIE MY PROTEGÉ! I'LL TAKE HIM TO THE OFFICE AND SHOW HIM THE ROPES!

WHO KNOWS? MAYBE THIS IS JUST WHAT HE NEEDS TO TAKE THINGS MORE SERIOUSLY!

THE NEXT WEEK...
HI, DADDY! I CAME BY TO SEE HOW ARCHIE WAS WORKING OUT!

WELL, HE'S NOT MUCH OF A WORKER...
SECRETARIAL POOL

...BUT THE INTERNS SEEM TO LIKE HIM!

SMITHERS, OLD MAN, I'M GIVING YOU A RAISE...
...THIS IDEA OF YOURS WORKED OUT BEAUTIFULLY...
IS THE YOUNG LAD BUCKLING DOWN, SIR?
BETTER THAN THAT...

... I DON'T THINK WE'RE GOING TO BE SEEING ARCHIE FOR AT LEAST A MONTH!!
WHACK!
The End

BETTY!
HI, VERONICA! YOU READY TO HIT THE MALL!?

WHATEVER FOR?
WHY, FOR ONE OF YOUR FAVORITE PASTIMES, OF COURSE! BACK TO SCHOOL SHOPPING!

yawn!
YOU GO ON WITHOUT ME! I JUST DON'T FEEL UP TO IT TODAY!
WHAT?!?

SCRIPT: KATHLEEN WEBB PENCILS: T.J. KIRSCH INKS: JON D'AGOSTINO
LETTERS: JACK MORELLI

Betty and Veronica in DROP The SHOPPING

Huh?! Wha-?! WHAT'RE YOU DOING?!

YOU DON'T FEEL LIKE YOU HAVE A FEVER!
AND YOUR PULSE IS NORMAL!

STILL-- SMITHERS! CALL FOR A DOCTOR!
WHAT ON EARTH FOR?

YOU'RE SICK! YOU HAVE TO BE! YOU DON'T WANT TO GO SHOPPING!
BECAUSE I DON'T NEED TO!

I'M HAVING MY ENTIRE FALL WARDROBE DONE BY THAT DESIGNER, ELANA THREDBAYRE! IT'LL BE SO UNIQUE!

TOO BAD YOU HAVE TO BUY ALL YOUR CLOTHES WHERE EVERYONE ELSE SHOPS!
YEAH!
sigh!
TOO BAD!

Phooey! She just took all the fun out of shopping for back-to-school clothes!

Not to mention she's right! I'll look like every other girl who shops at the mall!
Unless...

Here's where those sewing lessons from Mom come into play!
Fay's FABR
SALE

We're having a sale today! All our patterns are 50% off!
Wow! Now I can afford the more exclusive ones!

And speaking of--! There are patterns here for Elana Thredbayre's designs!!
Elana Thredbayre

If I use clearance priced fabrics, they won't look exactly like Ron's, but they'll be good enough for me!

AND SO, BETTY IS KEPT IN STITCHES FOR A WHILE...
RRRRRRRR

UNTIL--!
THERE! MY NEW FALL WARDROBE IS FINISHED!
VERONICA IS HERE TO SEE YOU, BETTY!

HI, RON! WHAT'S UP?
ER... I JUST WANTED TO SEE IF YOU'D LIKE TO GO SHOPPING!

BACK-TO-SCHOOL SHOPPING, THAT IS!
HUH? BUT I THOUGHT THAT YOU ALREADY HAD YOUR FALL WAR-DROBE!

ELANA THREDBAYRE BROKE HER FIBULA WHILE HEMMING A GOWN! MY WHOLE WARDROBE WON'T BE READY FOR WEEKS!

EVEN WORSE, BY THE TIME IT'S FINISHED, IT'LL BE OUT OF STYLE!!
THAT'S TOO BAD!

SO YOU'VE DECIDED TO GO SHOPPING FOR CLOTHES AT THE MALL?
AT THIS LATE DATE, I HAVE NO OTHER CHOICE!!

SHALL WE BE OFF, THEN?
YOU GO ON WITHOUT ME! I DON'T NEED TO VISIT THE MALL!

MOM!
DO WE HAVE ANY SMELLING SALTS?!

FOR HEAVEN'S SAKE, WHY NOT?!
I'VE ALREADY SEWN-UP MY BACK-TO-SCHOOL THINGS!

SEE? AND THEY'RE EVEN ELANA THREDBAYRE DESIGNS, JUST LIKE YOURS!

SHE'S OUT AGAIN--?
I PROBABLY SHOULDN'T HAVE OFFERED TO SEW HER UP AN OUTFIT OR TWO WITH MY LEFTOVER FABRIC!!
THE END

Monkey Business

SCRIPT AND PENCILS: **DAN PARENT** INKING: **RICH KOSLOWSKI** LETTERING: **JACK MORELLI**

AFTER WE FINISH OUR CONCERT, WE CAN HIT THE PARK!
I CAN'T WAIT!
THANKS, EVERYBODY!!
HAVE FUN HERE AT THE PARK!
WOW! WE'VE BEEN SIGNING AUTOGRAPHS FOR AN HOUR!
YOU'RE THE BEST, ARCHIE! I LOVE YOU!!
WATCH IT, SISTER! HE'S TAKEN!
VERONICA! I HAVE SUCH A CRUSH ON YOU!
Hmph!
Oh, ARCHIE!
IT DOESN'T FEEL SO GOOD WHEN THE SHOE IS ON THE OTHER FOOT, DOES IT?
2

COME ON! LET'S HIT THE PARK!
SOON...
THIS RIDE BETTER BE WORTH IT! THIS LINE IS SO LONG!
WHAT'S THAT?
THE PERSON IN THAT APE SUIT HAS BEEN STARING AT ME!
I THINK YOU'D MAKE A LOVELY COUPLE!
SHADDUP, LOSER!!
IT'S PROBABLY JUST YOUR IMAGINATION!
LATER...
OOOO! I LOVE THE LOG FLUME!
Omigosh! LOOK!
3

THERE'S THE APE ON THE LOG BEHIND US!
RON! HE PROBABLY JUST WANTS TO GO ON THE RIDES, TOO!
WHY IS HE IN FULL COSTUME?
THAT IS RATHER ODD!
SPLASH
THAT WAS FUN!
EEK! HOW CREEPY!!
THAT WET APE IS STARING OUR WAY!!
I'M CREEPED OUT! LET'S GET OUT OF HERE!!
FLUME
SO... RON! WE'RE NOT GOING TO LEAVE! WE HAVE A SHOW TONIGHT!
THAT NOSEY APE IS RUINING MY DAY!

PLUS, WE STILL HAVE TO RIDE THE FIREBLASTER 3000!!
FB 3000
IT'S THE TALLEST ROLLERCOASTER IN THE WORLD!!
IT'S THREE LOOPS ARE ALMOST GUARANTEED TO MAKE YOU LOSE YOUR LUNCH!
COOL!!
ALL RIGHT! BUT I'M HOLDING ON TO YOU TIGHT!
SO AM I!
SO...
OH! THIS IS GOING TO BE SCARY!
SORT OF LIKE WHEN YOU DON'T HAVE ANY MAKE-UP ON!!

I'LL DEAL WITH YOU WHEN AND IF I SURVIVE THIS!
Whoa!! THIS IS FREAKY!!
I CAN SEE ALL OF RIVERDALE!
I THINK I CAN SEE EUROPE FROM HERE!!
KA-CHUNG
WHAT WAS THAT?!
THAT DIDN'T SOUND GOOD!
WHAT'S GOING ON?!
ATTENTION, PASSENGERS! WE HAVE A TECHNICAL PROBLEM!
PLEASE BE PATIENT WHILE WE TRY TO ADDRESS THE PROBLEM!
I--I DON'T THINK I CAN HANDLE THIS!!
Huh? SOMEONE'S CLIMBING UP THE ROLLERCOASTER!
WHO?
6

OH, NO!! IT CAN'T BE!!
IT'S...IT'S...
THAT APE!!
HE'S COMING TO GET ME!!
DON'T WORRY, I'LL PROTECT YOU!!
I'D BETTER STEP IN!!
I DON'T KNOW WHO YOU ARE, BUT LEAVE ME ALONE!
YEAH! BUG OFF!!
GRAB
EEK!
HE'S GOT ARCHIE!
HE'S CLIMBING TO THE TOP WITH ARCHIE!
IT'S LIKE A LOW RENT VERSION OF KING KONG!

THE RESCUE CREWS ARE HERE TO GET US DOWN!
BUT WHAT ABOUT ARCHIE?

Oh, HE'LL BE FINE WITH KONGA!
KONGA?!

WHAT'S GOING ON HERE?
TAKE OFF YOUR MASK, YOU THUG!
FLOP
Huh?!

YOU'RE A GIRL!!
HEY, I REMEMBER! I SIGNED AN AUTOGRAPH FOR YOU EARLIER!

YOU REMEMBER ME!! Oh, ARCHIE, I'VE HAD A CRUSH ON YOU SINCE THE FIRST TIME I SAW YOU IN CONCERT!!
!

SO YOU WERE FOLLOWING ME ALL ALONG?
VERONICA THOUGHT YOU WERE AFTER HER!
?

YEAH, SHE'S QUITE SELF-CENTERED, ISN'T SHE?
WELL, SHE IS WHO SHE IS!
R

HOW CRAZY ARE YOU TO CLIMB THIS THING?!
I'M A TRAINED PROFESSIONAL!
?

I WORK AT THE "KONGA" ATTRACTION!
I'M A STUNT WOMAN! I CLIMB THINGS LIKE THIS ALL THE TIME!

WOW! I'M IMPRESSED!
REALLY?!

WHAT'S GOING ON UP THERE?!
THEY'RE LOOKING PRETTY CHUMMY!!

LET ME USE YOUR BINOCULARS, KID!
GAK
THAT APE IS A GIRL!!
AND SHE'S MAKING MOVES ON OUR ARCHIE!!

C'MON! I'M CLIMBING TO THE TOP OF THIS THING TO PUT AN END TO THIS!!
COME WITH ME, BETTY!!

WAIT! THEY'RE COMING DOWN!
GOOD! THAT APE IS CRUISIN' FOR A BRUISIN'!!

SO...
GIRLS! THIS IS DEBBIE, OTHER-WISE KNOWN AS "KONGA"!
I REMEMBER YOU! YOU HAD EYES FOR MY ARCHIE!

SHE WORKS AT THE "KONGA" ATTRACTION!
HOW CLASSY!
R

SORRY IF I CAUSED ANY TENSION!
I HAVE TO GET BACK TO WORK! SEE YOU LATER, ARCHIE!
WHAT?!/ YOU'RE GOING OUT WITH THAT MONKEY GIRL?!/
WELL, SHE DID SAVE MY LIFE... SORT OF!

AWWWW... COME ON, GIRLS!
LET'S NOT GET UPSET BEFORE OUR SHOW!
LET ME BUY YOU TWO A SPECIAL TREAT!
WELLLL... OKAY!

Veronica in "My "Hiccup" Runneth Over"

YAWN! I GUESS IT'S TIME TO GET UP!

12 HOURS OF SLEEP IS HIC

Script & Pencils: Dan Parent / Inks: Jon D'Agostino / Letters: Bill Yoshida

... PLENTY!
HMM! HICCUPS! THAT'S HIC ODD!

A LITTLE SIP OF HIC WATER SHOULD DO IT!

THERE, THAT'S BETTER!
HIC

HMPH! I'LL JUST GO ABOUT MY BUSINESS! THEY'LL GO AWAY!
HIC

SOUNDS LIKE YOU'VE GOT A CASE OF THE HICCUPS, DEAR!
YES! HIC FOR ALMOST AN HOUR NOW!

DRINK SOME WATER, DEAR!
I'VE ALREADY HAD A GALLON! HIC

TAKE DEEP BREATHS! IT'LL CLEAR YOUR AIR PASSAGES!
OKAY! I'LL HIC TRY!

AH... AH... HOOM!!
NICE AND EASY! THERE YOU GO!
2

I THINK IT WORKED! HIC
OH, DARN!!

I'LL GO TO POP'S! MAYBE NOT THINKING ABOUT IT WILL HIC HELP!
GOOD LUCK, DEAR!

WHAT'S UP, RON?
OH, JUST HIC THIS HICCUP SITUATION!
POP'S

OH, WHEN I GET HICCUPS, I ALWAYS HOLD MY BREATH!
I'LL HIC TRY IT! I'M DESPERATE!!
POP'S

I'LL TELL YOU WHEN 30 SECONDS PASSES! START NOW!
MMPH!!

HMM! RON'S TURNING BLUE! AND IT HAS BEEN A LONG 30 SECONDS!
UH-OH! SOMETHING'S WRONG...

MY WATCH IS BROKEN!
RON! START BREATHING!

PSAW!!! I ALMOST PASSED OUT!
BUT IT SOUNDS LIKE YOUR HICCUPS ARE...

Hic!
...CURED? RATS!

THIS IS GETTING FRUSTRATING!
GETTING FRUSTRATED WON'T HELP!

POP!!
EEK!!
ARCHIE!!

GETTING STARTLED WORKS FOR ME!
I HOPE IT : HIC : WORKS FOR ME! OH, DRATS!

THAT'S IT! I'M DOOMED! I READ ABOUT THAT GUY IN THE WORLD BOOK OF RECORDS WHO HAD HICCUPS FOR 42 YEARS! I GUESS I'M NEXT!
HIC!

I'LL JUST PUT ON A SWIMSUIT AND HANG HIC OUT BY THE POOL BY MYSELF!

EEEEK!
I'VE BEEN ROBBED! ALL MY CLOTHES ARE GONE!

I WAS TIRED OF YOUR OVERSPENDING!
I SENT BACK YOUR SUMMER WARDROBE AND CUT OFF YOUR CREDIT CARDS!

EEEEK!! HOW COULD YOU?! WHY WOULD YOU?
EASY!! I NEEDED TO TRULY FRIGHTEN YOU OUT OF YOUR HICCUPS! AND...

THEY'RE GONE! IT WORKED! THIS TIME IT WORKED!
BUT YOU ARE JUST KIDDING ABOUT THE CREDIT CARDS, RIGHT, DAD? RIGHT...?
END

Script: George Gladir / Pencils: Stan Goldberg / Inks: Mike Esposito / Letters: Bill Yoshida

PAMELA, I STILL DON'T KNOW WHY YOU DRAGGED ME ALONG ON THIS DUMB SAFARI!

TO FIND LORD ARCHIBALD!

WHEN HE VISITED AFRICA AS A TEN-YEAR-OLD, SOME APES RAN OFF WITH HIM!

ARE YOU CHAPS LOOKING FOR A CHEAP TOUR GUIDE?

IT'S *HE*... IT'S *LORD ARCHIBALD!*

THIS PICTURE IN MY LOCKET PROVES YOU'RE LORD ARCHIBALD!

CHEE! AND I THOUGHT I WAS JUST SOME KIND OF *ODD-LOOKING APE!*

AND THIS POCKET MIRROR PROVES YOU WEREN'T WRONG!
CEDRIC!!

I'M AFRAID I'M GOING TO HAVE TO COME BETWEEN YOU AND THIS YOUNG LADY!
OH, YEAH! HOW COME?

'CAUSE IF I DON'T COME BETWEEN YOU TWO, THAT NASTY RHINO WILL!

YOU HAVE TO COME BACK TO ENGLAND WITH US, LORD ARCHIBALD!
PLEASE DON'T CALL ME LORD ARCHIBALD... IT SOUNDS SO FORMAL!

ALL MY JUNGLE FRIENDS CALL ME "OOGA BOOGA CHEE CHEE GEECHI OOH HAH"!
OOGA BOOGA CHEE CHEE GEECHI OOH HAH!

UH, I THINK I'LL STICK WITH "LORD ARCHIBALD"!

WHY SHOULD I GO BACK? HERE I HAVE A LOVELY TREETOP HOME!

...AND A LOVELY MATE!
HI, EVERYBODY!

BUT BACK IN ENGLAND YOU'RE A RICH MAN! EVERYTHING WOULD BE AT YOUR FINGERTIPS!
AND EVERYTHING HERE IS AT MY FINGERTIPS!

...AND NO PESTICIDES!

BUT HERE IN THE JUNGLE YOU DON'T HAVE ANY NEAT CARS!
WHO NEEDS CARS?

FOR TRANSPORTATION WE HAVE THESE VINES!

WE ALSO HAVE THESE ELEPHANTS!
AND WE DON'T HAVE GRIDLOCKS OR ENGINE BREAK-DOWNS TO WORRY ABOUT!

BUT WHAT ABOUT TV?
YEAH! YOU GUYS DON'T HAVE ANY TV!
4

IT'S TRUE WE DON'T HAVE TV!
...BUT WE ALSO DON'T HAVE BORING COMMERCIALS, OR OLD SUMMER RERUNS!

BESIDES, WE HAVE SOMETHING BETTER TO DO WITH OUR SPARE TIME THAN WATCH TV!
SMOOCH!
SMOOCH!

YOU ALSO DON'T HAVE A BIG, BIG MANSION LIKE THE ONE YOU SEE HERE!

BUT WE ALSO DON'T HAVE BIG, BIG MORTGAGE PAYMENTS AND THE TAXES THAT GO WITH BIG, BIG MANSIONS!

YES, BUT DO YOU HAVE DISCO DANCING?
AND ROCK MUSIC?

PRACTICALLY EVERY NIGHT!

SIR GREENBUCKS, WE'VE JUST RECEIVED WORD YOUR DAUGHTER PAMELA AND CEDRIC HAVE LOCATED MISSING LORD ARCHIBALD!

FANTASTIC! GET THEIR EXACT LOCATION AND WE'LL RESCUE THEM!

PAMELA!
DADDY! DADDY!

OUR HELICOPTER IS READY TO TAKE YOU BACK, DAUGHTER DEAREST!

BUT WHAT MAKES YOU THINK WE WANT TO GO BACK?
END

Mr. Weatherbee "Mr. Lucky"

IF WE HURRY, WE CAN TEE OFF BEFORE THE CROWD FORMS, MR. WEATHERBEE!
OH NO!
RIP!

Script & Pencils: Dick Malmgren / Inks: Jon D'Agostino / Letters: Bill Yoshida

IF THIS IS HOW MY DAY IS GOING TO START, MAYBE I SHOULD FORGET ABOUT PLAYING GOLF, ARCHIE!
6

WHY SHOULD I TEMPT FATE?
DON'T BE SILLY, MR. WEATHERBEE!
1

HERE! MY LUCKY RABBIT'S FOOT WILL PROTECT YOU!
YOU'RE KIDDING!

IF YOU BELIEVE IN IT, A RABBIT'S FOOT WILL BRING YOU GOOD LUCK!
I'LL TRY ANYTHING!
POW! POP!

DO YOU BELIEVE ?
I BELIEVE! I BELIEVE!

TOCK!

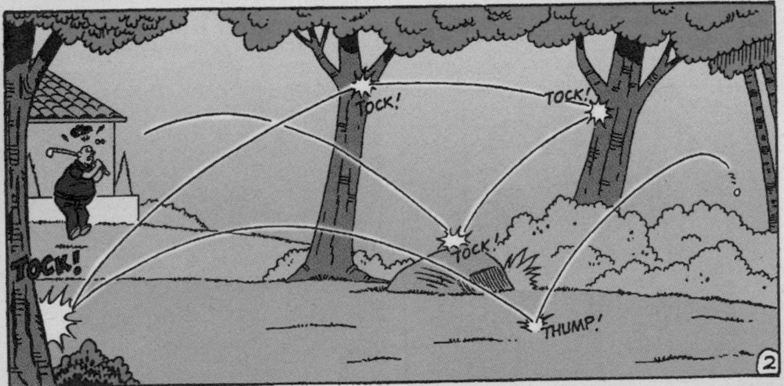
TOCK!
TOCK!
TOCK!
TOCK!
THUMP!
2

I'M IN THE WOODS! IS THAT WHAT YOU CALL LUCK?
MAYBE YOU'LL FIND A FEW BALLS IN THERE!

WATCH ME! I BELIEVE!
TOCK!

SEE?
GOOD GRIEF!
TOCK!
TOCK!
TOCK!
TOCK!
TOCK!
THUMP!

I DON'T BELIEVE THAT GUY! HE ALMOST GOT A HOLE IN ONE BY BOUNCING OFF TREES!

LET'S SEE IF LUCK CAN GET ME OUT OF THESE WOODS!
TOCK
3

TOCK!
YIPE!

TOCK!

I'M SORRY ABOUT THAT, MADAM!
YOU HIT THAT BALL IN THE WRONG DIRECTION!
YOUR GREEN IS THAT WAY!

IT WAS AN ACCIDENT!
SO IS THIS, MISTER!
WHAP!

YOU'D BE A HAZARD ON A MINIATURE GOLF COURSE!
?

I KNEW I SHOULD HAVE STAYED HOME TODAY!
NONSENSE! YOU HAVE MY LUCKY RABBIT'S FOOT!

CLUNK!
CRUNCH!
CLATTER!
RRRRRRRRRRR

THAT MAN RAN OVER MY NEW CLUBS WITH HIS LAWN MOWER!
YOU SHOULDN'T HAVE LEFT THEM IN THE TALL GRASS!

YOU CAN USE MY CLUBS!
WHAT ELSE CAN GO WRONG?
RUMBLE!

RUMBLE!
I HAVE A STRANGE FEELING THAT HE'S NOT GOING TO GIVE ME BACK MY LUCKY RABBIT'S FOOT!
END

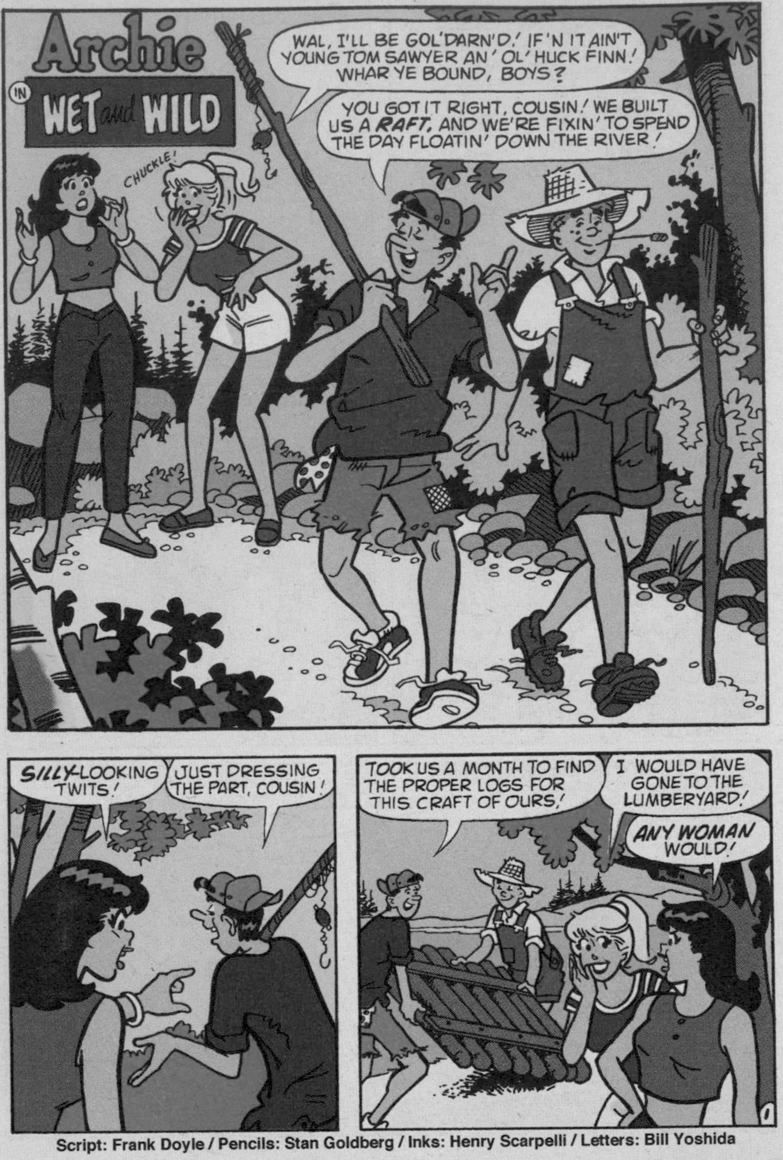

Archie in WET and WILD

WAL, I'LL BE GOL'DARN'D! IF 'N IT AIN'T YOUNG TOM SAWYER AN' OL' HUCK FINN! WHAR YE BOUND, BOYS?

YOU GOT IT RIGHT, COUSIN! WE BUILT US A *RAFT*, AND WE'RE FIXIN' TO SPEND THE DAY FLOATIN' DOWN THE RIVER!

CHUCKLE!

Script: Frank Doyle / Pencils: Stan Goldberg / Inks: Henry Scarpelli / Letters: Bill Yoshida

IT'S NOT HALLOWEEN, IS IT, JENNY? THOSE BOYS SEEM TO BE IN COSTUME!
NO, PENELOPE! IT MUST BE ONE OF THOSE CRAZY, TEENAGE FADS!

THERE! ISN'T SHE A BEAUTY?
THUMP!

LOOKS LIKE A BUNCH OF OLD DRIFTWOOD LASHED TOGETHER!
LOOSELY AND BADLY! I WOULDN'T TRUST THAT IN A BACKYARD POOL!

HAH! JEALOUSY AND ENVY! CAST OFF, MATEY!
AYE, AYE, SIR!
SHOVE!

FORTUNATELY THEY'RE BOTH GOOD SWIMMERS!
THEY'LL BE PUTTING *THAT* TO THE TEST REAL SOON!

AH! THIS IS THE LIFE!
WHAT'S WITH THE CORNCOB PIPE? YOU DON'T SMOKE!

HUCK FINN DID! THIS IS EMPTY! IT'S JUST FOR EFFECT!
HEY! THIS IS NOT FLOATING STRAIGHT! WE SHOULD HAVE PUT SOME PADDLES OR POLES ABOARD!

WOW! IT'S GETTING ROUGH! I SEE WHITE WATER AHEAD!
I DON'T LIKE THIS!
SWIRL!

I DON'T CARE IF THE WATER IS WHITE, PURPLE, PINK OR PUCE!-- I WANT IT CALM!!
HANG ON! I DIDN'T COUNT ON THIS!!

THIS RAFT IS NOT WELL-MADE! COME ON, CAP'N! LEAD US INTO STILL WATERS!
THAT SOUNDS BIBLICAL! I WISH I COULD!
SNAP

YIPE! ABANDON SHIP! WE'RE BREAKING UP!!!

THAT THING CAME APART LIKE A CHEAP SUIT! ... START SWIMMING!!
WE CAN'T MAKE IT TO THE MAINLAND! HEAD FOR SANDSPUR ISLAND!!

GASP! AT LAST! I WAS BEGINNING TO POOP OUT!
THIS OL' CHUNK OF LAND IS A WELCOME SIGHT!!!

HUCK! YOUR PIPE IS BLOWING BUBBLES! IS THAT SOME KIND OF SIGNAL?
THAT STUPID LAUNDRY DOWN-STREAM IS LEAKING DETERGENT INTO OUR RIVER AGAIN!

WE'LL FILE A COMPLAINT WHEN WE GET HOME! --NOT THAT WE HAVE ANY HOPE OF GETTING HOME!!

WELL!!
IMAGINE MEETING YOU HERE!!
HUH? HOW'D YOU GET HERE?
4

ONE OF MY OUTBOARDS! C'MON! WE'LL TAKE YOU TO THE MAINLAND!
OUR RAFT BROKE UP AND FLOATED AWAY!!

DARN! THE ENGINE WON'T START AGAIN! YOU BOYS TRY IT!
IT BETTER START! IT'S OUR ONLY WAY HOME!!
SPUT!
YANK!

WHEW! I GIVE UP! THIS STUPID THING IS NOT ABOUT TO COOPERATE!
WHAT GOOD'S A BOAT WITH-OUT POWER?
SPUT!
WHEEZE!

NO SWEAT, BOYS! WE JUST SWITCH TO EMERGENCY POWER!

...AND THE SERVANTS ROWED CLEOPATRA AND HER LITTLE KNOWN SIDEKICK DOWN THE NILE...
BONG! BONG!
AW, SHUT UP!!
The End

Betty and Veronica

THE RIVERDALE EXPRESS!

WHERE IS ARCHIE?

SHOULDN'T HE BE HERE ALREADY?

HE SAID HE MIGHT BE A LITTLE LATER!

HE'S GOING GREEN AND RIDING HIS BIKE MORE PLACES!

HAR!

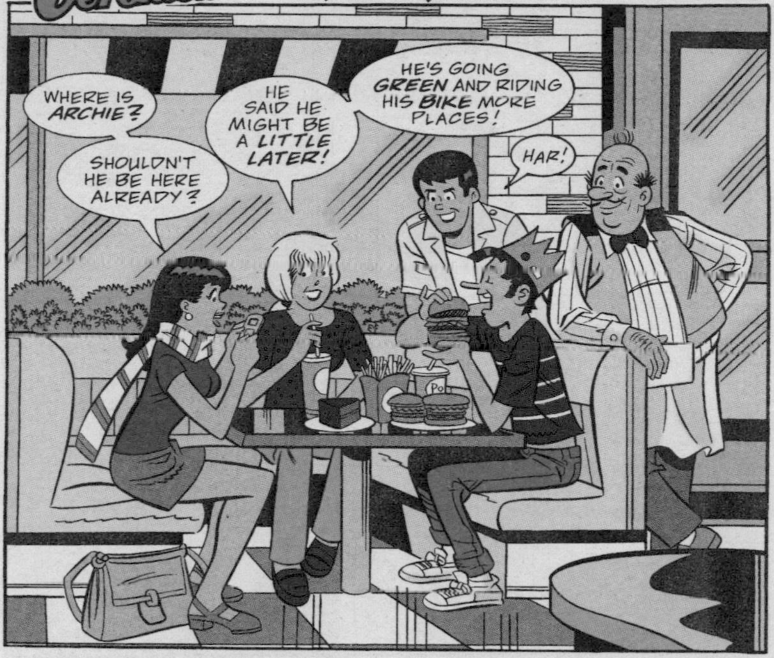

Script: BILL GOLLIHER Pencils: PAT KENNEDY Inks: MARK MCKENNA Letters: PHIL FELIX

HONK!
SCREECH!
OH, NO! THAT'S ARCHIE!
HE WAS ALMOST IN AN ACCIDENT!

ARCHIE, ARE YOU OKAY?
=URF!= I THINK SO! THAT CAR SEEMED TO IGNORE ME, FORCING ME TO RUN INTO THE CURB!

IT'S A GOOD THING YOU WERE WEARING YOUR HELMET!
YOU COULD HAVE BEEN HURT!
OR THE CURB! HEH! HEH!
KNOCK! KNOCK!
THERE'S NOT A SAFE PLACE TO RIDE A BIKE IN THIS TOWN! WE NEED BIKE LANES!
GOOD LUCK WITH THAT!

OUR CYCLING CLUB ASKED THE CITY COUNCIL ABOUT THAT BEFORE!
THEY SAY THE ROADS AREN'T WIDE ENOUGH AND THEY DON'T HAVE THE FUNDS!

THERE MUST BE A WAY!
MORE PEOPLE ARE RIDING BIKES AROUND TOWN AND WE NEED TO DO IT SAFELY!

THE IDEA IS TO SAVE GAS AND GET SOME EXERCISE, NOT RISK OUR LIVES!!
THERE ARE OTHER PLACES YOU CAN RIDE!
LIKE WHERE?

OFF-ROAD TRAILS! I'M TAKING MY MOUNTAIN BIKE OUT TOMORROW!
YOU CAN JOIN ME, IF YOU'RE UP TO IT!
OF COURSE I AM! I'LL BE THERE!

NEXT DAY...
HOW'D YOU FIND THIS TRAIL, REGGIE?
SOME OTHER BIKERS SHOWED ME! IT'S NOT FAR FROM TOWN AND IT'S QUIET A STRETCH!

IT'S A BUMPY COURSE FOR SOMEONE WHO'S USED TO STREET RIDING!
AW! DOES THE BABY WANT TO GO BACK?

I CAN HANDLE IT JUST FINE! BRING IT ON!
OH, ARCHIE, I FORGOT TO MENTION...

YOU DON'T HAVE TO MENTION ANYTHING! I'M READY FOR WHATEVER COMES MY WAY!
WHOOPS!
BUT, ARCHIE...

OOF!

ARE YOU OKAY?
I THINK SO! WHAT HIT ME?

YOU MEAN, WHAT DID YOU HIT!
IT WAS THE OLD RAILROAD TRACK I WAS TRYING TO WARN YOU ABOUT!

RAILROAD TRACK?!
IT'S IN AWFUL CONDITION! HOW ARE THE TRAINS SUPPOSED TO STAY ON IT?
THEY HAVEN'T FOR YEARS!

THIS IS THE TRACK THE TRAINS USED TO TAKE DOWN-TOWN!
NOW THE NEW STATION IS ON THE OTHER SIDE OF TOWN!

NOW THIS TRACK IS JUST A HINDRANCE!
Hmm! YOU SAY IT RUNS ALL THE WAY DOWNTOWN?

WHAT ARE YOU THINKING?
IT'S KIND OF A WAY-OUT IDEA! BUT I WANT TO WAIT AND DISCUSS IT WITH THE REST OF THE GANG!

AND SO...
ARCHIE, THAT'S BRILLIANT!!
TURNING THE OLD RAIL LINE INTO A PAVED BIKE TRAIL!
POP'S

BUT WON'T IT BE BUMPY WITH ALL THOSE TRACKS?
NO, SILLY! WE'LL HAVE ALL THE TRACKS REMOVED!
POP'S

BUT IT'S ALREADY SMOOTH AND LEVEL WHERE IT RUNS, SO IT COULD BE PAVED!
EXACTLY!

IT WOULD RUN FROM THE OUTSKIRTS RIGHT INTO THE CENTER OF TOWN!
A SAFE, FUN WAY FOR PEOPLE TO TRAVEL INTO TOWN ON THEIR BIKES!
RIVERDALE

YOU KNOW THE CITY WILL SAY THEY CAN'T AFFORD IT!
I THINK WE SHOULD VISIT THE CITY OFFICES AND SEE WHO OWNS THAT RAIL LINE!

SOON...
HERE WE ARE! THE TRANS-UNION RAIL COMPANY STILL OWNS THE LINE!
LET'S GO VISIT THEM AND SEE WHAT THEY THINK OF OUR IDEA!
CITY RECORDS

AND SO...
YOU WANT US TO REMOVE THE RAILS AND CROSS-TIES FOR AN OLD TRACK WE DON'T EVEN USE ANYMORE?
WHY WOULD WE DO THAT?

IT'S PRETTY DANGEROUS LIKE IT IS!
ARCHIE HERE TOOK QUITE A SPILL WHEN HE RAN INTO IT!
HE DID?

BESIDES, IT WOULD BE QUITE A PUBLIC RELATIONS MOVE FOR YOUR COMPANY IF THE CITY AGREES TO TURN IT INTO A BIKE PATH!

AND DONATING THAT STRIP OF LAND WOULD DO WONDERS FOR YOUR TAXES!
THESE KIDS MAKE SOME GOOD POINTS! LET'S GO VISIT THE CITY COUNCIL!

PAVING A FIVE-MILE-LONG OLD RAIL LINE SEEMS LIKE A BOONDOGGLE TO ME!
NOT AT ALL! THE LAND IS DONATED AND WE ALSO TALKED TO SOME ASPHALT COMPANIES!

THAT WILL PROBABLY COST A FORTUNE!
ACTUALLY, NO!

AND SO...
FOR PLACEMENT OF DISCREET ADVERTISING SIGNS ALONG THE PATH, ACME ASPHALT HAS AGREED TO PAVE THE PROPOSED TRAIL!
Humph!
ACME
ASPHALT
PAVING
6

IN THE DAYS THAT FOLLOW...
WOW! THIS IS LOOKING AMAZING!
AND EVERYONE KEEPS ASKING WHEN IT OPENS!

FINALLY...
THE TRAIL IS COMPLETED! NOW WE CAN ALL ENJOY A PEACEFUL BIKE RIDE INTO TOWN!
BY THE WAY, THE CITY WANTS TO KNOW IF YOU HAVE AN IDEA FOR A NAME!

HOW ABOUT THE SAME NAME AS OUR TRAIN THAT USED TO RIDE IT BACK IN THE DAY...
...THE RIVERDALE EXPRESS!

FINALLY...
I CAN'T BELIEVE IT'S HERE! TOMORROW IS THE GRAND OPENING OF THE RIVERDALE EXPRESS!
I'M REALLY EXCITED ABOUT IT!
GRAND OPENING
POP'S

AND TO THINK WE OWE IT ALL TO YOU, CARROT-TOP!
HA! HA! NO!
PLEASE! REGGIE'S SAYING SOMETHING NICE... GO WITH IT!

AND SO...
WELL, IF IT ISN'T THE CITY COUNCIL!
WE CAME TO CHECK OUT THE GRAND OPENING, BUT NO ONE'S HERE!
GRAND OPENING! RIVERDALE EXPRESS

I KNEW IT WAS A BOONDOGGLE!
OH, NO! IT'S NOT! LISTEN UP!
CHOO CHOO CHOO CHOO CHOO!

CHOO CHOO CHOO CHOO!
WHAT'S THAT?
THE SOUND OF SOME HAPPY BIKERS!

THEY DECIDED TO DO THE FIRST RUN AT THE SAME TIME THE OLD RIVERDALE EXPRESS USED TO!
CHOO CHOO!
AMAZING! I DIDN'T REALIZE THERE WERE SO MANY BIKERS IN THE AREA!

AND NOW WE'RE ALL HEADED DOWNTOWN WHERE WE'LL PROBABLY SHOP AND VISIT RESTAURANTS!
I LIKE THAT! WE SHOULD HAVE LISTENED TO YOU KIDS FROM THE START!

ARCHIE, SINCE THIS WAS YOUR IDEA, WE WANT YOU TO LEAD THE CROWD FROM HERE!
IT WOULD BE AN HONOR! YUK! YUK!

ARCHIE, THIS WAS YOUR IDEA? YOU'RE A GENIUS!
HOW CAN WE EVER THANK YOU?
?!
HEY, ARCH!

I WANT TO RIDE BESIDE HIM!
SO DO I!
ME, TOO!

LET'S ROCK!!
IT LOOKS LIKE WE'RE GOING TO HAVE TO FALL BACK NOW THAT ARCHIE'S SO POPULAR!

SOON...
WHAT AN AWESOME TRAIL!
...AND HERE WE ARE IN RIVERDALE!
I WANT TO RIDE IT EVERY DAY WITH YOU, ARCHIE!

THAT DOES IT!!
WE'VE GOT TO DO SOMETHING ABOUT THIS!
YOU BET!

Hmm!
MIKE'S BIKES

SOON...
ARCHIE, WE'RE SO PROUD OF YOUR ACCOMPLISHMENT, WE GOT YOU A GIFT!
OH, GIRLS! YOU DIDN'T NEED TO DO THAT!
IT'S A NEW BIKE...!
WHOA!! AND THEN SOME!
YES! A BICYCLE BUILT FOR THREE!
BUT WHY?
?
SO WE CAN RIDE THE RIVERDALE EXPRESS TOGETHER!
WON'T THAT BE SWEET?!
AND SO...
HI, ARCHIE!
NO! NO! ARCHIE, KEEP THOSE EYES ON THE ROAD!
YES, SAFETY FIRST! DON'T LOOK ON THE OTHER SIDE, EITHER!
AND THAT'S THE END!

Veronica in "Dear Aunt Sadie"

I'M SORRY, MIDGE! LET'S NEVER FIGHT AGAIN!

OH, IT WAS ALL MY FAULT, MOOSIE! I KNOW YOU WERE UPSET BECAUSE YOU *LOVE* ME!

JA + HA

SCRIPT: GREG EHRBAR
PENCILS: DAN PARENT
INKS: JIM AMASH

D-DUH, YEAH! WHO TOLD YA?
LET'S JUST SAY I WOKE UP AND SMELLED THE COFFEE!
BINGO! JUST LIKE I WROTE IT!

SCORE ANOTHER ONE FOR OL' "AUNT SADIE"!
VERONICA, HOW IS THAT ADVICE COLUMN FOR RIVER-DALE'S BLUE & GOLD COMING ALONG?

OH, SWIMMINGLY, MISS GRUNDY! THANK YOU FOR THE ASSIGNMENT! I MAY HAVE FOUND MY TRUE CALLING IN LIFE!
REALLY?

ABSOLUTELY! NO ONE IS MORE OF A "PEOPLE PERSON" THAN I! BESIDES, AS A LODGE, I CAN UNDERSTAND THE INNER WORKINGS OF MINDS FAR LESS SUPERIOR TO MY OWN!
HOW COMPAS-SIONATE OF YOU!

WELL, HERE ARE THE LATEST LOVE-LORN QUESTS FOR "AUNT SADIE'S" WIS-DOM! YOU CAN WORK ON THEM DURING THE NEXT STUDY PERIOD!
OOH! GOBS OF LIVES TO IMPROVE! I CAN'T WAIT!
FWIP!

SEVERAL LETTERS LATER...
"DEAR AUNT SADIE... THE BOY I LIKED CANCELLED OUR DATE FOR THE TENTH TIME TO GO OUT WITH MY BEST FRIEND! SHOULD I GIVE UP? SIGNED, FAIR-HAIRED GIRL!"

" DEAR FAIR-HAIRED GIRL... DON'T GIVE UP! NEXT TIME, NIP IT IN THE BUD! TURN HIM DOWN!"

HEY, RON! THAT NEW TOM FRANKS MOVIE OPENS TONIGHT! WANNA SEE IT?
ACTUALLY, ARCHIE, I HAVE SOME, UH... CORRESPONDENCE TO ANSWER TONIGHT...
WHADDAYA SAY, BETS? THIS MOVIE'S GETTING GOOD BUZZ!
EH, NO, ARCHIE! AND I'M NOT GOING TO THE ZOO WITH YOU SUNDAY, EITHER, THANK YOU!
B-BUT, BETTY! I THOUGHT YOU LIKED TOM FRANKS?
WHAT I DON'T LIKE, MR. ANDREWS, ARE ALL THE DATES YOU HAVE BROKEN! I'M GOING TO NIP THIS IN THE BUD!
GASP!
GOSH! I'M SORRY, BETTY! PLEASE RECONSIDER! I'LL EVEN TAKE YOU TO THE DANCE SATURDAY!
HOLD IT, JOCKO! THAT'S MY DATE YOU'RE TOSSING AROUND...
...LIKE SOME KOOSH BALL!

I KNOW, RON, BUT I REALLY OWE IT TO BETTY! BESIDES, YOU HAVE ALL THAT CORRESPONDENCE TO DO!
OH, INDEED I DO! AND THERE'S ONE IN PARTICULAR THAT I MUST ATTEND TO RIGHT AWAY!
3

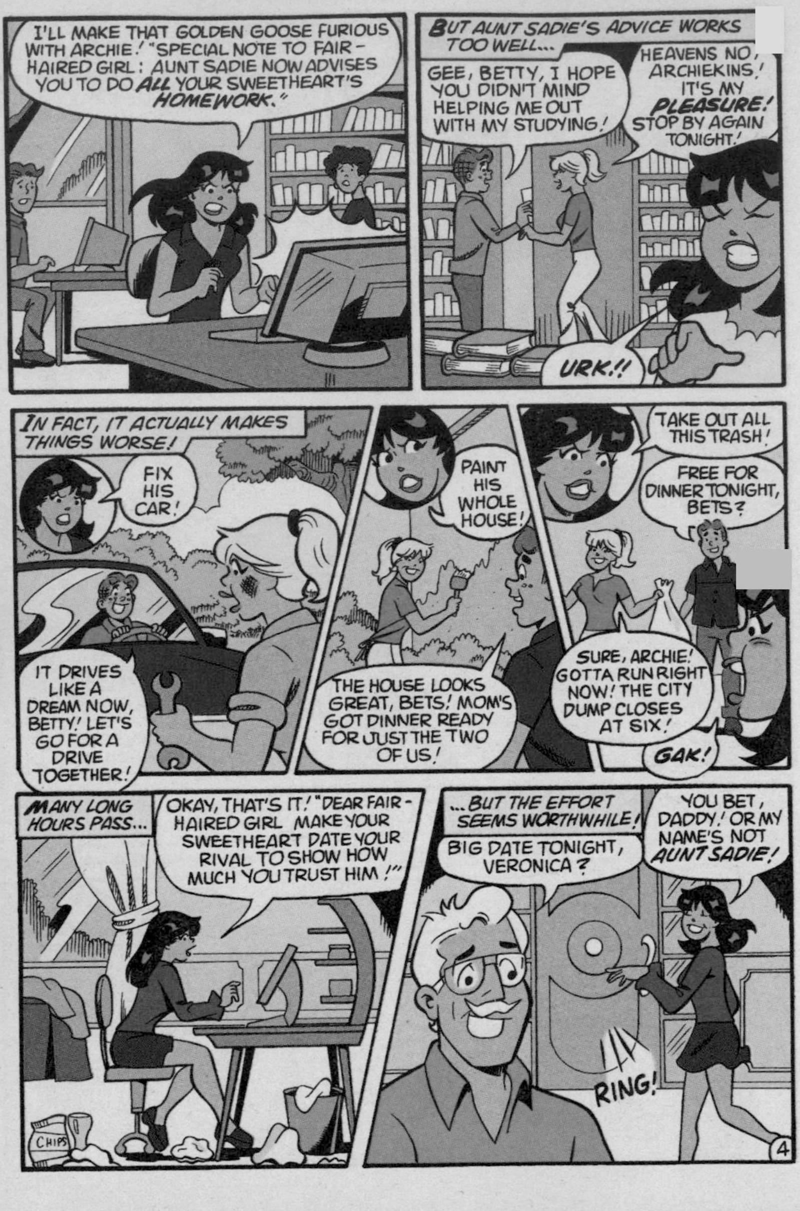

I'LL MAKE THAT GOLDEN GOOSE FURIOUS WITH ARCHIE! "SPECIAL NOTE TO FAIR-HAIRED GIRL: AUNT SADIE NOW ADVISES YOU TO DO **ALL** YOUR SWEETHEART'S **HOMEWORK**."

BUT AUNT SADIE'S ADVICE WORKS TOO WELL...

GEE, BETTY, I HOPE YOU DIDN'T MIND HELPING ME OUT WITH MY STUDYING!

HEAVENS NO, ARCHIEKINS! IT'S MY **PLEASURE!** STOP BY AGAIN TONIGHT!

URK!!

IN FACT, IT ACTUALLY MAKES THINGS WORSE!

FIX HIS CAR!

IT DRIVES LIKE A DREAM NOW, BETTY! LET'S GO FOR A DRIVE TOGETHER!

PAINT HIS WHOLE HOUSE!

THE HOUSE LOOKS GREAT, BETS! MOM'S GOT DINNER READY FOR JUST THE TWO OF US!

TAKE OUT ALL THIS TRASH!

FREE FOR DINNER TONIGHT, BETS?

SURE, ARCHIE! GOTTA RUN RIGHT NOW! THE CITY DUMP CLOSES AT SIX!

GAK!

(GASP) JUGHEAD! WHAT ARE YOU DOING HERE?
ARCHIE PAID ME **FIVE BUCKS** TO TAKE HIS PLACE! WANNA SPEND IT ON SOME PIZZA AT POP'S?
AREN'T YOU GONNA EAT ANY? IF NOT, GIVE ME YOUR SHARE!
TAKE THE WHOLE THING FOR ALL I CARE!
BOY, YOU SURE ARE ACTING WEIRD LATELY! MAYBE YOU SHOULD WRITE TO THIS AUNT SADIE LADY!
THAT'S IT! QUICK! FINISH STUFFING YOUR FACE AND TAKE ME TO THE NEAREST WORD PROCESSOR!
"DEAR RAVISHING RONNIE: THE BEST THING FOR FRIENDS TO DO IS TALK ABOUT WHAT'S BOTHERING THEM! TELL YOUR FRIEND THE **TRUTH!**"
HEY! YOU MEAN **YOU'RE** AUNT SADIE? I DIDN'T THINK YOU HAD IT IN YOU!
THANK YOU SO MUCH, JUGHEAD JONES! YOU DIDN'T THINK I HAD THE CAPACITY TO HELP OTHERS? EXCUSE ME, WHILE I FIND ARCHIE AND BETTY TO TELL THEM THE **TRUTH!**
YOU WON'T HAVE TO LOOK FAR! THEY'RE JUST CHECKING OUT SOME BOOKS OVER THERE!
5

ULP! RONNIE! HOW'S THE "CORRESPONDENCE" COMING?
I HAVE SOMETHING TO TELL YOU TWO! I'VE BEEN TRYING TO SEND YOU BAD ADVICE! YOU SEE, I'M, I'M-
IT'S OKAY, RON! WE KNOW YOU'RE AUNT SADIE!
YOU DO? WHAT BLABBERMOUTH TOLD YOU?
THIS BLABBER-MOUTH!
GASP! MISS GRUNDY!
YOU WERE USING THE SCHOOL PAPER FOR PERSONAL GAIN! BETTY AND ARCHIE TALKED ME OUT OF GIVING YOU DETENTION BY MAKING YOUR CRAZY ADVICE WORK!
SORRY, RON! IT MUST'VE DRIVEN YOU NUTS
MORE THAN USUAL, THAT IS!
I'M SO SORRY, BOTH OF YOU! I GUESS I'M OUT OF THE ADVICE BUSINESS NOW!
NOT AT ALL! I'VE BEEN CARRYING AROUND THE VERY THING TO GET YOU REINSTATED AS AUNT SADIE!
JUST PAINT MY HOUSE!
END

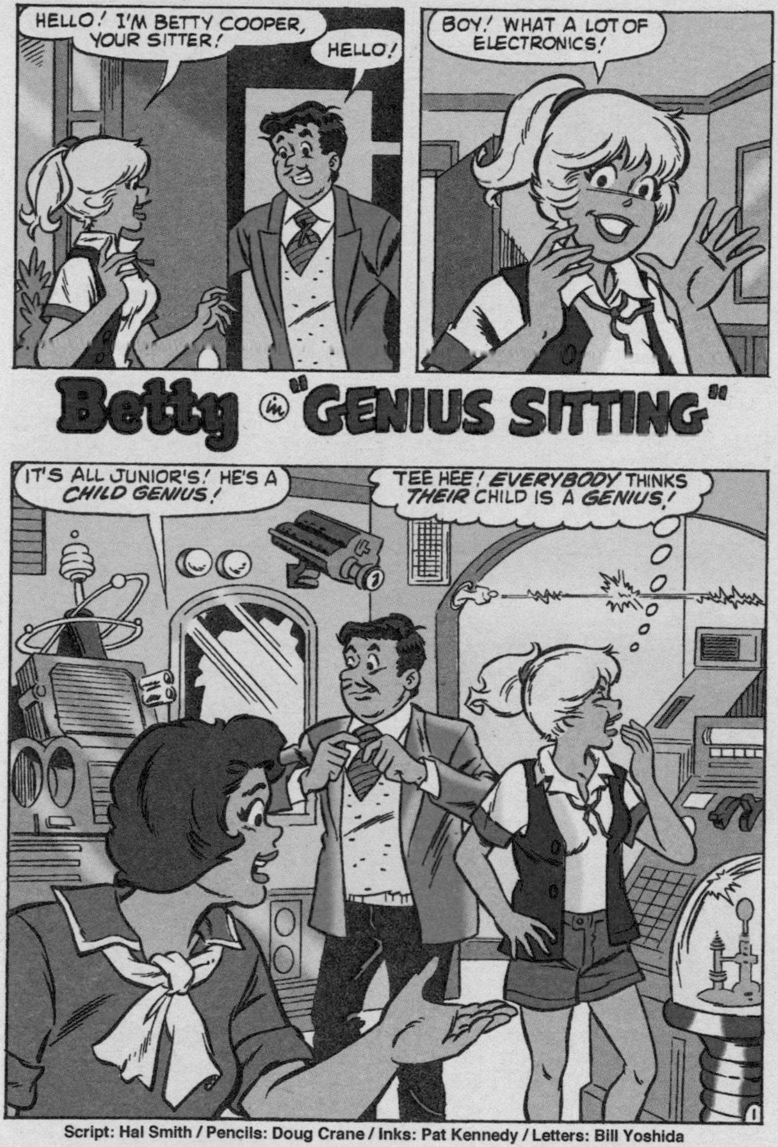

Betty in "GENIUS SITTING"

IT'S ALL JUNIOR'S! HE'S A *CHILD GENIUS*!

TEE HEE! *EVERYBODY* THINKS *THEIR* CHILD IS A *GENIUS*!

1

Script: Hal Smith / Pencils: Doug Crane / Inks: Pat Kennedy / Letters: Bill Yoshida

HELLO! YOU MUST BE JUNIOR!
A REASONABLE ASSUMPTION!

I'M BETTY! WHAT WOULD YOU LIKE TO DO?

COMPLETE THE EQUATION FOR CIRCUMNAVIGATING THE UNIVERSE!

(TEE-HEE!) THAT'S CUTE!

LATER...
IT'S BEDTIME, JUNIOR!
IN A MINUTE! I'M NOT FINISHED WITH MY COMPUTATIONS...

FINISH IT TOMORROW, JUNIOR! IT'S BEDTIME!
NO WAY!
2

EEEEEEEEEK!!
THIS IS MY ANTI-GRAV DEVICE!

GET ME DOWN!
OKAY!

WHOOOSH!
WHUMP!

WHY, YOU... OWW!
BLAM!!

AN INVISIBLE WALL?
A FORCE FIELD!

ROBOT! PROTECT!
BLIP!
BLIP!

THIS IS RIDICULOUS!
PROTECT... PROTECT...
BLIP!

HOW DO YOU COPE WITH A GENIUS?
PROTECT... PROTECT...
BLIP!

WHY, WITH ANOTHER GENIUS, OF COURSE!

I NEED HELP, DILTON!
IT'S AN INTERESTING CHALLENGE, BETTY! I'LL BE RIGHT OVER!

I THINK I'VE NEUTRALIZED THE FORCE FIELD...

AND NOW TO OVERRIDE THE ROBOT'S COMMANDS...

HEY! WHAT...?!
I'VE GOT MY OWN GENIUS!

I'LL PUT HIM TO BED, BETTY!

I WONDER HOW DILTON IS DOING! IT'S BEEN A HALF-HOUR!

JUNIOR? DILTON? WHERE ARE YOU?
IN HERE!

DILTON! IT'S PAST JUNIOR'S BEDTIME!
IN A MINUTE...

WE'RE CLOSE TO A BREAKTHROUGH IN ARTIFICIAL INTELLIGENCE!
!
END

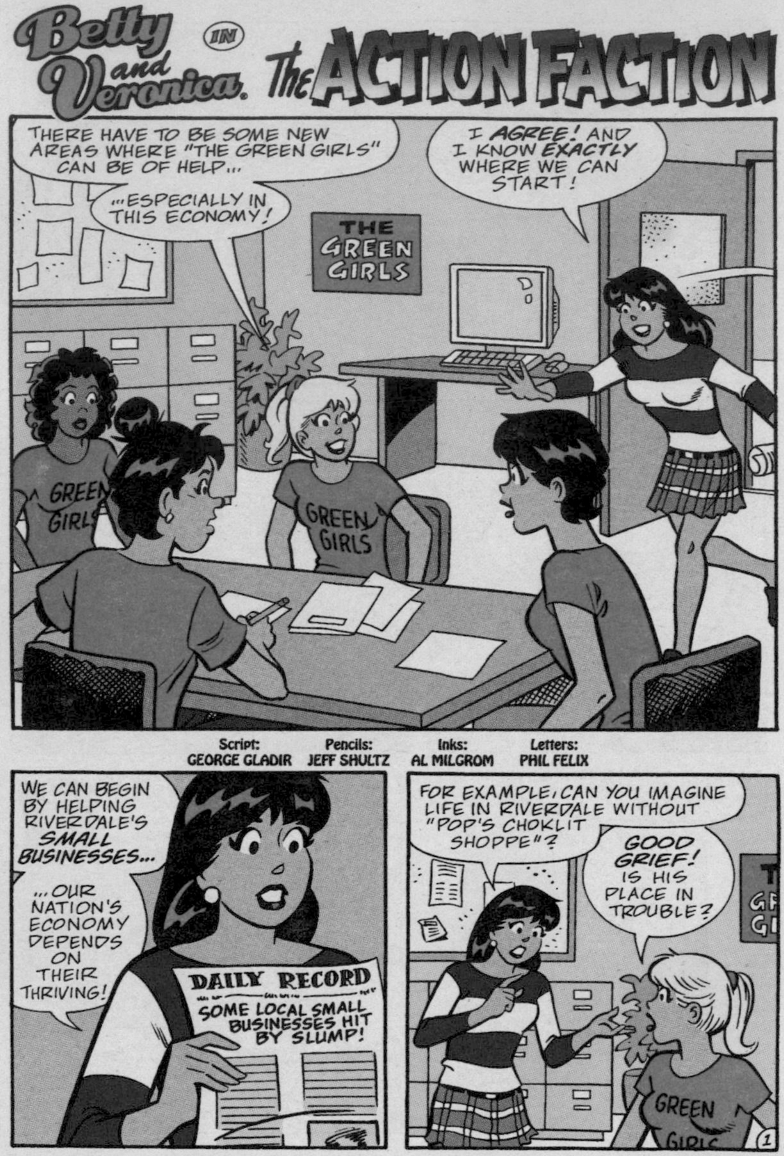

Betty and Veronica in The ACTION FACTION

THERE HAVE TO BE SOME NEW AREAS WHERE "THE GREEN GIRLS" CAN BE OF HELP...

...ESPECIALLY IN THIS ECONOMY!

I AGREE! AND I KNOW EXACTLY WHERE WE CAN START!

THE GREEN GIRLS

Script: GEORGE GLADIR Pencils: JEFF SHULTZ Inks: AL MILGROM Letters: PHIL FELIX

I CERTAINLY HOPE NOT!
WE'D HAVE TO MEET IN THE PARK TO DISCUSS THE LATEST GOSSIP!
WOW! I CAN JUST IMAGINE US MEETING IN THE PARK...
GREEN GIRLS

IT'S STARTING TO DRIZZLE!
LET'S HOPE IT DOESN'T RAIN!
HE SAYS HE'S OUT OF EVERY-THING EXCEPT MAPLE WALNUT!
I *HATE* MAPLE WALNUT!
ICE CREAM
BOY! DO I MISS HAVING POP'S LARGE SELECTION OF GOODIES!

GIRLS! *STOP WHINING!* WE HAVE TO THINK *POSITIVE!*
IF POP'S IS REALLY IN TROUBLE, WE HAVE TO FIGURE SOME WAY OF HELPING HIM!
SLAM!

AND WE'LL NEVER FIND OUT BY JUST GABBING AWAY HERE!
WE HAVE TO GO AND CHECK OUT THE STORE FOR OURSELVES!

OH, DEAR! LOOK AT THE MOB SCENE IN FRONT OF POP'S!
I HOPE THEY AREN'T CREDITORS FORCING HIM TO FORECLOSE!
POP'S

PLEASE LET US THROUGH! WE'RE FRIENDS OF THE OWNER!
AREN'T WE ALL?

GIRLS, YOU'LL HAVE TO WAIT YOUR TURN! THERE'S AT LEAST A FIFTEEN MINUTE WAIT FOR A TABLE!
GREEN GIRLS

YOU MEAN-- POP'S IS DOING OKAY?
THAT'S WHY I WAS HIRED!
HIS BUSINESS HAS NEVER BEEN BETTER!

LET THE GIRLS IN, TOM! THEY'RE MY REGULAR CUSTOMERS!
I ALWAYS KEEP A SPECIAL TABLE IN RESERVE JUST FOR THEM!

WHEW! IT'S SUCH A RELIEF TO FIND OUT YOUR STORE IS DOING SO WELL!
AND WHY SHOULDN'T WE BE?

THE HUGE PROMO WE HAD A YEAR AGO CELEBRATING THIS STORE'S CENTENNIAL STILL BRINGS IN NEW CUSTOMERS... MANY FROM OUTLYING TOWNS!
POP'S

AND THAT SIGN ALSO HELPS BRING IN PEOPLE BY THE DROVES!
GO GREEN!
NOTHING BUT ONE OF POP'S DOUBLE BURGERS WILL DO!
DOUBLE BURGER
EVERYONE FOR MILES AROUND KNOWS ABOUT JUGHEAD'S INSATIABLE BUT DISCRIMINATING APPETITE!

ETHEL'S RECIPE FOR VEGGIE BURGERS MAKES FOR ANOTHER YUMMY ATTRACTION!
AND LIQUADO, THAT FRUIT DRINK I INTRODUCED, IS ALSO A HUGE FAVORITE HERE!
GO GREEN!
SPECIAL

SIGH! I SOMETIMES WISH OUR BUSINESS WASN'T QUITE SO BUSY... JUST KIDDING, OF COURSE!

BY THE WAY, VERONICA, HOW ARE THINGS AT YOUR DAD'S MALL?
I HEAR THERE ARE A FEW STORES THERE THAT MIGHT BE HAVING PROBLEMS!
GREEN GIRLS

MY FATHER'S MALL? GEE, I DON'T KNOW...
...I'LL HAVE TO ASK HIM!
SODA $1.25

COME TO THINK OF IT, I DO RECALL DADDY SAYING A FEW PLACES WEREN'T DOING WELL!

WE COULD HELP THE TROUBLED STORES BY PASSING ON THE WORD ABOUT THEIR SALES...
...AND WE COULD VOLUNTEER TO HELP UNTIL THINGS GOT BETTER!
POP'S

AND ALSO GET CAROL NORITA TO DO HER CARTOON BUSINESS SIGNS AT REDUCED RATES!
I'M SURE THERE ARE DOZENS OF WAYS WE CAN HELP SMALL BUSINESSES IN OUR COMMUNITY!
GREEN

GEE, POP! THOSE GIRLS WERE SORTA DOWN WHEN THEY FIRST CAME IN... AND NOW THEY ALL LOOK SO PLEASED!
AND WHY WOULDN'T THEY BE, TOM?
GREEN GIRLS

MY SPECIAL SODAS AND DESSERTS HAVE THAT EFFECT ON EVERYBODY!

WE HAVE TO LEAVE, POP!
OH, AND MUCHO THANKS FOR ALL THAT IMPORTANT INFO YOU GAVE US ON THE MALL!
IMPORTANT INFO ABOUT THE MALL?
GREEN GIRLS

NOW WHAT WAS SHE TALKING ABOUT?
OH, MAN! HERE COMES ANOTHER BIG CROWD!
WHEW! DOESN'T IT EVER LET UP AROUND HERE?
Menu
END

DEAR DIARY, VERONICA AND I FOUGHT OVER ARCHIE AGAIN TODAY...
POP'S

POP'S

...I DON'T LIKE TO, AND IT'S BEGINNING TO MAKE ME WONDER...

Betty's Diary
LIFE WITHOUT ARCHIE!

...WHAT WOULD LIFE BE LIKE...

...IF THERE WASN'T AN ARCHIE ANDREWS TO FIGHT OVER ?!

LE

1

Script: Kathleen Webb / Pencils: Bob Bolling / Inks: Mike Esposito / Letters: Rod Ollerenshaw

WHAT IF ARCHIE HAD NEVER BEEN BORN... OR LIVED SOME-WHERE ELSE?

WOULD VERONICA AND I BE BETTER FRIENDS?!

...OR WOULD WE FIND SOME OTHER BOY TO FIGHT OVER? ...LIKE REGGIE, PERHAPS?!

STATE CHAMP
...AND HOW WOULD REGGIE BE AFFECTED BY ARCHIE'S ABSENCE?

WHO WOULD HE HAVE TO PLAY TRICKS ON THEN?

...CERTAINLY NOT MOOSE!!

AND AS FOR SCHOOL... MR. WEATHERBEE COULD RETIRE EARLY!

...AND MISS GRUNDY MIGHT NOT BE QUITE SO STERN AND SEVERE...
...AND THE NEIGHBOR'S DOG ATE ALL MY HOMEWORK!
THERE, THERE... NO PROBLEM! YOU CAN'T HELP HIS APPETITE!
NO HOMEWORK TODAY

I CAN'T IMAGINE WHAT WOULD HAPPEN TO JUGHEAD...

HE MIGHT NOT HAVE ANY FRIENDS!

WITHOUT ARCHIE STANDING LOYALLY BESIDE JUGGIE...
JUGHEAD'S APPETITE AND INDIFFERENCE TOWARDS WOMEN WOULD MAKE HIM A TOTAL OUTCAST!!

OF COURSE, NOT EVERY-BODY WOULD MISS ARCHIE...
WITHOUT ARCHIE'S TAB, POP TATE COULD PAY HIS BILLS ON TIME...
DAILY BUDGET
BALANCED

...AND AS FOR MR. LODGE'S NERVES...

WHY... HE COULD HAVE ALL THE FINE CHINA AND ANTIQUE FURNITURE HE WANTED...

...WITHOUT ARCHIE AROUND TO BREAK IT!

NOT TO MENTION ALL THE OTHER DAMAGE ARCHIE COSTS HIM!
RRIP!

AS FOR ME, DEAR DIARY, I CAN'T IMAGINE NOT HAVING ARCHIE IN MY LIFE...
TRIP!
FOR ALL HIS FAULTS, I'D RATHER HAVE HIM AROUND THAN NOT...

...EVEN THOUGH HE CAUSES ME TO FIGHT WITH MY BEST FRIEND...AND EVEN THOUGH HE SOMETIMES BREAKS MY HEART...

GUESS WHO?
!
EVEN THOUGH HE IS A RED-HEADED, FRECKLE-FACED TROUBLE MAKER ...

...THE TROUBLE ARCHIE ANDREWS MAKES IS THE NICEST KIND!!
I KNEW IT ALL ALONG!
?
5 END

Archie
"DESERT SAGA"
PART 1
OH, DADDY! YOUR FRIEND'S HOME IS LIKE A DESERT DREAM!
YES, MY OLD PAL, LES NIKK, HAS QUITE A MANSION!
NIKK
SCRIPT: GEORGE GLADIR
PENCILLING: STAN GOLDBERG
INKING: BOB SMITH
LETTERING: BILL YOSHIDA
HIRAM! YOU OL' HORNSWAGGLER!
LES! IT'S BEEN SO LONG!
AND THIS IS MY DAUGHTER VERONICA AND HER TWO FRIENDS, ARCHIE AND BETTY!
PLEASED TO MEET YOU ALL!

WELCOME TO MY LITTLE SPREAD!
"LITTLE"? GOSH! IT'S MORE LIKE A ROYAL PALACE, MR. NIKK!

OHMIGOODNESS! LOOK AT THE DISPLAYS OF JEWELRY!
AS A DIAMOND DEALER, I LIKE TO HAVE A FEW AROUND FOR SHOW!

WHENEVER I SEE DIAMONDS, MY EYES LIGHT UP!
AND HER FATHER'S WALLET GETS NERVOUS PALPITATIONS!

WHICH ARE THE MOST VALUABLE GEMS HERE, MR. NIKK?

THAT'S EASY TO ANSWER!
THE MOST VALUABLE GEMS ARE THE TWO GIRLS WHO JUST ARRIVED!
MEET MORTY, MY SHIFTLESS NEPHEW!
WATCH OUT FOR HIS SLICK LINE OF GAB, LADIES!
HI, MORTY!
2

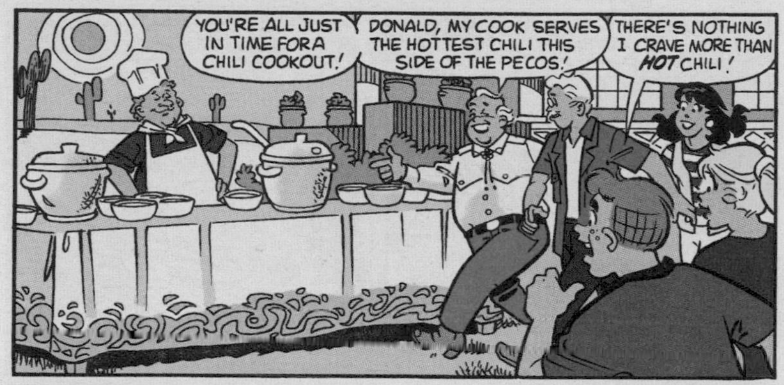

YOU'RE ALL JUST IN TIME FOR A CHILI COOKOUT!
DONALD, MY COOK SERVES THE HOTTEST CHILI THIS SIDE OF THE PECOS!
THERE'S NOTHING I CRAVE MORE THAN HOT CHILI!

I'LL TAKE MINE AS HOT AS YOU CAN MAKE IT, DONALD!
YOU GOT IT!

OH, BOY! THIS IS SIMPLY...

EEEAGHH!!

GLUB! GLUB! GLUB!
3

HEH! HEH! NOBODY MAKES CHILI LIKE MY OL' SCHOOL CHUM DON!
GASP!

WHILE HIRAM AND I DISCUSS BUSINESS, WHY NOT SHOW THE GANG THE LOCAL COWBOY MUSEUM?
GOOD IDEA, UNC!

YOUR UNCLE OWNS QUITE A COLLECTION OF DIAMONDS!
WOULDN'T MIND GETTING MY MITTS ON SOME OF IT MYSELF!

YOU'RE IN LUCK! AFTER TODAY WE'RE CLOSING FOR ALTERATIONS!
COWBOY MUSEUM
INFORMATI

THIS MUSEUM HAS THE FINEST COLLECTION OF COSTUMES WORN BY MOVIE AND TV COWBOYS!...
OUTFIT WORN BY BUZZ BANCROFT FOR TV SERIES "SIX SHOOTE

...INCLUDING AN AUTOMATED REPLICA OF BUCK SADDLESORE, THE WEST'S FAMOUS GUN-SLINGER!
4

WATCH WHAT HAPPENS WHEN I PRESS THIS BUTTON...

...OL' BUCK SHOWS YOU HOW HE SLAPS LEATHER!

UH, WE BETTER BE HEADING BACK! UNCLE LES HAS A WESTERN PARTY PLANNED FOR TONIGHT!
COWBOY MUSEUM
INFORMATION

BUT, MORTY, WE DIDN'T BRING ANY WESTERN CLOTHES WITH US!
NO PROBLEM! WE HAVE CLOSETS FULL OF WESTERN DUDS!

WELL, HOW DO I LOOK, PARTNER?
LIKE KITTY CARSON HERSELF!

ARCHIE! HOW ARE YOU DOING?
COME IN AND SEE FOR YOURSELF!
RAP! RAP! RAP!

THIS WAS THE ONLY OUTFIT THEY HAD ANYWHERE NEAR MY SIZE!

THIS IS GOING TO BE SUCH FUN!
PROVIDING I DON'T TRIP OVER MY CHAPS!

MR. NIKK, IS THIS SUPPOSED TO BE A MASQUERADE?
NO, ARCHIE!

THEN WHY ARE THOSE TWO WEARING MASKS?
MAYBE THEY'RE DRESSED AS STAGECOACH ROBBERS! HA! HA!

EVERYBODY GET YOUR HANDS UP AND MOVE OVER TO THAT CORNER!
THIS IS A REAL HOLDUP!
KRRACK!
CONTINUED
6

"DESERT SAGA"
PART 2
THAT'S IT! GRAB EVERY-THING!!
NOBODY MAKE A MOVE FOR TEN MINUTES!
...IF YOU KNOW WHAT'S GOOD FOR YOU!

GOOD GRIEF! THE ALARM SYSTEM AND THE PHONES HAVE ALL BEEN DISCONNECTED!
S'OKAY! I'LL CALL THE POLICE ON MY CELL PHONE!
I WONDER IF THIS WAS AN INSIDE JOB!

WE GOT HERE AS SOON AS WE COULD, MR. NIKK!
POLICE

WE'VE GOT ALL THE ROADS BLOCKED, BUT THERE'S NO SIGN OF THEM!
WHERE COULD THEY HAVE DISAPPEARED TO?

YAWN! WHA HAPPENED?
YOUR UNCLE LES WAS JUST RIPPED OFF... BIG TIME!

WHERE'VE YOU BEEN ALL THIS TIME?
IN MY ROOM, I WASN'T FEELING WELL!
...DON'S CHILI! MUST'VE DID ME IN!

THAT'S ODD! HE SEEMED OKAY AT THE MUSEUM!
AND DID YOU NOTICE ONE OF THE MASKED BANDITS ALSO HAD RED HAIR?

DON'T WORRY! MR. NIKK! WE'LL NAB 'EM SOONER OR LATER!
I SURE HOPE IT'S SOONER!
POLICE

ARCHIE, I THINK I SEE THE WHEELS TURNING IN YOUR HEAD! WHAT'S UP?
PLENTY!
THE COSTUMES ON THOSE TWO ROBBERS LOOKED VERY FAMILIAR!

I'VE A HUNCH! WE'RE GOING BACK TO THE COWBOY MUSEUM!

SEE! THE COSTUMES ON THE STAGECOACH ROBBERS ARE MISSING!
...I WAS RIGHT! THEY MUST HAVE WORN THEM TO TONIGHT'S PARTY!

ALL RIGHT, EVERYONE! UP WITH YOUR HANDS!
CLICK!

IT'S... IT'S MORTY! ...MR. NIKK'S NEPHEW!

OH, IT'S ONLY YOU KIDS!
...I THOUGHT MAYBE THE THIEVES MIGHT BE OUT HERE!

MORTY... WATCH IT!!
MUSEUM HOURS

SLIM, TIE UP ALL THESE SNOOPERS!
WE'LL MAKE OUR GETAWAY IN THE MORNING!
HE'S STANDING NEAR THE AUTOMATED GUNSLINGER!
IF I CAN JUST PRESS THE AUTOMATION'S BUTTON...
CLICK!
REACH FOR THE SKY!
SPIN!
WHAT THE?
NOW'S MY CHANCE!
GET THE GUN, SLIM!
10

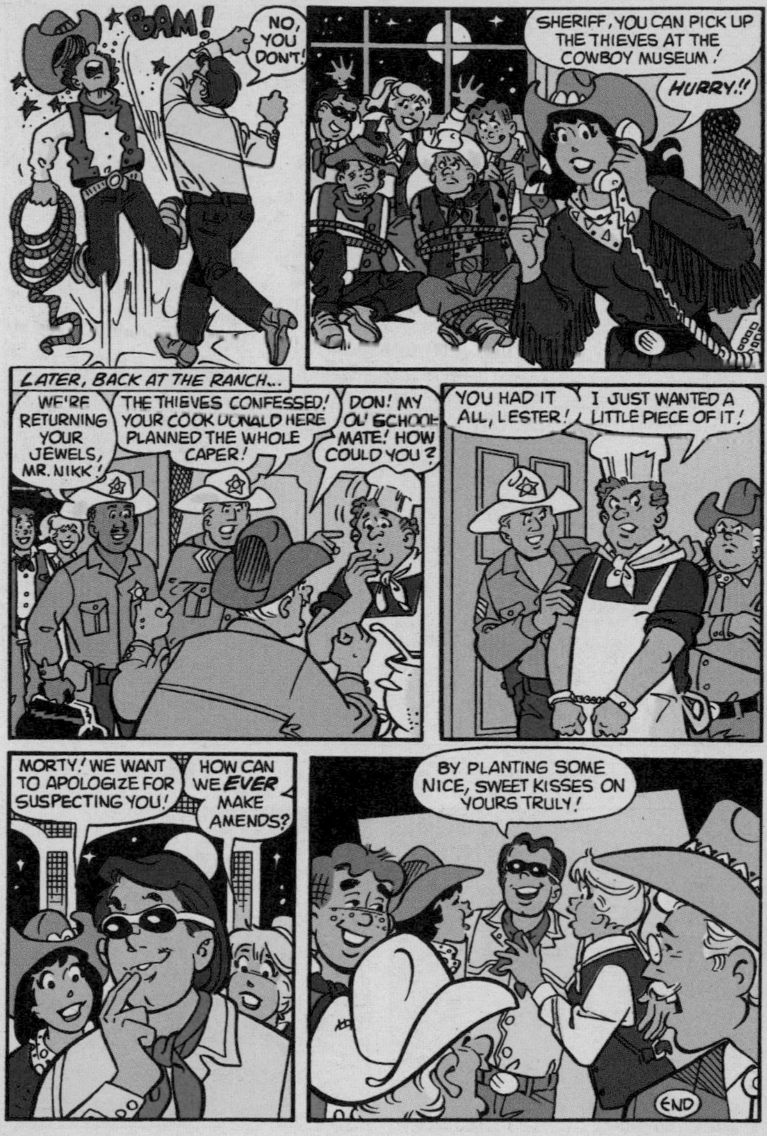

BAM!

NO, YOU DON'T!

SHERIFF, YOU CAN PICK UP THE THIEVES AT THE COWBOY MUSEUM!

HURRY!!

LATER, BACK AT THE RANCH...

WE'RE RETURNING YOUR JEWELS, MR. NIKK!

THE THIEVES CONFESSED! YOUR COOK DONALD HERE PLANNED THE WHOLE CAPER!

DON! MY OL' SCHOOL-MATE! HOW COULD YOU?

YOU HAD IT ALL, LESTER!

I JUST WANTED A LITTLE PIECE OF IT!

Archie in The PLOT THICKENS!

SCRIPT: MIKE PELLOWSKI
PENCILS: STAN GOLDBERG
INKS: BOB SMITH

SQUEAK

THERE'S AN OLD SAYING...THE BASIC PLOT OF LIFE'S STORY IS SIMPLE!
CHIRP
BUZZ BUZZ

IT STARTS WITH A BOY!

SOON A GIRL ENTERS THE PICTURE!
Puff! Puff!
SQUEAK
AND THEN...
SQUEAK
BONK!
BOY MEETS GIRL!
OOF!!
Whoa!! EXCUSE ME!!
BOY LOSES GIRL!
NO PROBLEM! IT WAS ALL MY FAULT! SORRY! BYE!
B-BYE!
GOSH! SHE SURE IS PRETTY! I'D REALLY LIKE TO GET TO KNOW HER!

AND THEN... THE PLOT THICKENS!
HEY! SHE DROPPED HER BRACELET!
YOO-HOO! WAIT! STOP! YOU LOST SOME-THING!!
Puff! Puff! MAYBE IF I CAN TAKE A SHORTCUT I CAN CATCH HER BEFORE SHE EXITS THE PARK!
TRIP
YEOW!
FLIP
Whoa!
oh!!
OUCH!
UGH!!

YUK!
SPLASH

WELL, AT LEAST I STILL HAVE THE BRACELET! I'M NOT GIVING UP YET!
SPLISH
SPLOSH
SPLOOSH

SQUEAK
SLOG
SQUEAK
SQUEAK
SLOG

SQUEAK
SQUEAK
SQUEAK

HEY! BEAT IT, YOU CRAZY SQUIRREL!! SCRAM!!
SQUEAK
CHIP CHIP
SQUEAK!

YES! I'M IN TIME! THERE SHE IS!!
EXIT

LIKE WE ALREADY SAID, THE BASIC PLOT OF THE STORY OF LIFE IS SIMPLE...
MISS, WAIT! YOU DROPPED THIS!

BOY LOSES GIRL, BOY FINDS GIRL!
OH! THAT'S MY FAVORITE BRACELET! THANKS EVER SO MUCH!

BOY MEETS GIRL!
MY NAME IS SARA JOHNSON! I'M NEW IN TOWN!
MY NAME IS ARCHIE ANDREWS!

GIRL LIKES BOY, ROMANCE BLOOMS!
CAN I REWARD YOU BY BUYING YOU LUNCH OR SOMETHING, ARCHIE?
LUNCH WOULD BE NICE, SARA, REAL NICE!

BUT WHEN YOU'RE ARCHIE ANDREWS, IT'S THE UNTOLD PARTS OF THE PLOT THAT ARE THE REAL STORY ... AND IT'S USUALLY A FUNNY STORY!
GOSH! YOU'RE SOAKING WET! WHAT HAPPENED?!
YOU WOULDN'T BELIEVE IT IF I TOLD YOU!
EXIT
THE END

HI, ARCHIE! *READY* TO GO TO THE *BEACH?*

YEAH! I JUST HAVE TO MAKE A FEW *STOPS!*

LOOK AT THIS *LINE!* I SHOULD HAVE MAILED THIS PACKAGE YESTERDAY!

WANTED

U.S. POST OFFIC
STAMPS · MONEY O

Archie in The HANDLE Waiter

1

SCRIPT: HAL SMITH PENCILS: FERNANDO RUIZ INKS: JIM AMASH LETTERS: BILL YOSHIDA

WE'VE ONLY GOT TWENTY MINUTES BEFORE THE BANK CLOSES!
U.S. POST OFFICE

IF I DIDN'T NEED TO CASH THIS $25 CHECK WE'D BE OUTTA HERE!
RIVERDALE FIRST NATIONAL

FINALLY, WE'RE ON OUR WAY!

THERE'LL BE A FIFTEEN MINUTE WAIT FOR PARKING!
BEACH PARKING LOT #3

I FEEL LIKE SOME ICE CREAM!
I'LL GO GET SOME!

LATER...
WHERE'S THE ICE CREAM?
THE LINE IS SIX MILES LONG!
2

WE'LL FIND A DRIVE-THRU WHERE WE CAN GET A BITE TO EAT!

THIS IS MORE LIKE A PARK-AND-WAIT-THRU!
BURGERS TO

LET'S GO TO THE AMUSEMENT PARK!
OKAY!

EVERY RIDE HAS A LONG LINE WAITING FOR IT!
RIDE THE SCREAME
1 HR WAIT FROM THIS POINT

I HAVE TO USE THE REST ROOM!

I HOPE YOU'RE NOT IN ANY PARTICULAR HURRY!
LADIES

THIS PLACE IS TOO CROWDED
LET'S GO TO A MOVIE!

OKAY, BUT, FIRST WE'LL HAVE TO STOP AND GET GAS!
PRIZES

BY THE TIME WE GET TO THE PUMP, CARS WILL BE POWERED BY NUCLEAR ENGINES!
GAS

WE'LL NEVER GET INTO THAT MOVIE!
ATTACK OF THE KILLER MOTHS
ATTACK OF THE

THE MALL IS TOO CROWDED, TOO!
RIVERDALE MALL

I'M SORRY THE DAY DIDN'T TURN OUT SO GOOD!
THAT'S OKAY, ARCHIE! IT WAS AN ADVENTURE!
4

HELLO, ARCHIE, HOW WAS YOUR DAY?
FRUSTRATING! EVERY PLACE YOU GO, THERE ARE LONG LINES!
I JUST WISH I COULD FIND ONE PLACE WHERE I WOULDN'T HAVE TO WAIT ON LINE!
I KNOW SOME PLACE THAT HAS IMMEDIATE ADMISSION! THERE'S NEVER A LONG LINE TO GET IN!
IT'S A PLACE WHERE YOU CAN PLAY VIDEO GAMES AND LISTEN TO CD'S!
ADMISSION IS FREE AND IT'S WITHIN WALKING DISTANCE!
OH, WOW, DAD! WHAT IS THIS PLACE?
YOUR ROOM! YOU PROMISED TO CLEAN IT UP, REMEMBER?
RIV
R
JINOS
5 THE END

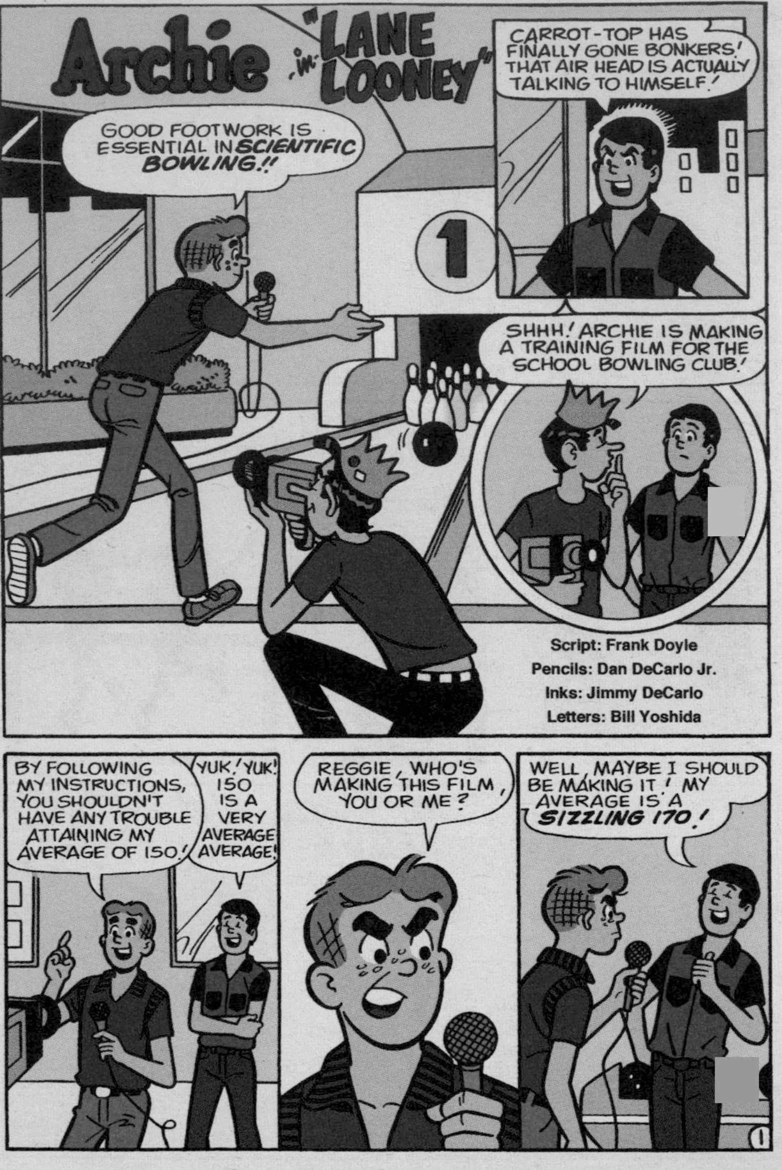

Archie in "LANE LOONEY"

GOOD FOOTWORK IS ESSENTIAL IN *SCIENTIFIC BOWLING!!*

CARROT-TOP HAS FINALLY GONE BONKERS! THAT AIR HEAD IS ACTUALLY TALKING TO HIMSELF!

SHHH! ARCHIE IS MAKING A TRAINING FILM FOR THE SCHOOL BOWLING CLUB!

1

Script: Frank Doyle

Pencils: Dan DeCarlo Jr.

Inks: Jimmy DeCarlo

Letters: Bill Yoshida

REG, BUZZ OFF!
WHAT'S WRONG? AREN'T TWO HEADS BETTER THAN ONE?

NOT IF ONE OF THOSE HEADS IS INFLATED TO THREE TIMES THE NORMAL SIZE!

DID YOU DEMONSTRATE THE FULL FINGER-TIP GRIP TO INCREASE THE HOOK OF THE BALL?

WELL, I'M GLAD TO SEE WE AGREE ON SOMETHING!
MAYBE WE CAN MAKE THIS TRAINING FILM TOGETHER!

CRASH
WHAT WAS THAT?

OOPS! I DROPPED THE BALL!
THOSE GABBY GISELDAS ARE GONNA RUIN OUR FILM WITH ALL THE NOISE THEY'RE GONNA MAKE!

AND LOOK AT THE WAY THEY'RE DOING EVERYTHING WRONG!
HMM! THAT GIVES ME ONE OF MY USUAL BRILLIANT IDEAS!

WHY DON'T WE FILM THEM AS THE PERFECT EXAMPLE OF HOW NOT TO BOWL?
RIGHT! ONLY WE DON'T LET ON WHAT WE'RE UP TO!

GIRLS, HOW'D YOU LIKE TO HELP US WITH A TRAINING FILM WE'RE SHOOTING?
WHAT DO WE HAVE TO DO?

NOTHING SPECIAL, JUST BOWL THE WAY... UH, YOU USUALLY DO!
FINE!

YOU'LL HAVE TO EXCUSE ME WHILE I FIX MY HAIR AND MAKE-UP!
ME, TOO!

THAT'S THE FIRST MISTAKE NOVICE BOWLERS MAKE! THEY'RE MORE CONCERNED WITH THEIR APPEARANCE THAN WITH THEIR BOWLING!

ALL RIGHT ARCHIE, WE'RE ALL SET!

THIS IS A PERFECT EXAMPLE OF WHAT NOT TO DO! HER APPROACH IS JERKY, AND SHE'S OFF BALANCE AS SHE DELIVERS THE BALL...

OH, LOOK... A STRIKE!

UH, THAT'S WHAT MAKES BOWLING SO FASCINATING! EVEN BAD BOWLERS CAN GET LUCKY ONCE IN AWHILE!

AND NOW LET US OBSERVE THE SCIENTIFIC BOWLER... NOTICE HOW CAREFULLY HE POSITIONS HIS BODY... HIS FEET... THE BALL...
... AS HE RELEASES THE BALL, OBSERVE HIS SMOOTH FOLLOW THROUGH!

POOR REGGIE! ONLY GOT THREE PINS!
1
2
TIC!

AGAIN WE HAVE ANOTHER PERFECT EXAMPLE OF HOW NOT TO BOWL... HER TIGHT CLOTHES... HER GRIP... EVERYTHING IS WRONG!

STRIKE
GULP!

MY PARTNER WILL NOW OFFER AN EXAMPLE OF SCIENTIFIC BOWLING AT ITS BEST!
NOTICE HOW HE CAREFULLY ALIGNS THE BALL WITH THE DOTS AND ARROWS ON HIS LANE!

RATS! ONE MISERABLE PIN...
PING!

LATER
WE CREAMED THE BOYS! WE AVERAGED 190 TO THEIR 150!
I GUESS THEY KNEW WHAT THEY WERE DOING WHEN THEY INVITED US TO MAKE THE FILM!

TA! TA! SEE YOU BOYS AT MY PARTY TONIGHT!

THIS VIDEO TAPE WE MADE IS WORTHLESS! WE MIGHT AS WELL THROW IT AWAY!
NO, DON'T DO THAT!
TRASH

I WANT TO STUDY IT!

WHO KNOWS, MAYBE I CAN LEARN TO BOWL 190 THE UNSCIENTIFIC WAY!
END

WAH!

ISN'T THAT TRUDY SMITH, THE THIRD GRADER WHO LIVES ON YOUR STREET?

YEAH! IT IS!

SHALLOW WATER! NO SWIMMING

Archie in JUMPING TO CONCLUSIONS!

SCRIPT: MIKE PELLOWSKI PENCILS: HOLLY G. INKS: RICH KOSLOWSKI
COLORS: FRANK GAGLIARDO LETTERS: BILL YOSHIDA

WHAT'S WRONG, TRUDY?
SOB! IT'S MY PET FROG, MR. HOPPY!

HE'S WAY OUT IN THE MIDDLE OF THE POND!
RIBBIT!

WAH! I RAISED HIM FROM A TINY TADPOLE!
THERE, THERE, TRUDY! DON'T CRY!

I CAN GUESS EXACTLY WHAT HAPPENED!
?
SNIFF!

"YOU WERE TAKING MR. HOPPY FOR A WALK WHEN HE HOPPED OUT OF THE BOWL AND JUMPED INTO THE LAKE..."
MR. HOPPY, NO!!
SPLISH!
RIBBIT!

...AND NOW YOU WANT HIM BACK!
YES! YES! I WANT HIM BACK!

SORRY, TRUDY! IT LOOKS LIKE MR. HOPPY IS GONE FOR GOOD!
WAH!

SOB! MR. HOPPY! PLEASE COME BACK! PLEASE!
HMMM...

WHAT DO YOU SAY, JUG? THE POND IS ONLY KNEE-DEEP!
GO IN AFTER A FROG? NO WAY!
SHALLOW WATER NO SWIMMING
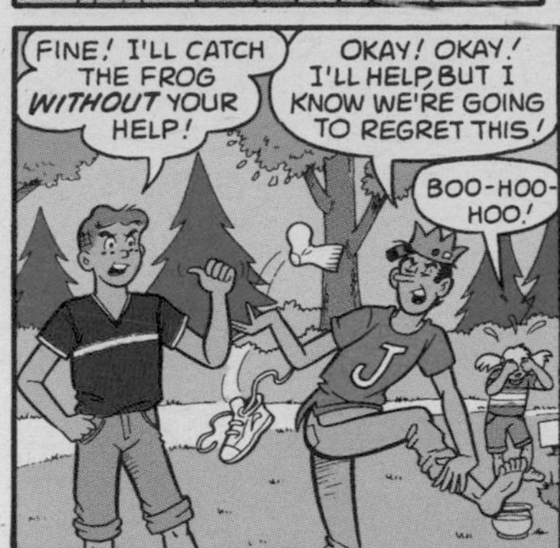
FINE! I'LL CATCH THE FROG WITHOUT YOUR HELP!
OKAY! OKAY! I'LL HELP, BUT I KNOW WE'RE GOING TO REGRET THIS!
BOO-HOO-HOO!

EEYUK! THE BOTTOM IS SLIMY!
SOB!
DON'T WORRY ABOUT THE SLIME! WORRY ABOUT SNAKES AND SNAPPING TURTLES!
SLOP!
SPLASH! SPLASH!

YIKES!!
RELAX! I'M KIDDING!

HEY! THERE'S THE FROG! LET'S GET HIM!
EASY! DON'T SCARE HIM!
RIBBIT!

YOU MISSED HIM, ARCH! HE'S GETTING AWAY!
OOF! UGH!
RIBBIT!
SPLAT!

QUICK! GRAB HIM, JUG!
COME BACK HERE, FROG!
SPL!SH!
HOP!
HIP!

UH-OH!
YEOW!!
CROAK!
SPLASH!

THIS WAY, JUG! AFTER HIM!
GRRRR!!
HOP!
HOP!

BE MAD LATER, JUG! HURRY! FOLLOW THAT FROG!
GASP!
SPLASH!
HIP!
HOP!

QUIET NOW! WE'VE GOT HIM SURROUNDED!
TAKE IT NICE AND SLOW!

GOTCHA!!
GOOD WORK, ARCH! LET'S GET HIM TO SHORE!
RIBBIT!
ZOOM!

WE'RE A MESS, BUT WE MADE TRUDY HAPPY!
HOORAY! HOORAY! YOU CAUGHT MR. HOPPY!
SPLASH!
SLOOSH!

HERE'S YOUR PET, TRUDY!
OH, THANK YOU SO MUCH, ARCHIE AND JUGHEAD!

ISN'T THAT SWEET!
I LOVE YOU SO MUCH, MR. HOPPY!

NOW, DON'T YOU FEEL GOOD?
MESSY, BUT GOOD, I GUESS!
SMACK!
5

HUH ? TRUDY! NO.!!
OKAY, MR. HOPPY! YOU'RE FREE!

T-TRUDY... W-WHY ? WHY DID YOU DO THAT ?
'BYE!
SHALLOW WATER NO SWIMMING
HIP!
HOP!

MY DAD SAID I HAVE TO LET MR. HOPPY GO NOW THAT HE'S GROWN! THAT'S WHY I CAME HERE!
WHAT!

BUT THEN, WHY DID YOU WANT US TO CATCH HIM ?
I DIDN'T GET A CHANCE TO KISS HIM GOODBYE!

UGH !!
I KNEW IT! I TOAD YOU WE'D REGRET THIS!
'BYE, GUYS! THANKS AGAIN FOR YOUR HELP!
BZZZZ!
RIBBIT!
SHALLOW WATER NO SWIMMING
END

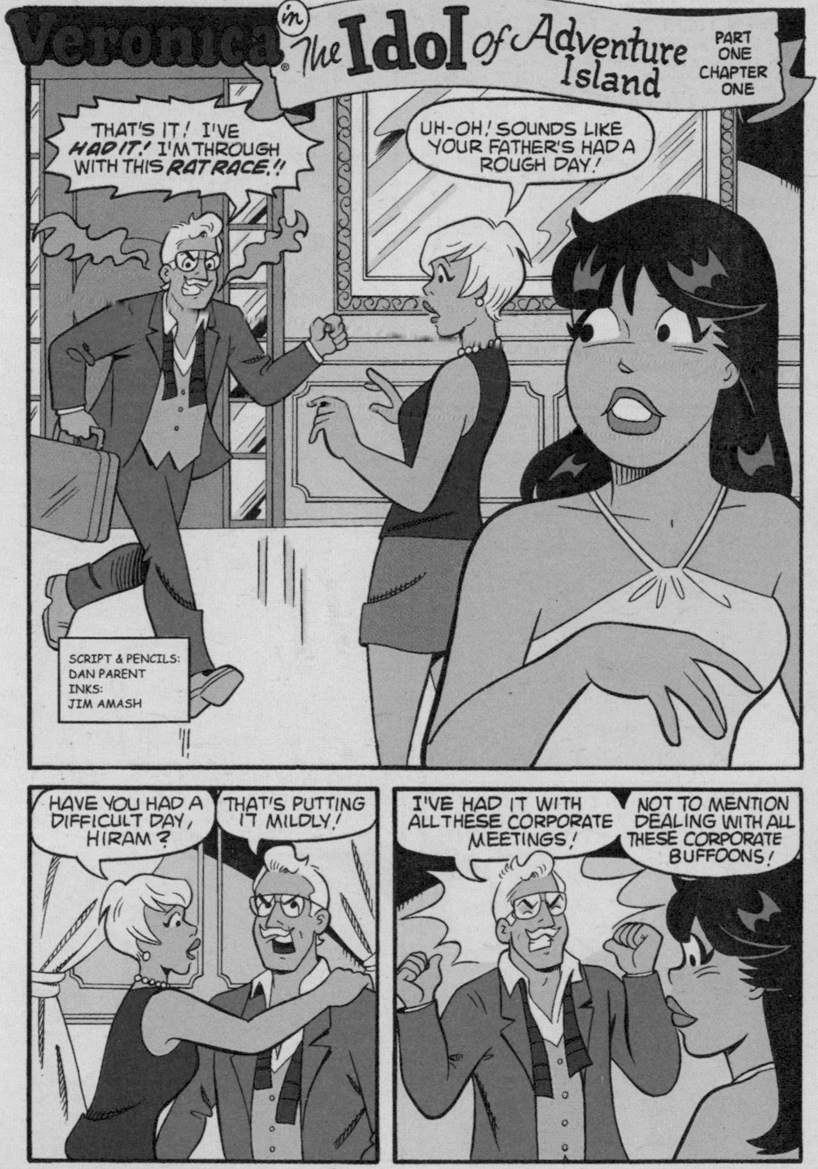

Veronica in The Idol of Adventure Island

PART ONE CHAPTER ONE

THAT'S IT! I'VE *HAD IT!* I'M THROUGH WITH THIS *RAT RACE!!*

UH-OH! SOUNDS LIKE YOUR FATHER'S HAD A ROUGH DAY!

SCRIPT & PENCILS: DAN PARENT
INKS: JIM AMASH

THEN I GET TO SIT IN TRAFFIC FOR AN HOUR!!
SIT DOWN, DEAR! WE'LL GET YOU A CUP OF TEA AND YOUR PAPER!!
THANKS! I...
RING!
OOPS! IT'S MY CELL PHONE!
WHAT? THE HELMSFORD MERGER DIDN'T GO THROUGH?
HE WANTS TO MEET WITH ME TONIGHT?
IN A WORD... NO!!
GEE, DADDY! WASN'T THAT AN IMPORTANT CALL?
MY SANITY IS MORE IMPORTANT!
THAT'S WHY WE'RE GETTING AWAY-- ALL OF US-- AS SOON AS POSSIBLE!
OOH!! WE'RE GOING ON VACATION!
2

CAN WE GO TO HAWAII ?
I'D LOVE TO VISIT THE SOUTH OF FRANCE!
FORGET IT!

I DON'T WANT TO GET STUCK IN SOME TOURIST TRAP!
WE'RE GOING TO JAVAKUMBA ISLAND!

WHERE IS THAT?
IT'S A REMOTE ISLAND I'M PLANNING TO DEVELOP, OFF THE AFRICAN COAST!

IT'S A BEAUTIFUL, RUSTIC ENVIRONMENT WITH WONDERFUL, ALBEIT VERY FEW, PEOPLE!

RUSTIC ? DOESN'T THAT MEAN "NO SHOPPING" AND "NO NIGHTLIFE"?!
YOU SAID IT!

COUNT ME OUT!
NO! WE'LL COUNT YOU IN!

WE COULD ALL USE A QUIET, PEACEFUL FAMILY GETAWAY!

THANKS, GIRLS! WE'LL LEAVE TOMORROW!

WHO KNOWS...

MAYBE WE'LL LIKE IT SO MUCH THAT WE'LL WANT TO ***LIVE*** THERE!

!

!

I HOPE HE'S KIDDING!

SO...
WOW!! WE'VE BEEN FLYING FOR HOURS! WHERE IS THIS ISLAND?

THERE IT IS.!! JUST LOOK AT IT ON THAT VIBRANT BLUE OCEAN!
WE'RE COMING IN FOR A LANDING!
GOOD! I'M READY FOR A MEAL, DADDY!
WE WILL HAVE HOT MEALS, WON'T WE?
OF COURSE! WE'RE STAYING IN A CABIN! THE TOWNSPEOPLE ARE GOING TO SUPPLY US WITH HOT MEALS!
WELL, THAT DOESN'T SOUND SO BAD!
HEY, WHERE ARE THE REST OF MY BAGS?!
WE "REORGANIZED" YOUR BAGS! WE ONLY HAVE ROOM FOR A FEW BAGS IN OUR SMALL CABIN!
WHAT? HOW WILL I SURVIVE ON ONLY ONE SUITCASE FULL OF CLOTHES?
LOOKS LIKE YOU'LL HAVE TO SURVIVE LIKE A NORMAL PERSON!
SHEESH!
5

SOON...
THIS IS OUR CABIN? IT'S MORE LIKE A SHED!
BUT LOOK AT THAT VIEW! IT'S SPECTACULAR!

BOING!!
YOU KNOW, I FINALLY AGREE WITH YOU ON SOMETHING!

OH, HI, EVAN! HE'S AN INHABITANT OF JAVAKUMBA! HE'S GOING TO BE OUR TOUR GUIDE!
AND I'VE BROUGHT YOU SOME FOOD!

AND WHO IS THIS?
THIS IS IMANA! SHE HELPS ME PREPARE YOUR MEALS! AND SHE'S A TOUR GUIDE, TOO!

HMMPH! LOOKS LIKE COMPETITION!
...OH, AND BY THE WAY, SHE'S MY SISTER!

IMANA! HOW NICE TO MEET YOU!

Veronica
in
"The IDOL of Adventure Island"
(PART ONE) CHAPTER TWO
SO, VERONICA! HOW DO YOU LIKE ADVENTURE ISLAND?
"ADVENTURE ISLAND"? I THOUGHT IT WAS CALLED JAVAKUMBA ISLAND!?
TECHNICALLY, YES! BUT ADVENTURE ISLAND IS WHAT WE'RE CALLED BY MANY PEOPLE!
THAT'S BECAUSE THE ISLAND IS A HAVEN TO ALL KINDS OF ACTIVITIES, LIKE HAND-GLIDING, MOUNTAIN CLIMB-ING, SPELUNKING...

OOH! THERE'S AN OLD CREEPY CAVE!!
SHALL WE EXPLORE IT?

THAT'S NOT A GOOD IDEA!
THERE ARE SOME CREEPY ARTIFACTS IN THOSE CAVES! SOME DANGEROUS, SOME RUMORED TO BE CURSED!

SOUNDS INTERESTING!
NOW, LET'S TAKE A TOUR OF THESE WATERFALLS!

SOON
I KNOW I'M NOT SUPPOSED TO, BUT I'VE GOT TO CHECK OUT THIS CAVE!

WOW! CHECK IT OUT! ALL KINDS OF OLD TRUNKS AND URNS!
I WONDER WHO STASHED THESE ITEMS HERE?

SOMETHING'S GLISTENING OVER THERE! I'LL JUST WHIP OUT THIS FLASHLIGHT AND...
8

WOW! SOME SORT OF JEWELED IDOL!!
THIS IS GORGEOUS!

I'VE GOT TO SHOW THIS TO EVAN AND IMANA!
THEY'LL PROBABLY KNOW WHAT IT IS!

SOON...
JUST A FEW HUNDRED YARDS TO OUR CABIN!
I'M EXHAUSTED! AND THIRSTY!

WOULD YOU LIKE SOME PINEAPPLE JUICE, YOUNG LADY?
SURE! THAT WOULD HIT THE SPOT!

(GASP!)
HEY, I KNOW I'M NOT LOOKING MY BEST, BUT I'VE BEEN HIKING...

NO! WHAT'S THAT?
IT'S AN OLD IDOL I FOUND IN A CAVE! COOL, HUH?

YOU MUST RETURN IT!! YOU COULD CURSE YOURSELF, AS WELL AS THIS WHOLE ISLAND!
NOW, NOW!! DON'T BE SO SUPERSTITIOUS!

I'M WARNING YOU!! RETURN IT WHILE YOU CAN!
ER-THANKS! I'LL THINK ABOUT IT, LADY!

ALMOST HOME!
OOPS!!
TRIP!

OUCH!! OOH! MY ANKLE! I THINK I TWISTED IT!
VERONICA! ARE YOU ALL RIGHT?

I HURT MY ANKLE!!
I'LL CALL THE ISLAND DOCTOR!
SO...
IT'S A SLIGHT SPRAIN! JUST REST IT FOR A FEW DAYS...
SHE SHOULD HAVE NO PROBLEM TAKING IT EASY!

LATER...
WHAT'S THAT CREAKING NOISE?
LOOK OUT!!
CRASH
THAT MIRROR ALMOST SLAMMED INTO YOU, DEAR!!
BOY! WE'VE HAD SOME BAD LUCK LATELY!! COULD IT BE THAT CURSED IDOL?
STOP IT, VERONICA! HOW COULD YOU BE SO SILLY?
VAGUE
A LITTLE BAD LUCK IS JUST A COINCIDENCE!
RUMBLE! RUMBLE!
HMM! WHY IS EVERYBODY RUNNING?
COOKACHEWA VOLCANO IS STARTING TO ERUPT!!
WHAT?!
LOOK WHAT YOU'VE DONE, YOU STUPID IDOL!
CONTINUED...

Veronica in
The Idol of Adventure Island
PART 2 CHAPTER 3
HERE'S A RE-CAP FROM THE FIRST PART OF "THE IDOL OF ADVENTURE ISLAND", PART 1...
"MY FATHER, FEELING FLUSTERED FROM WORK, DECIDED WE WERE GOING TO GET AWAY FROM IT ALL ON AN ISLAND HE WAS DEVELOPING CALLED JAVAKUMBA ISLAND, A.K.A. ADVENTURE ISLAND!
"THERE'RE LOTS OF SUPERSTITIONS ON THE ISLAND, INCLUDING RUMORS OF BAD LUCK CONCERNING AN IDOL I FOUND! I DIDN'T BELIEVE IT, BUT SOME BAD THINGS HAVE BEEN HAPPENING...
"...INCLUDING THE ERUPTION OF COOKACHELLA VOLCANO!! YIKES!!"

LATER THAT DAY, THE VOLCANO'S ERUPTIONS BEGIN TO SUBSIDE...
IT LOOKS LIKE THE VOLCANO'S ERUPTION IS DYING NOW!
THANK GOODNESS!
IT'S SAFE TO RETURN TO OUR HOMES NOW!!
FORTUNATELY, LITTLE DAMAGE WAS DONE!
THIS TIME AT LEAST!
WHAT ARE YOU TALKING ABOUT, VERONICA?
ER-UH... WELL, I MIGHT AS WELL TELL YOU!!
I THINK I CAUSED THAT VOLCANO TO ERUPT!
WHAT? HOW COULD YOU DO THAT?
I SORT OF TOOK THIS IDOL FROM ONE OF THE CAVES!
YOU WHAT?!
2

I WAS GOING TO BRING IT BACK! HONEST!
THEN AN OLD WOMAN TOLD ME THE IDOL WAS BAD LUCK!!

I DIDN'T BELIEVE HER, BUT THEN I HURT MY ANKLE!
AND ALMOST IMMEDIATELY AFTER, A MIRROR ALMOST FELL ON MY MOTHER!

THEN BEFORE I KNEW IT, THE VOLCANO ERUPTED!
VERONICA, I THINK THOSE WERE JUST COINCIDENCES!

SOME PEOPLE ON THIS ISLAND ARE SUPERSTITIOUS, BUT WE'RE NOT!

WELL, I SUPPOSE WE SHOULD RETURN THE IDOL, THOUGH!
LET'S DO IT RIGHT NOW BEFORE SOMETHING ELSE HAPPENS!

WE'LL PUT IT BACK TOMORROW! IT'S GETTING DARK NOW ANYWAY!! LET US HOLD ON TO THIS FOR SAFEKEEPING!
WELL, OKAY!!
3

I'M EXHAUSTED! I NEED SOME SLEEP AFTER THIS DAY!
YOUNG LADY! DO YOU SEE WHAT'S HAPPENED BECAUSE OF THAT IDOL YOU TOOK?
YEAH, I'M FULLY AWARE, LADY!
MY FRIENDS ARE RETURNING IT TOMORROW!

THEY CAN'T DO IT! YOU MUST DO IT! AND ALONE!!
THE CURSE CAN'T BE LIFTED UNTIL THE APPREHENDER RETURNS IT AND BEGS FOR FORGIVENESS!
WHAT?
DO IT BEFORE THE WHOLE ISLAND ERUPTS!

GREAT! LIKE I NEED THAT HANGING OVER MY HEAD!
I'D BETTER DO IT NOW, OR I'LL NEVER GET ANY SLEEP TONIGHT!
OH, NO! EVAN AND IMANA HAVE THE IDOL!!
I'LL SNEAK OVER TO THEIR HOUSE AND GET IT!
4

ER- MOM, I'M GOING TO GET A SNACK FROM THE GRILL!
WHY NOT HAVE EVAN OR IMANA DELIVER IT?
FASHION BUZZ

ER... THAT'S OKAY! I NEED TO STRETCH MY ANKLE!
OKAY, BUT HURRY! IT'S GETTING DARK!

I HATE TO SNEAK IN AND GRAB IT, BUT I KNOW THEY WOULDN'T APPROVE OF MY GOING UP THERE ALONE!
I THINK IT'S IN EVAN'S KNAPSACK!! OH, GOODY, THIS WINDOW IS OPEN!!

SOUNDS LIKE HE'S IN THE SHOWER! I'LL JUST GRAB IT AND...

UH-OH! HE'S COMING OUT OF THE SHOWER! THIS ISN'T GOOD!

HE SPENDS MORE TIME IN FRONT OF THE MIRROR THAN I DO!
KNOCK! KNOCK!

C'MON, EVAN! IT'S TIME FOR DINNER!
OKAY! LET ME GET DRESSED!

THINK FAST!
FLOP!

HEY! WHO'S IN HERE?!
NOW TO MAKE A MAD DASH FOR IT WHILE HE CAN'T SEE!!

WHAT'S GOING ON?!
THERE WAS SOMEONE IN MY ROOM!! THEY THREW A BLANKET ON ME!

SO...
LET'S SEE! IT WAS THE THIRD CAVE ON THE RIGHT, I BELIEVE!
OR WAS IT THAT CAVE?!

DOESN'T THIS PLACE HAVE A DIRECTORY LIKE THE MALL HAS?!

Veronica in The Idol of Adventure Island

PART 2
CHAPTER 4

THERE! I THINK I'VE FINALLY FOUND IT.!!
NOW I JUST HAVE TO ***RETURN*** THE IDOL TO ITS RIGHTFUL ***SPOT*** AND ASK FOR FORGIVENESS!!

NOT SO FAST, YOUNG LADY!
YIKES! YOU SCARED ME!

YOU'RE ON SACRED GROUND! ON THIS ISLAND THAT'S PUNISHABLE BY LAW!
ESPECIALLY WHEN YOU STEAL OUR ARTIFACTS!

I SHOULD'VE KNOWN! YOU HAVE A BIG MOUTH, LADY!
I DID EVERYTHING YOU SAID! I RETURNED IT SAFELY! NOW I HAVE TO BE GOING!

WELL, YOU'LL HAVE TO STAY IN THIS CAVE UNTIL WE'RE SURE THE CURSE IS LIFTED!!
I CAN'T DO THAT! I HAVE FASHION MAGAZINES TO READ!

IF THE ISLAND DOESN'T BLOW UP, YOU'RE OFF THE HOOK!
WE'LL JUST BLOCK THE ENTRANCE WITH A BOULDER SO YOU DON'T GO RUNNING OFF!

WHAT?! MY PARENTS WILL FREAK OUT!!
WE WON'T HURT YOU!! IT'S YOU WHO ARE DANGEROUS!

LET HER GO, YOU THREE!
YOU GIVE US INHABITANTS OF THIS ISLAND A BAD NAME!
THOSE WHO AID AND ABET CURSED ONES ARE JUST AS GUILTY!!
WHAT ARE YOU GOING TO DO ABOUT IT?

SO...
GREAT! NOW WE'RE ALL STUCK HERE TOGETHER! AND THE ENTRANCE IS REALLY BLOCKED!
I'M AT LEAST GLAD YOU CAME AFTER ME!!

I SENSED THAT WAS YOU IN MY BEDROOM!
WHEN WE SAW THE IDOL WAS GONE, WE KNEW WE'D BETTER FIND YOU!

LATER THAT NIGHT...
VERONICA'S NOT BACK! THIS ISN'T LIKE HER!
I'LL CALL EVAN AND IMANA!

THEY'RE GONE, TOO!
HOPEFULLY VERONICA IS WITH THEM!

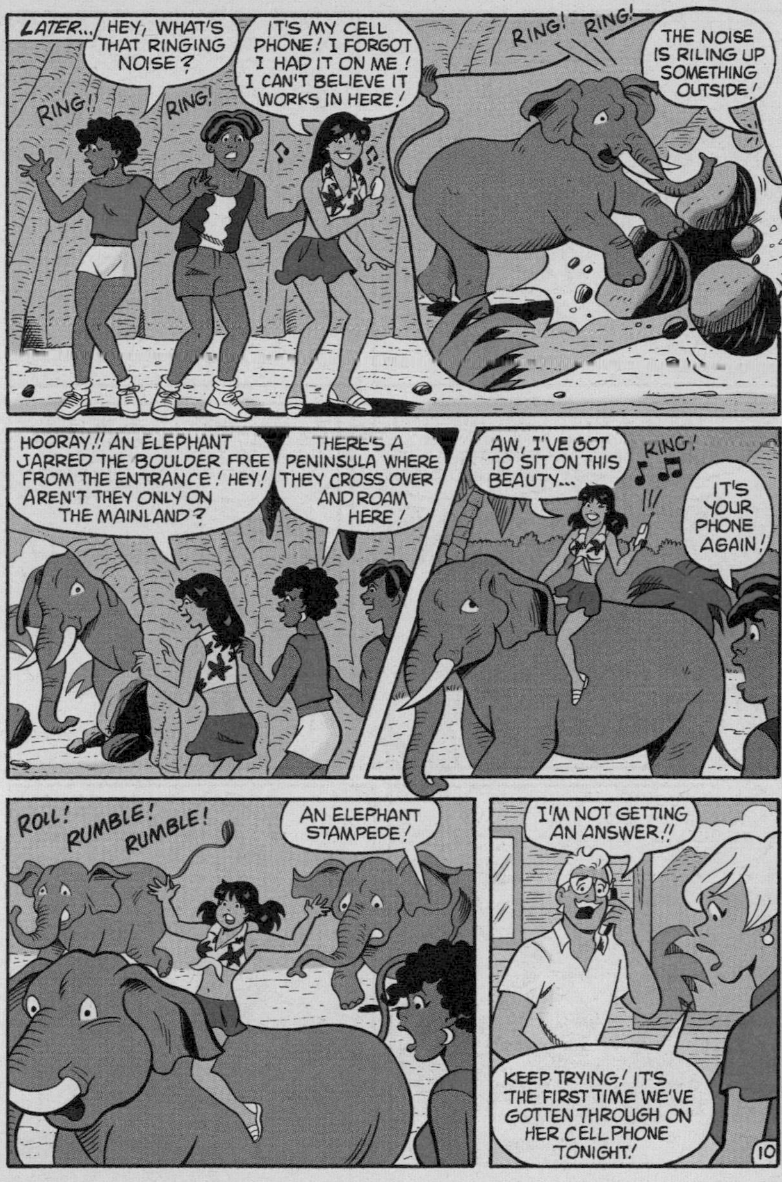

LATER...
HEY, WHAT'S THAT RINGING NOISE?
RING! RING!
IT'S MY CELL PHONE! I FORGOT I HAD IT ON ME! I CAN'T BELIEVE IT WORKS IN HERE!
RING! RING!
THE NOISE IS RILING UP SOMETHING OUTSIDE!

HOORAY!! AN ELEPHANT JARRED THE BOULDER FREE FROM THE ENTRANCE! HEY! AREN'T THEY ONLY ON THE MAINLAND?
THERE'S A PENINSULA WHERE THEY CROSS OVER AND ROAM HERE!
AW, I'VE GOT TO SIT ON THIS BEAUTY...
KING!
IT'S YOUR PHONE AGAIN!

ROLL! RUMBLE! RUMBLE!
AN ELEPHANT STAMPEDE!
I'M NOT GETTING AN ANSWER!!
KEEP TRYING! IT'S THE FIRST TIME WE'VE GOTTEN THROUGH ON HER CELL PHONE TONIGHT!

HELLO?
VERONICA! THANK GOODNESS! WHERE ARE YOU?

RIGHT HERE, DADDY!
PLEASE TELL ME I'M DREAMING!

SOON...
WE'RE SORRY WE TRIED TO DETAIN YOUR DAUGHTER!!
WELL, WE DIDN'T MEAN TO INTERFERE WITH YOUR ISLAND CUSTOMS!
WE'RE NOT ALL AS SUPERSTITIOUS AS THESE OLD-TIMERS!

I DON'T THINK I SHOULD TRY TO DEVELOP THIS ISLAND!!
SOME THINGS ARE BETTER LEFT UNTOUCHED!

SO...
I'M GLAD YOU CAME! AND PLEASE VISIT US OFTEN!
WE WILL!

I CAN'T TAKE A STRENUOUS VACATION LIKE THAT AGAIN!
I NEED TO GET BACK TO THE RAT RACE AND RELAX!!
END

HOW PERFECTLY PEACEFUL! THE RIPPLING SOUND OF THE WATER, THE SOFT WHISPER OF THE WIND IN THE TREES, THE TWITTERING OF THE BIRDS...

ALL THE TWITS AREN'T IN THE TREES!

Betty and Veronica in "UP THE CREEK"

Script: Frank Doyle / Pencils: Dan DeCarlo / Inks: Jimmy DeCarlo / Letters: Bill Yoshida

AREN'T YOU ENJOYING THIS?
I'M BORED!

YOU'RE BORED BY NATURE?
OF COURSE NOT!

...BY THE COMPANY!
?

THAT'S RIDICULOUS! WHAT COMPANY? WE'RE ALONE! NOBODY HERE BUT YOU AND... UH-OH!

NO OFFENSE, BUT A LITTLE MALE COMPANIONSHIP WOULD LIVEN THINGS UP A BIT!
THANKS A BUNCH!

HEY!
OVER THERE! THE LONE FISHERMAN! IS THAT WHAT YOU'RE CRAVING?

CAN'T BE SURE FROM THIS DISTANCE! BUT BEGGARS CAN'T BE CHOOSERS!

SORRY ABOUT THIS, GIRL!
HEY! WAIT!!

FLIP!
2

HELP! HELP ME!
I'M DROWNING!
?

I'M COMIN'! I'M COMIN'!

DON'T PANIC! RELAX! I'LL HAVE YOU OUT IN NO TIME!

OH! YOU SAVED ME! YOU'RE A HERO! HOW CAN I REPAY YOU?
LATER! YOUR FRIEND IS STILL OUT THERE!

HANG ON, SIS! I'M COMIN' TO GET YOU!!

DON'T BOTHER! I'LL WALK IN MYSELF! IT'S ONLY HIP DEEP!

SONOFAGUN! LOOK HOW SHALLOW THAT WATER IS!
NOT HALF AS SHALLOW AS MY FRIEND!

COME ON IN! PUSH THE CANOE IN AND WE'LL RIGHT IT!
IN A MINUTE! I'M SEARCHING!

WHAT FOR?
I THINK RONNIE LOST HER EXPERT SWIMMER'S MEDAL WHEN WE CAPSIZED!

NICE GOING, PAL! CAN YOU SAY "VENGEANCE"?
WHERE'S YOUR SENSE OF HUMOR? ARE YOU COMING WITH ME?

WHY DON'T YOU GIRLS STAY AND HAVE LUNCH WITH ME?
WHAT A DELIGHTFUL IDEA!

THREE'S A CROWD! I'LL JUST PADDLE ON!
THAT WILL EARN A LITTLE FORGIVENESS!
4

TALLYHO! ENJOY YOURSELVES!
YOU CAN COUNT ON IT!

I HOPE YOUR MOUTH IS ALL SET FOR A LUNCH OF NICE FRESH FISH!
OH, IT IS! IT IS!!

OKAY! YOU GUT AND CLEAN THESE WHILE I CATCH A FEW MORE!

YOU WANT ME TO WHAT??
GUT AND CLEAN THE...

WAIT!!
HOLD UP, FRIEND! COMPANION! OLD BUDDY! I'M COMING!!
WELL... I GUESS I CAN'T LEAVE HER UP THE CREEK WITHOUT A PADDLE!
END

Betty in "GOLF GAFF"
Doyle / Goldberg
Lapick / Yoshida
SIGH! I CAN'T BELIEVE IT'S JUST THE TWO OF US! WHAT A ROMANTIC WAY TO SPEND AN EVENING!
PUTT-ERAMA
FAMILY FUN
OOPS!
DARN! WHERE DID IT GO?
ARE YOU LOOKING FOR THIS, ARCHIE?
ALICE ... ALICE GUMM!
1

GEE, ALICE! I HAVEN'T SEEN YOU IN AGES!
OUR FAMILY MOVED TO CENTERVILLE!

HATE RUSHING YOU, ARCHIE, BUT THERE ARE PEOPLE WAITING BEHIND US!
SEE YOU LATER, ARCHIE!
6

THEY SAY THE SECRET BEHIND GOOD PUTTING IS CONCEN...
7

BONK!

OH, DEAR! I'M SO SORRY! THE CLUB JUST SLIPPED OUT OF MY HAND!
S'OKAY! NO HARM DONE!
UH, MAYBE I CAN GIVE YOU SOME PUTTING TIPS!
5

SEE? THIS IS THE *PROPER* GRIP!
LOOKS LIKE AN *IMPROPER* GRIP TO ME!
PUTT

ARCHIE, LET ME EXAMINE THE BUMP ON YOUR HEAD!
IT'S NO BIG DEAL, BETTY!

BUT I INSIST!

WHY DON'T WE TAKE A BREAK? I'LL GO GET SOME SODAS!
OKAY!

THIS HAS BEEN A FUN EVENING!
IT STARTED OUT THAT WAY!

I SEEM TO HAVE LOST MY SCORE-CARD!
BUT YOU HAD IT JUST A MOMENT AGO!

LOOKING FOR THIS, ARCHIE?
MY SCORE-CARD!
ALICE AGAIN!
3

GEE! THERE ARE SOME FUNNY-LOOKING NUMBERS ON THIS CARD OF MINE!
THAT ALICE! SHE WROTE DOWN HER PHONE NUMBER!

LET ME REPLACE YOUR CARD WITH A FRESH ONE!
13

WE'LL JUST DISPOSE OF YOUR OLD, DIRTY CARD!

WE'D BETTER MOVE ON! PEOPLE ARE WAITING BEHIND US!
THAT'S OKAY!
12

TAKE AS LONG AS YOU WANT! I DON'T MIND!

JUST ONE MORE HOLE TO GO AND WE'RE FINISHED!
BOY! I REALLY WORKED UP A THIRST! BE RIGHT BACK!

THAT'S THE *THIRD* SODA HE'S HAVING!
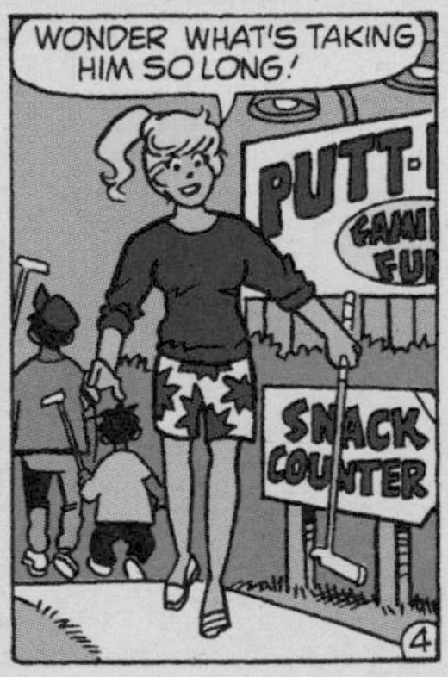
WONDER WHAT'S TAKING HIM SO LONG!
SNACK COUNTER

SO HOW LONG HAVE YOU BEEN WORKING HERE, MELISSA?
BURG
SODA
HOTDOG
CHEES

TOO LONG!

BETTY, HAVE YOU HEARD THE NEWS?
DADDY JUST BOUGHT THE LOCAL MINIATURE GOLF COURSE!

NOW I'LL BE ABLE TO INVITE ALL MY BOYFRIENDS TO PLAY THERE WITH ME!

OH, YOU POOR, POOR GIRL!
END

THE FULL MOON THAT SHINES DOWN UPON BONGO BEACH ILLUMINATES THE DOZENS OF SURFCASTERS THAT LINE ITS SHORE... TONIGHT SHOULD BE A GOOD NIGHT FOR STRIPED BASS...
LOOK, MR. WEATHERBEE... HERE COMES A SCHOOL OF STRIPERS NOW!
RARF!
I SEE THEM, ARCHIE!... NOW IF THEY'LL JUST COME IN CLOSER...
Archie IN "BAD BREAKS ON BONGO BEACH"

SWISH!

OOOF!

1

Inks: Chic Stone / Letters: Bill Yoshida

DRAT! THOSE FISH ARE STAYING OUT OF REACH!
NO ONE ON THE BEACH CAN CAST A LURE THAT FAR!

WHAT A PITY! LOOKS LIKE A SCHOOL OF BIG ONES GOING PAST OUT THERE!
(SIGH!) IT'S THE ONLY KIND OF SCHOOL I LIKE TO BE AROUND!

BUT NOW I SEE THERE IS SOMEONE WHO'S GOING TO CATCH STRIPED BASS TONIGHT!

- AND THEY'RE ALL ON MR. LODGE'S SPORTS FISHING BOAT!
BONNIE RONNIE

MR. LODGE HAS A BOAT FOR EVERY PURPOSE... FROM A CANOE TO A YACHT... HE'S SHOWED THEM ALL TO ME!
THE ONLY VESSELS HE'S EVER SHOWED ME WERE RAPIDLY FILLING WITH BLOOD!
RARF!

DADDY! I CAN SEE ARCHIE AND MR. WEATHERBEE SURFCASTING FROM BONGO BEACH!... OH! I WISH ARCHIE WAS ABOARD WITH US!
WELL, I DON'T, VERONICA!

I CAN'T TAKE THE CHANCE OF HAVING ARCHIE OUT HERE... MR. MCJITTERS BACK THERE IS AN IMPORTANT CLIENT OF MINE AND-

-HE'S A HIGHLY NERVOUS TYPE! ... YOU KNOW HOW ARCHIE WOULD AFFECT HIM!
YOU'RE RIGHT, AS USUAL, DADDY!

BESIDES, VERONICA, THE LAST TIME WE TOOK ARCHIE OUT IN THIS BOAT, HE GOT HIS FISHING LINE FOULED IN THE PROPELLER!
...CAUSING THE WATER PUMP TO BURN OUT, THEN YOU DID A SLOW BURN, I GOT A SUN-BURN AND WE ALL GOT TOWED IN BY THE COAST GUARD!

(SIGH!) I REMEMBER ONE OF THOSE SAILORS WAS REAL CUTE!
STANDBY! WE'RE TROLLING PAST A BIG SCHOOL OF STRIPERS NOW!

I'VE HOOKED ONE!
BONNIE RONNIE
GOOD FOR YOU, MR. MCJITTERS! I'LL IDLE THE ENGINE WHILE YOU PLAY HIM!

SOMEBODY'S JUST BOATED A STRIPER!
RON SAID THEY WERE TO HAVE AN IMPORTANT CLIENT ON BOARD TONIGHT... THAT'S WHY HER DAD DIDN'T WANT ME AROUND... I CAN'T UNDERSTAND WHY HE THINKS I'M A JINX!

THAT'S A BEAUTIFUL SCHOOL OF BASS OUT THERE! IF ONLY WE COULD CAST THAT DISTANCE!
WHY BOTHER!? C'MON, SPOTTY, LET'S GO HO-

BLAP! BLAP! VROOOM!
IT'S DILTON DOILEY!
IN HIS DUNE BUGGY!

HI! ANY LUCK? I HEARD THE STRIPERS WERE OUT HERE TONIGHT!
YEAH, TOO FAR OUT... CAN'T REACH 'EM, DILT!... IT'S HOPELESS!

GOOD! VERY GOOD!

NOW YOU CAN DO SOMETHING ABOUT GETTING YOUR LURE TO GO FARTHER!
YEAH? SINCE WHEN DO YOU KNOW SO MUCH ABOUT SURF-CASTING!
1540
SINCE I CREATED THIS–
?
–THE SURFCASTER'S HANDY "REACH 'EM 'N' BEACH 'EM ROCKET"... NOW YOU TOO, CAN GET TO THE BIG ONES!

IS THIS ANOTHER OF YOUR WILD INVENTIONS?
NO, SIR! THIS ONE I'VE THOROUGHLY TESTED AND I'VE BEEN WAITING FOR A NIGHT SUCH AS THIS!
HOW DOES IT WORK?

THE LURE AND LINE ARE ATTACHED TO THIS SPECIAL RELEASE CLIP ON MY ROCKET, WHICH IS ACTIVATED BY ME HERE ON SHORE... I CAN DROP YOUR LURE RIGHT NEXT TO A SCHOOL OF STRIPED BASS!

THESE CONTROLS WILL SET OFF THE ROCKET!
SOUNDS NEAT, DILT!

–I'M SETTING THEM TO HAVE THE LURE-RELEASED AT ABOUT... HMMM... EIGHTY YARDS OUT... NOW, WHO WANTS TO BE THE FIRST TO CATCH BASS?
MIND IF I TRY FIRST, SIR?
–ER– NOT AT ALL, ARCHIE... IN FACT, I ENCOURAGE IT!

OKAY! CONTROLS SET! READY?
READY!
RARF!

GOOD! JUST HOLD YOUR POLE STEADY, ARCH!
RARF!
WOOSH

GRRRR!
CLICK!
CLICK!
CLICK!

FUNNY! THE ROCKET SHOULD'VE DROPPED YOUR LURE BY NOW...
IT HAD BETTER HURRY UP... I'M RUNNING OUT OF-

L-I-I-I-NE

DADDY! SOMETHING WEIRD JUST FLEW UP IN THE AIR FROM BONGO BEACH!
LET'S HAVE A LOOK!

A ROCKET!! TOWING SOMETHING!... URK! IT CAN'T BE! BUT IT IS -

-ARCHIE!

A-A- R-ROCKET!?

BETTER REEL IN, MR. MCJITTERS!

CLICK!

W-WE'RE UNDER A ROCKET ATTACK! DID YOU HEAR THAT SPLASH!??
IT'S ALL RIGHT, MR. McJITTERS... WE'RE AQUAINTED WITH THE SPLASHEE!
SPLASH!

(COUGH!) (SPUTTER!)
ARCHIE! ARE YOU ALL RIGHT?
BONNIE RON

HE MUST BE ALL RIGHT... HE NEVER LET GO OF HIS FISHING ROD!
NOT A CHANCE! THIS IS A BRAND NEW RIG!
IT'S GOT TO BE FATE THAT HAS ME CONSTANTLY ENTWINED WITH THIS TEEN-AGE TWIT!

BETTER REEL IN... AT LEAST MY LURE GOT OUT HERE... HEH! HEH!

HEY! GOT ONE!

15 MINUTES LATER...
(WHEW!) MUST BE A WHOPPER!... I CAN'T GET HIM TO SURFACE!
GOOD GRIEF! LOOK AT THE TEMPERATURE GAUGE!! WE'RE OVERHEATING!
BONNIE RONNIE

NO WONDER! ARCHIE'S LINE IS FOULED IN THE PROP AGAIN! THE WATERPUMP'S PROBABLY BROKEN!
DADDY! THE ENGINE JUST QUIT!
BONNIE RONNIE
BLURP!
GURGLE! BLURP!

WE'RE ADRIFT... AT THE MERCY OF THE CRUEL SEA!
IT'S ALL RIGHT, MR. McJITTERS! WE'RE THROWING OUT THE ANCHOR AND CALLING THE COAST GUARD!
COME ON UP ON THE BOW, ARCHIE, IT'S SAFER UP THERE!

YEAH! ARCHIE'S OKAY! I CAN SEE HIM ABOARD LODGE'S BOAT!
LOOK! HE'S SCARED THAT SCHOOL OF STRIPERS TOWARD SHORE!

I HAVE ONE!

MINUTES LATER -
LOOKS LIKE ALL THE SURFCASTERS ARE DOING THIS WELL... THANKS TO ARCHIE AND YOUR ROCKET!

YOU AND ARCHIE ARE INVITED TO A STRIPED BASS DINNER AT MY HOUSE TOMORROW NIGHT!
GREAT! I'LL GIVE YOU A LIFT BACK TO YOUR CAR AT THE BEACH PARKING LOT!

- AND I'LL TAKE SPOTTY WITH ME AND DROP HIM OFF AT ARCHIE'S HOUSE!

MEANWHILE...
WHO'S YOUR DAD'S CLIENT? HE SEEMS KINDA JUMPY!
MR. MCJITTERS, FOUNDER OF THE FIDGETY FUDGE FIRM... DADDY WANTS TO SELL HIM A FACTORY IN FRANCE!
WHY FRANCE?
CHOCOLATE-COVERED SNAILS!
HERE COMES THE COAST GUARD!
IT'S THE LODGE BOAT AGAIN!

NEXT EVE...
HI, DILT! READY FOR THE BEE'S BIG BAKED BASS BASH?
HI, ARCH! YEAH! C'MON IN!

CHEER UP, ARCH... YOU'LL CATCH A STRIPER... NEXT TIME I'LL *STAY* AT THE CONTROLS!

(SIGH!) IT DOESN'T MATTER!

HEY! YOU DON'T SEEM TOO HAPPY!?!

I'M NOT... I'M GONNA MISS RONNIE!

SHE'S SAILING FOR THE CARIBBEAN WITH MR. MCJITTERS ON HER DAD'S YACHT... *TONIGHT!*

HMMPH! MR. LODGE SAID HE'LL BE SAFE FROM ME WAY DOWN THERE!

ARCH-

-WOULD YOU STEP OUT BACK FOR A MOMENT?
THE END

Jughead in The Tightening Web
RIPP
ANY HINT OF LAUGHTER I DETECT WILL WEIGH AGAINST YOU WHEN SCHOOL IS BACK IN SESSION!
THINKING ABOUT SAD THINGS!
TSK! THE NYLON WEBBING MUST'VE GROWN WEAK WITH AGE!
YEAH! THAT MUST BE WHAT DID IT!
SCRIPT: CRAIG BOLDMAN
PENCILS: REX LINDSEY
INKING: RICH KOSLOWSKI
LETTERING: JACK MORELLI

FORTUNATELY, I HAVE SOME ROLLS OF NYLON WEB IN MY GARAGE! I CAN DO THE REPAIR!

WHY DON'T YOU JUST BUY A NEW CHAIR? CAN'T COST MORE THAN A FEW BUCKS!
I ENJOY FIXING THINGS!

IF I THREW OUT EVERYTHING THAT DIDN'T WORK QUITE RIGHT, RIVERDALE HIGH WOULD BECOME A LONELY PLACE!
GOTCHA!

IN FACT, I MIGHT AS WELL REPLACE THE NYLON IN ALL MY LAWN FURNITURE!
MIGHT AS WELL!

IS THERE A REASON YOU'RE HANGING AROUND?
I ENJOY WATCHING OTHER PEOPLE WORK!

HERE! MAKE YOURSELF USEFUL! TAKE THE OLD SEATING OFF THESE!

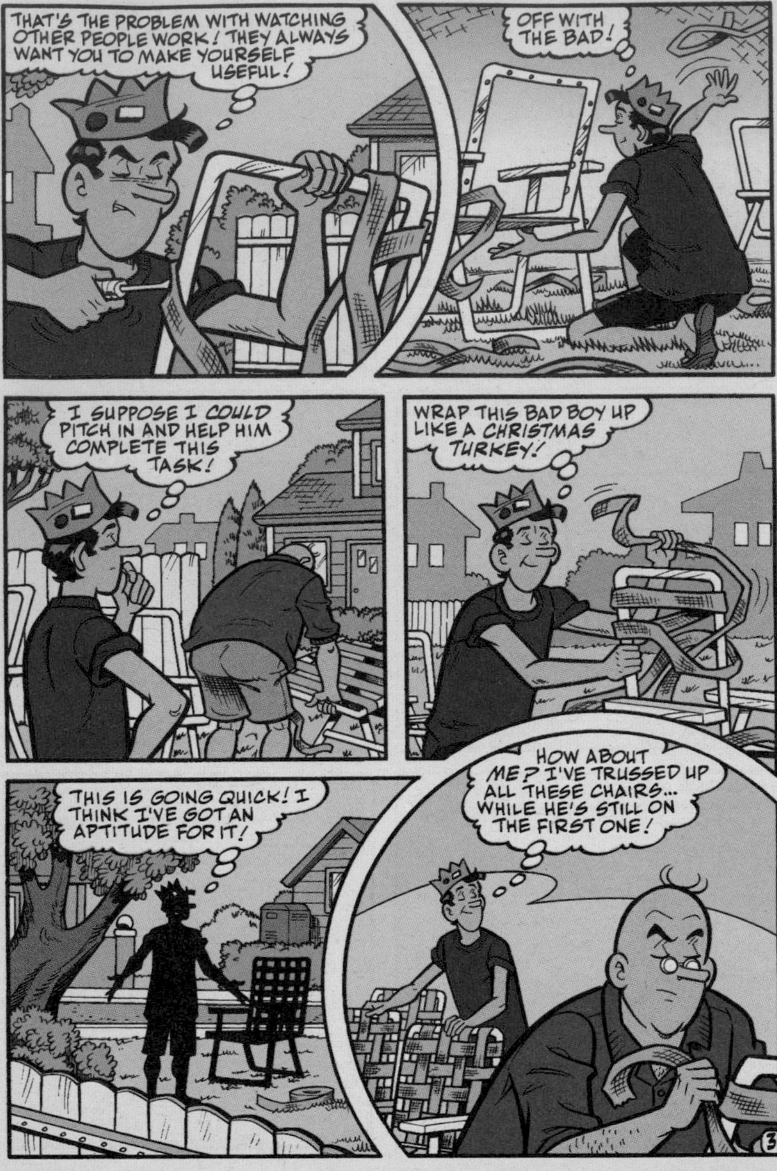

I SUPPOSE I COULD PITCH IN AND HELP HIM COMPLETE THIS TASK!

WRAP THIS BAD BOY UP LIKE A CHRISTMAS TURKEY!

THIS IS GOING QUICK! I THINK I'VE GOT AN APTITUDE FOR IT!

HOW ABOUT ME? I'VE TRUSSED UP ALL THESE CHAIRS... WHILE HE'S STILL ON THE FIRST ONE!

OKAY! I'VE GOT 'EM ALL WRAPPED! BUT THEY'RE NOT YET FASTENED!
I GUESS THAT'LL TAKE A RIVET GUN! IT MUST BE IN THE GARAGE!
Oh, DEAR! THIS BENDING DOES TAKE A TOLL ON MY BACK!
I GUESS I'VE EARNED A SIT-DOWN IN ONE OF THESE OLD CHAIRS!
ER... HOLD UP! I DON'T THINK YOU WANNA SIT ON THAT--
FLOP

THERE SHOULD BE A LAW AGAINST SETTING BOOBY TRAPS FOR YOUR PRINCIPAL!
HEY! WATCH IT! YOU'VE GOT ME, NOW!
WHAT A MESS!
I CAN'T TELL WHERE I STOP AND THE LAWN FURNITURE BEGINS!
WE'RE STUCK TIGHT! I CAN'T MOVE A MUSCLE!
YEAH, I'D SAY WE DID QUITE A JOB!
DON'T KEEP STRUGGLING! YOU'RE JUST LOCKING US UP TIGHTER!
I CAN'T HELP IT! I WANT TO GET OUT OF HERE BEFORE THREE O'CLOCK!
THREE O'CLOCK? WHAT HAPPENS AT THREE O'CLOCK?
THAT'S WHEN MY SPRINKLER SYSTEM COMES ON!
SPRTZZ
DO YOU SUPPOSE... BLUB THERE'S A MORAL TO THIS STORY?
GLUG IF THERE IS, IT'S GOTTEN TOO SOGGY TO MATTER! GLUG
THE End

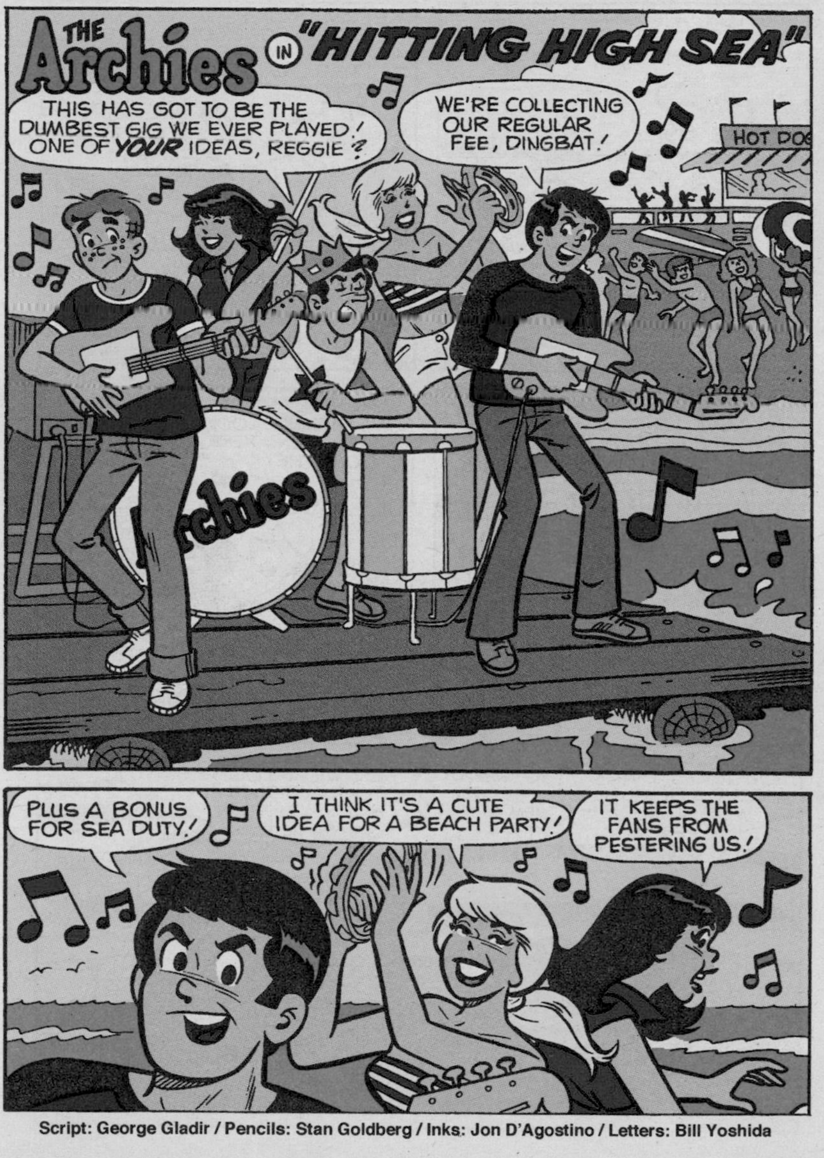

THE Archies IN "HITTING HIGH SEA"

THIS HAS GOT TO BE THE DUMBEST GIG WE EVER PLAYED! ONE OF *YOUR* IDEAS, REGGIE ?

WE'RE COLLECTING OUR REGULAR FEE, DINGBAT!

HOT DOG

Script: George Gladir / Pencils: Stan Goldberg / Inks: Jon D'Agostino / Letters: Bill Yoshida

HOW LONG WILL THAT POWER PACK KEEP US IN SOUND?
LONG ENOUGH TO FINISH THIS GIG!

WE CAN'T RISK FULL ELECTRICAL POWER ON A STAGE AS WET AS THIS ONE!
OKAY! LET'S HIT NUMBER TWENTY-THREE!

HEY! YOU CALL THAT MUSIC?
THEY SOUND LIKE THEY'RE GOING DOWN FOR THE THIRD TIME!

MAN! THEY'VE GOT SOME STRANGE LOOKING FISH AROUND HERE, DON'T THEY?
MUST BE A RESULT OF ALL THAT POLLUTION!

HOW ABOUT THAT? A COUPLE OF MUSICAL WISE GUYS!
NO WONDER THEY SET THEM ADRIFT!
HEY! WE'RE LOSING SIGHT OF OUR AUDIENCE! FOG'S ROLLING IN!
2

WHAT SAY WE TREAT THOSE WISE GUYS TO A LITTLE OCEAN VOYAGE ?
A SURPRISE CRUISE ! WHAT A GREAT IDEA !

CLIK!
CLIK!

I'D WAVE BYE-BYE, IF I THOUGHT THEY COULD **SEE** US !
HAW!

Y'KNOW, THE CROWD ON THE BEACH HAS GROWN VERY QUIET !
HEY ! THAT DUMB FOG IS LIFTING !

ACK ! WE'RE ADRIFT ! I CAN'T SEE THE SHORE !
WE'VE BROKEN LOOSE OF OUR MOORING !
WHICH WAY IS HOME ?
THE Archies

MAYBE IF WE YELL, SOMEBODY WILL HEAR US!
WHO? THERE'S NOBODY IN SIGHT!

WE PLAY LOUDER THAN WE YELL!
HIT IT! NUMBER SIX!

ARGH! STOP! WE'RE DRAWING SHARKS!!
THAT'S NO SHARK!
SPLASH!

THAT'S A DOLPHIN! HE SEEMS TO LIKE OUR MUSIC!
THEY'RE VERY FRIENDLY ANIMALS!

KEEP PLAYING! HE'S SWIMMING CLOSER AND CLOSER!
WHAT DO YOU HAVE IN MIND?

I'VE READ OF DOLPHINS ACTUALLY SAVING PEOPLE WHO ARE IN TROUBLE AT SEA!
4

MAYBE WE SHOULD PLAY, "SHOW ME THE WAY TO GO HOME."
NO! KEEP IT UP! HE LIKES ROCK!

HEY! HE LET ME GRAB HIM! HOLD MY FEET, SOMEBODY!

ARE YOU ALL RIGHT, ARCHIE?
GLUB! J-JUST FINE! L-LET'S TAKE IT FROM THE TOP AGAIN!
ZOOM!
Archies

WE'RE SAVED! HE BROUGHT US TO SHORE!
TALK ABOUT MUSIC APPRECIATION--

BEST AUDIENCE WE EVER PLAYED FOR! RIGHT, ARCH?
HE'LL ANSWER YOU AS SOON AS WE PUMP HIM OUT!
BLAGH!
END

Script: Craig Boldman / Pencils: Rex Lindsey / Inks: Rudy Lapick / Letters: Bill Yoshida

THE STRAIGHT MAN AND THE GOOFY SIDEKICK!
YEP!

`COURSE, I'D ORDINARILY NEVER REFER TO YOU AS A "GOOFY SIDEKICK"!

WAIT A MINUTE! YOU'RE THE FUNNY ONE!
ME? OH, COME ON!

I'M THE DASHING DEAN MARTIN-TYPE LEADING MAN! YOU'RE MY JERRY LEWIS!
COLA

NO WAY! IF ANYTHING, I'M THE SMOOTH ABBOT TO YOUR SILLY COSTELLO!
GET OUT!

I'M THE SERIOUS HALF OF THIS ACT! YOU'RE AROUND FOR COMIC RELIEF!
ARCH!!
CLUNK!
SWISH!
2

YOU KNOCKED MY SODA DOWN THE ALLEY!
I DID?
WELL, IT'S DONE FOR GOOD!
SLOOP!
POP!
SPLURT!
FOR A STRAIGHT MAN, YOUR MATERIAL KILLS, ARCH! CHORTLE!
WHAT'S ARCH SULKING ABOUT?
HE'S UNHAPPY WITH HIS PLACE IN THE UNIVERSE!
IT'S BEEN POINTED OUT THAT HE IS THE FOPPISH FOZZIE TO MY STEADFAST KERMIT!
HOP!

AFTER ALL, I'M THE MEASURED, STUDIOUS TYPE WHO'S ALWAYS SOLVING HIS MESSES!
YOU'D MAKE A STRONGER CASE IF YOU WEREN'T SITTING ON MY FRESHLY VARNISHED COUNTER!
KEEP OFF WET VARNISH
HO HO! SO YOU'RE THE STRAIGHT MAN?
ANYONE CAN HAVE AN OFF DAY!
DON'T BE TOUCHY, JUG! THE WORLD LOVES A CLOWN!
AFTER ALL, ED SULLIVAN GOT TOP BILLING, BUT THAT TOPO GIGO...
ARCH!!
WHUMP!
4

BUMP!
BOING!

CRASH!

WHICH WOULD YOU SAY IS THE FUNNIEST ONE?
IT'S HARD TO SAY...

LET'S BOWL A FEW FRAMES AND SEE WHICH ONE GETS THE BIGGEST LAUGH!
END

Archie & FRIENDS in "The NOISE of SUMMER"

AH, THE OLD SCHOOL CERTAINLY SEEMS *PEACEFUL* IN THESE *LAST DAYS* OF *SUMMER*!

RIVERDALE HIGH SCHOOL

I SEE SVENSON REPLACED THE BROKEN GLASS IN MY OFFICE WINDOW!

"I CAN STILL REMEMBER *HOW* IT BROKE! IT WAS THE DAY OF SUP'T. HASSLE'S *INSPECTION*...
BONK!
CRASH!

Script: Fernando Ruiz / Pencils: Jeff Shultz / Inks: John Lowe / Letters: Bill Yoshida

"OF COURSE IT WAS NO SURPRISE WHO IT BELONGED TO..."

SIGH! TO THINK I'M IN FOR ANOTHER NINE MONTHS OF TRYING TO KEEP THAT BOY UNDER CONTROL!

OF COURSE, FOR ONE MORE WEEK I'M ARCHIE FREE!
BWA-HA-HA!

I'M GOING TO SAVOR MY LAST FEW DAYS OF PEACE AND QUIET WITH A GOOD BOOK AT THE BEACH!

EGAD!
WHAT A RACKET!!
2

IT'S ARCHIE! MUST HE HAUNT ME EVEN HERE??

I'D BETTER SLIP AWAY QUIETLY BEFORE HE SEES ME AND...

EEYOOWWW!
WHAM!

GULP! IT'S THE BEE.!!
I THINK YOUR REMOTE CONTROLLED CAR WIPED HIM OUT!

LET'S HELP HIM UP!
I'VE GOT HIS LEG!
MAN, WHAT A LOAD!
OUCH! PUT ME DOWN, YOU FOOLS!

SORRY, MR. WEATHERBEE! WE WERE JUST TRYING TO HELP!
I'LL HELP MYSELF TO THE OTHER SIDE OF THE BEACH!
3

THERE'S GOT TO BE A SPOT ON THE BEACH WHERE I WON'T RUN INTO ANY STUDENTS!

WHOOPS!
AAAAKKK!
WHAM!

DUH-H... SORRY, MR. WEATHERBEE... I WAS GOING FOR THE GOAL!
WAS THE GOAL TO POUND ME?

OUCH!
OUCH!
OOF!
GROAN!

CAN IT BE...

A WHOLE SECTION OF THE BEACH... ALL TO MYSELF!

WHOA! THERE'S BETTY AND VERONICA!

WELL, THEY SEEM TO BE READING QUIETLY! HOW MUCH TROUBLE COULD THEY BE?

WHAT AM I SAYING?! IT'S BETTY AND VERONICA!
HMM? OH NO!

OOOOFFFF!

HEY! LET'S HAVE A BEACH BARBECUE?!
I'LL BRING THE TUNES!

THIS IS GONNA BE A GREAT BASH!
I HAVE HAD ENOUGH OF THIS! IT'S TIME I CHANGED MY VACATION SPOT!

AND I KNOW JUST WHERE TO GO!

I'VE GOT TO GET THE CAFETERIA READY FOR SCHOOL!

HUH?

DON'T ASK ME! HE'S BEEN SITTING THERE ALL WEEK!